MY BIG TOE

BOOK 2:

D I S C O V E R Y

Section 3
Man in the Loop:
How You Fit into the Big Picture –
Ego, Body, Mind, and Purpose

Section 4
Solving the Mystery
Mind, Matter, Energy and Experience

The *My Big TOE* reality model will help you understand your life, your purpose, the totality of the reality you experience, how that reality works, and how you might interact most profitably with it.

A half dozen independent test readers of various backgrounds were asked to evaluate the My Big TOE *trilogy and record their impressions of it. This is what they said:*

■ ■ ■

"Eureka! A Theory Of Everything that actually lives up to its name! *My Big TOE* not only unifies physics, but unifies philosophy and theology as well. You will be amazed!"
— PAMELA KNIGHT, PHYSICIST

"Reading *My Big TOE* has challenged my mind and widened my horizon. Expect your worldview to radically expand and your perspective to reach a new level of understanding."
— INA KUZMAN

"*My Big TOE* is utterly original, pioneering and bold. Campbell writes with clarity and humor as he explores and answers the hard questions in this comprehensive work about the ultimate nature of reality and consciousness. Full of fresh and profound ideas, you may be astonished to find that learning how reality works actually improves the quality of your life."
— LYLE FULLER, POWER ENGINEER

"The *My Big TOE* trilogy roared through my comfy no-brainer world like a category F5 tornado that makes you laugh ... when the dust finally settled, I was left with an incredibly clear view of how and why things are as they are."
— PEG ROCHINE, FOUNDER AND CEO, CLINICAL RESEARCH

"This trilogy will profoundly change you .... you will never look at your world in the same way again."
— INA KUZMAN

"Thoroughly challenging, engaging ... a transforming experience. *My Big TOE* marks the end of humanity's childhood."
— LYLE FULLER, POWER ENGINEER

"Unique, profound, and enriching are the words that most easily come to my mind to describe *My Big TOE*."
— TREVOR GOLDSTEIN, PHILOSOPHER AND FUTURIST

"If you have ever asked the questions: Is this all there is?, What's the purpose?, How am I related to the whole?, *My Big TOE's* logic, grounded in science, provides unequivocal answers that make you think. A profoundly fascinating read!"
— INA KUZMAN

MY BIG TOE

A TRILOGY
UNIFYING PHILOSOPHY,
PHYSICS, AND METAPHYSICS

BOOK 1:
AWAKENING

BOOK 2:
DISCOVERY

BOOK 3:
INNER WORKINGS

Thomas Campbell

Find the other two books of the *My Big TOE* trilogy:
http://www.My-Big-TOE.com
http://www.lightningstrikebooks.com
Phone orders: 1 – 800 – 901 – 2122

MY BIG TOE: A TRILOGY UNIFYING PHILOSOPHY, PHYSI CS, AND METAPHYSICS

BOOK 2: DISCOVERY

Lightning Strike Books
http://www.LightningStrikeBooks.com

Printed in the United States of America
First Edition: February, 2003

Book design by Michele DeFilippo, 1106 Design, LLC
Cover illustration by Frank Foster

Publishers Catalogue-in-Publication Data
Campbell, Thomas
My Big TOE: Discovery. Book 2 of a trilogy unifying philosophy, science, and metaphysics / Thomas Campbell
1. Science. 2. Philosophy. 3. Metaphysics. 4. Reality, model of.
5. Consciousness, theory of. 6. Spirituality. 7. Paranormal, theory of.
8. Theory of Everything. 9. TOE. 10. Theology (religion) and science.

ISBN 0-9725094-2-9 (Softcover)
ISBN 0-9725094-3-7 (Hardcover)

To Chris

To Bob & Nancy

To Dennis & Nancy Lea

To Todd, Lyle, Ina, and Trevor,
whose encouragement
was key to success

To those in need of
a new perspective

To all seekers of Big Truth

To Pamela, The One

To love within
A joyous
Heart

To Chris

To Bob & Nancy

To Dennis & Nancy Lea

To Todd, Lyle, Ina, and Trevor,
whose encouragement
was key to success

To those in need of
a new perspective

To all seekers of Big Truth

To Pamela, The One

To love within
A joyous
Heart

■ ■ ■

Synopsis
My Big Picture
Theory of Everything

My Big TOE – A trilogy unifying philosophy physics, and metaphysics

■ ■ ■

Book 1: Awakening

Section 1 provides a partial biography of the author that is pertinent to the subsequent creation of this trilogy. This brief look at the author's unique experience and credentials sheds some light upon the origins of this extraordinary work. The unusual associations, circumstances, training and initial research that eventually led to the creation of the *My Big TOE* trilogy are described to provide a more accurate perspective of the whole.

Section 2 lays out, logically justifies, and defines the basic conceptual building blocks needed to construct *My Big TOE*'s conceptual foundation. It discusses the cultural beliefs that trap our thinking into a narrow and limited conceptualization of reality, defines the fundamentals of Big Picture epistemology and ontology, as well as examines the inner-workings and practice of meditation. Most importantly, Section 2 defines and develops the two basic assumptions upon which this trilogy is based. From these two assumptions, time, space, consciousness, and the basic properties, purpose, and mechanics of our reality is logically inferred.

Book 2: Discovery

Section 3 develops the interface and interaction between "we the people" and our digital consciousness reality. It derives and explains the characteristics, origins, dynamics, and function of ego, love, free will, and our larger purpose. Finally, Section 3 develops the psi uncertainty principle as it explains and interrelates psi phenomena, free will, love, consciousness evolution, physics, reality, human purpose, digital computation, and entropy.

Section 4 describes an operational and functional model of consciousness that further develops the results of Section 3 and supports the conclusions of Section 5. The origins and nature of digital consciousness are described along with how artificial intelligence (AI), as embodied in AI Guy, leads to artificial consciousness, which leads to actual consciousness and to us. Section 4 derives our physical universe, our science, and our perception of a physical reality. The mind-matter dichotomy is solved as physical reality is directly derived from the nature of digital consciousness.

Book 3: Inner Workings

Section 5 pulls together Sections 2, 3, and 4 into a more formal model of reality that describes how an apparent nonphysical reality works, interacts, and interrelates with our experience of physical reality. Probable realities, predicting and modifying the future, teleportation, telepathy, multiple physical and nonphysical bodies, and the fractal nature of an evolving digital consciousness reality are explained and described in detail.

Section 6 is the wrap-up that puts everything discussed in Sections 2, 3, 4, and 5 into an easily understood personal perspective. Additionally, Section 6 points out *My Big TOE's* relationship with contemporary science and philosophy. By demonstrating a close conceptual relationship between this TOE and some of the establishment's biggest intellectual guns, Section 6 solidly integrates *My Big TOE* into traditional Western scientific and philosophical thought.

Contents

BOOK 2: Discovery

BOOK 3: Inner Workings

SECTION 5
Inner Space, the Final Frontier:
The Mechanics of Nonphysical Reality – A Model 43

■■■
Acknowledgements
■■■

The One. In a category all to herself, I wish to acknowledge the immeasurable contribution, in all possible forms, given by my most constant, consistent, and challenging teacher: Pamela – The One.

Fellow travelers. First and foremost, acknowledgement goes to Bob Monroe and his wife Nancy who enabled my exploration of the path that eventually led to the *My Big TOE* trilogy. Next, to Dennis Mennerich, my fellow explorer and traveling companion. We pulled each other along when neither of us knew much about where we were going or how we were going to get there. Then, to Nancy Lea McMoneagle who was not only a fellow traveler but also the primary enabler of Monroe's success. All gems, every one – I could not possibly have set out on this strange journey with a better collection of friends and mentors. Finally, to the un-named many who provided me with the opportunities that enabled me to be what and who I have become. I wish I could have made more of the opportunities you offered. In the end it is these tens, these hundreds, these thousands, who made this trilogy possible. Thank you all.

Major contributors. In a more direct and immediate vein, there are a few readers of indomitable fortitude to whom I am eternally grateful. The time and effort volunteered by these remarkable people made all the difference in the world. Together we have tried hard to make all three books as clear and understandable as possible.

Special thanks go to Lyle Fuller, Todd Phillips, Ina Kuzman, and Caroline Lampert for their effort to improve the readability and clarity of *My Big TOE*. All three were quick to point out where I had left stumbling blocks lying on the path to Big TOE understanding. Additionally, Todd's and Ina's questions served as a catalyst to ferret out much interesting material. Many thanks to Chris Nelson who started me writing in the first place. Without their selfless generosity and dedication beyond all reason, this trilogy would be a poor shadow of what you have before you.

In addition, I thank Nancy Lea McMoneagle and Dennis Mennerich for aiding and corroborating the accuracy of my memories of the early years at Whistlefield. Also heartfelt thanks to Lyle Fuller, Joel Dobrzelewski, Trevor Goldstein, and Eric Campbell for their encouragement and good questions. Special thanks to Steve Tragesser for asking questions that became the catalyst for much of Chapter 18, Book 3. Likewise, to Lyle Fuller for doggedly pursuing questions that eventually produced the discussion of free will found in Chapter 11, Book 2 and that added clarity to my exposition of the psi uncertainty principle. Similarly, to Trevor Goldstein whose experience and questions precipitated the discussion of mind tectonics in Chapter 6, Book 2; and to Ina Kuzman for initiating the discussion found in Chapter 23, Book 1 about the nature and practice of meditation. Also, thanks goes to Eric Campbell for precipitating a discussion about the natural constraints of a finite consciousness system. Credit goes to Tom Hand, Zane Young, Rhonda Ganz, and Kristopher Campbell for offering useful suggestions and comments. Finally, I wish to thank Steve Kaufman for being in the right place at the right time with his book, *Unified Reality Theory: The Evolution of Existence Into Experience*. I love it when a plan comes together.

Hired Help. Two ladies of great integrity and competency enabled *My Big TOE* to make the transition from an amateur creation to a professional product. Kate von Seeburg, owner of *K8 & Company*, edited the manuscript while Michele DeFilippo, owner of *1106 Design*, produced the interior and cover designs.

Family. Great appreciation goes to my wife and children, who patiently and cheerfully allowed me to work on "the book" when I should have been paying attention to them. I hope the final result will prove itself worthy of our collective sacrifice.

Non-contributors. Last, and certainly least, I wish to barely mention Kathy Cyphert and Peggy Rochine, who, along with many others too numerous to name, contributed absolutely nothing to this effort but wanted to see their names mentioned in it just the same. Additionally, Boldar, Kiana, Onyx, Joe, Nikki, Chico, Mr. Pickle, Sid, Moe, Sir Maximus, Snuffy, Sir Minimus, Kia, Gabrielle, Isabel, and Kuga-Bear also deserve honorable mentions as outstanding non-contributors.

—Tom Campbell,
Dec. 9, 2002

Preface: Author's Note to the Reader

Yes, you should read this preface.

I understand that many readers have little interest in, or patience for, lengthy prefaces or forewords. The first question is always: Should I take the time to read this ancillary text, or can I skip it without missing anything important?

Most of us are eager to zip past the preliminaries and immediately sink our teeth into the meat of the main text. Anticipation and expectation push us to get on with the real thing. We of Western culture are an impatient goal oriented people driven toward endpoints. In our rush to the finish line, we take little notice of the journey that gets us there. Such a misappropriation of emphasis often squanders our opportunities because, more often than not, the tastiest and most nourishing part of life lies in experiencing the process, not in attaining the goal.

By the end of Section 6, you will no doubt agree that these books are ... well ...different. As such, they require a different approach. The preface and foreword of the *MY Big TOE* trilogy **are** integral parts of the story. Because this trilogy blazes an original trail far off the beaten path, it is essential to include introductory material that can help prepare you for what lies ahead. I know you are eager to get on with it and discover if this trilogy delivers the goods, but rushing off toward that goal too quickly actually reduces the likelihood that you will get there at all.

The function of the preface and the foreword is to maximize the return on your reading investment. The preface provides an overview of the tone, structure, process, and mechanics of the *My Big TOE* trilogy. The foreword establishes a broad view of the trilogy's content and lays out a rough map of where you will be going on this unusual journey. It provides the context and focus wherein the trilogy's content is most easily understood. The foreword and preface together improve comprehension and minimize frustration by providing a global view of the forest before you begin your descent into the trees.

I strongly suggest that you adopt an attitude of patience toward gaining an understanding of the profound mysteries and ancient secrets that are logically unraveled by this new physics. My Big Picture Theory Of Everything (*My Big TOE*) will take you to both the beginning and to the end of time. It will dive deeply into the human heart as well as probe the limits of the human mind. It will define the significance of you, and provide new meaning to your existence. It will help you realize and optimize your potential. It will develop a wholly new scientific understanding of both your inside and outside world.

You may find it more productive to pace yourself by depth of comprehension than by percent of completion. Avoid rushing from concept to concept the way children pursue presents on Christmas day. Take your time. A feast for heart, head, and soul is best ingested little by little, bite by bite, with many thoughtful pauses and much careful cogitation to aid digestion. Genuine breakthroughs must be absorbed slowly as existing paradigms grudgingly dissolve. Familiar paradigms, like a favorite teddy bear, can be extremely difficult to let go.

Every successful journey, regardless of how long or difficult, begins with a single step that is animated by gumption, directed by goals, and repeated as often as necessary by dogged perseverance. On this particular journey, the preface is located at step one, the foreword at step two, followed by the three books: *Awakening*, *Discovery*, and *Inner Workings*.

I have carefully aimed the content of this scientific and philosophic exposition at a general audience of varied background. You do not need a scientific, philosophical, or metaphysical background to understand the content of the My Big Picture Theory Of Everything trilogy. No leaps of faith or beliefs are required to get to where these books will take you. A determined and tenacious truth seeker – a sturdy, independent intellect that is by nature open minded and skeptical – constitutes the optimal reader. There are no prerequisites. If you have a logical, open, and inquisitive mind – an attitude of scientific pragmatism that appreciates the elegance of fundamental truth and the thrill of breakthrough – you will enjoy this journey of personal and scientific discovery.

Under the best of circumstances the successful communication of this trilogy's content will require much from both of us. This work presents many unique and daunting challenges to the effective communication between author and reader. Worldviews are not casually picked, like fruit, from a vendor's cart: To make the necessary connections, we must dive deeply.

Far beneath the foundation of your intellect, your culture lays out the template for your worldview upon the core belief systems that define your perception of existence. The basic assumptions that support your notion of reality are not seen by you as assumptions at all – they are accepted, without question, as the most solid of all facts. That is simply the nature of culture – belief at the bone and sinew level of awareness. The point is: The concepts presented by this trilogy are likely to challenge the belief systems of your culture – regardless of what culture you come from.

Material within *My Big TOE* may challenge your familiar assumptions, beliefs, and paradigms to the point of serious discomfort. If that discomfort leads to a profitable resolution, I am pleased; if it does not, I am saddened. My goal is to be informative and helpful. I encourage you to take what you can profitably use and leave the rest.

There are enough new concepts and unusual perspectives presented here to support and generate a multitude of books. I have purposely left much unsaid at the periphery in order to stay focused on the central idea of developing a Big TOE. Though the trilogy remains, from beginning to end, tightly focused on its primary objective, I will occasionally take short side trips in the form of asides to add color, explore related connections, and insert topics of special interest and practical value. Hopefully, you will find these side trips so interesting and informative that you will gladly excuse their interruption. Some effort will be required on your part to bridge these asides in order to maintain the logical continuity of the larger discussion. To make sure that you are never confused about whether you are reading an aside or the main text, asides are indented, have their own special font, and are clearly marked (at the beginning and end) with dingbats that look like this: ▶. If a secondary aside resides within a primary aside, it is indented yet again and marked with double dingbats ▶▶. When an aside fills an entire page, it is difficult to judge how much the text is indented, consequently, when this condition occurs, dingbats are placed in the header to let you know that the text is part of an aside. Thus, a casual glance is all that is required to determine if the text that you are reading is part of an aside, and if so, at what level.

You may find the text to be challenging in some places and obvious in others. What is too challenging or too obvious to each reader is mostly dependent on the experience and understanding of that individual reader. It is my intent to never speed through this exposition at such a rate that you cannot appreciate the scenery, nor to wallow about repetitively in the obvious – though from time to time, depending on your background, some may feel that I occasionally do both.

Although the language of American English (the language in which these books were originally written) is decidedly poor in nonphysical conceptual descriptors, it does have the advantage of being unusually rich in communications and information technology descriptors. The latter, oddly enough, is what allows me to convey the former. As strange as that may seem, it is the pervasiveness of modern science and technology, especially communications and data processing technology, that provides the conceptual tools required to produce a model of the larger reality the Western mind – or more broadly, the Western attitude or more accurately, the Western belief system – can relate to, understand, and work with.

Science and technology have advanced to the point where their applications and understanding have begun to mirror some of the fundamental processes of existence. We of the twenty-first century have only recently acquired the necessary concepts to understand and appreciate the nature of the larger reality within the context of our contemporary Western point of view. Previously, knowledge and understanding of the Big Picture and our existence in it was comprehended and described by ancient sages in terms of metaphors that were pertinent to their cultures and specifically created for the benefit of their specific audiences. Today, we find these once practical descriptions to be largely symbolic and irrelevant to a modern scientific view of reality. Philosophy, theology, and science find themselves at odds over what is significant.

I am a scientist. This trilogy is the result of a long and careful scientific exploration focused upon the nature of reality and the individual. Preconceived notions will be more of a hindrance than a help. It is the task of this trilogy to clearly and completely construct your consciousness, your world, your science, and your existence in a general, logical, scientific way that comprehensively explains **all** the personal and professional data you have collected during a lifetime. An overarching Big Picture theory that explains **everything** may seem highly unlikely, if not absolutely impossible, but it is not. Take heart: Good science and human ingenuity have consistently delivered the impossible for at least two hundred years. Be open – history repeatedly demonstrates that the appearance of impossibility is most often the result of limited vision.

Patience will be required. This adventure of mind, science, and spirit is complex and will take significant time to properly unfold. If it were immediately obvious, it would either be old news or you would be reading a short journal article instead of a trilogy. A keen mind that is skeptical and open is the only ticket you need to take this journey.

Based on the feedback from those who have preceded you, I expect that you will find this voyage into the depths of elemental consciousness and fundamental reality to be personally enriching. You will be pushed to think a few big thoughts and ponder a few big ideas, but the conclusions you eventually come away with will be entirely yours, not mine. These are not books that set out to convince you of anything, or persuade you towards a particular point of view. At every turn you are strongly dissuaded from becoming a believer. Data, facts, and measurable results are the exclusive currency upon which this trilogy trades.

Reading the *My Big TOE* trilogy is not likely to be a passive experience. If you decide to seize the opportunity to climb out of the box, you will likely end up doing some difficult work. You will always be encouraged to think for yourself and come to conclusions that are based on **your** personal experience. Despite all the serious cogitation, we are also going to play, laugh, and have some fun as we go.

Much of what you believe to be true about yourself, your existence, and the nature of reality will be challenged. If you are open to exploring a bigger picture, these books will make you think, and think again. Most readers will not consider this trilogy to be an easy read – merely following the logical processes and sequences as they swallow up old paradigms will require some focused effort. On the other hand, significant growth and learning is rarely easy – if easy, it is rarely significant.

Contrary to my best efforts, Sections 2, 3, 4 and 5 remain somewhat conceptually interdependent. Each section will be better understood and make much more sense after reading the other sections. That could not be helped. Reality is a unified whole thing with each of its parts inexorably intertwined with the others.

This trilogy's three books and six sections develop the conceptual content of *My Big TOE* more or less sequentially. Consequently, reading the books or sections out of numerical order provides a less than optimal experience. However, understanding *My Big TOE* is much more dependent upon reading the entire trilogy than it is upon reading it in any particular order.

The nature of reality and of the typical reader is such that we must sneak up on *My Big TOE* one concept at a time. We will examine the Big Picture from multiple perspectives to ensure the design and structure of the whole becomes clearly visible. If things seem to get a little far out every once in a while, hang tough until it all pulls together into a coherent complete picture.

For the reasons stated above, a slow and careful reading will optimize your investment – take your time, and meander through these books at a relaxed and unhurried pace. If you become bogged down, it is better to go on (and come back later if you want to) than to feel as if you must read every word in the order in which it appears. It would be unfortunate for you to miss seeing a part of the forest that may be important to you because you became lost, exhausted, or discouraged wandering unproductively among the trees in another part.

Throughout *My Big TOE*, I have used a seeding technique to sneak up on some of the more difficult ideas. I often plant conceptual seeds (that briefly bring up or introduce an idea) within the sections, chapters, pages, or paragraphs that precede a full and thorough discussion of that idea. I do this because many readers will find the concepts presented within *My Big TOE* to be totally unfamiliar. Comprehension and understanding of this trilogy is significantly improved if the reader is at least somewhat prepared for the major conceptual discussions.

Questions may occasionally leap into your mind as you read. Hold on to your questions, or better yet, write them down as you go. Most will be answered within a few paragraphs or pages. If you have unanswered questions after completing Section 5, these can be productively used as the initial focus of your own quest for Big Truth – a subject that is taken up with gusto in Section 6.

Be careful not to lose sight of the Big Picture as a result of being overly focused on the details. It is easy to get twisted around details that strike an emotive resonance with your beliefs. The winning strategy here is to get a glimpse of the entire forest, not to argue about the color of the moss growing on specific trees. Control your passionate interest in the coloration of moss or you may entirely miss what is important.

One final note before you begin. Those who know me well, along with a few of the initial readers, have suggested that I forewarn you about my sense of humor. If you read something in these books that could be interpreted as humor, sarcasm, condescension, arrogance, silliness, inanity, or all of the above, it is probably only humor, or occasionally, humor with a touch of sarcasm. If you find yourself unsure of how offended you should be, I suggest that you temporarily suspend your judgment of the author's mind-set. I am told that eventually (by the end of Section 4) you'll be familiar with my stealthy humor and informal chatty style. Consequently, a later judgment may be more accurate.

The structural anatomy of *My Big TOE* is laid open like a frog on the dissecting table in the paragraphs below. Most readers will find that this overview provides a helpful perspective on how the book you are now reading fits into the overall *My Big TOE* trilogy.

My Big TOE is designed as a three book trilogy. It is packaged as separate books for those who are not sure of how big a bite they wish to take, and as a more economical three book set for those who are confident they want it all. Each book contains the identical dedication, synopsis, table of contents, acknowledgements, preface, and foreword, as well as its own acronym list and two unique sections of content. Though the table of contents displays the contents of all three books a the beginning of each book, the contents belonging to the other two books are cast in light grey instead of black. Although chapter and page numbering starts anew within each book, the six sections are numbered sequentially across the entire trilogy to add a sense of structural continuity.

Book 1: *Awakening* contains the first two sections. **Section 1** provides a partial biography of the author that is pertinent to the subject matter. Its function is to shed light on the origins of this unusual work by providing a look at the author's unique experiences and credentials that eventually led to the creation of *My Big TOE*. **Section 2** lays out the basic building blocks needed to develop this TOE's conceptual foundation. Many of the concepts initiated in Section 2 will be more fully explored in later sections.

Book 2: *Discovery* contains the middle two sections. **Section 3** takes the information gained in Section 2 and develops its implications in more detail and depth while relating it more directly to the reader's personal experience. **Section 4** pulls together the ideas of Sections 2 and 3, while developing the additional concepts required to bind it all together into one consistent whole. Sections 2, 3, and 4 are carefully designed to sequentially work together to produce the fundamental understanding that is necessary to comprehend Section 5.

Book 3: *Inner Workings* contains the last two sections. **Section 5** presents the formal reality model in detail. **Section 6** is the wrap-up that puts everything discussed into an easily understood perspective. Additionally, Section 6 points out *My Big TOE's* relationship with contemporary science and philosophy. By demonstrating a close conceptual relationship between this TOE and some of the establishment's biggest scientific and philosophic intellectual guns, Section 6 integrates *My Big TOE* into traditional Western science and philosophy.

There is a place in cyberspace [**http://www.My-Big-TOE.com** This URL is not case sensitive but the **hyphens are required**] set aside for you to share your experience, exercise your intellect, voice your opinions, vent your angst, or simply hang out with your fellow travelers. You can send email to both the author and the publisher from the **my-big-toe.com** web site, as well as acquire all Big TOE books. There, you can keep up with the latest in Big TOE info, happenings, chitchat, reviews, research, and discussion groups.

— Tom Campbell
Dec. 9, 2002

■■■
Foreword: A Conceptual Orientation
■■■

Without the proper perspective, clear vision produces only data. The point here is to give the reader an initial high altitude peek at the forest before we begin our trek into its depths. In this foreword, I will describe where you will be going and what you should expect to accomplish. It is always helpful to know where you are headed even if you have no idea of how you are going to get there. This conceptual fly-over is designed to minimize the disorienting affect of totally unfamiliar territory.

Both the structure and the content of your perception of reality are culturally dependent. How a Tibetan Buddhist monk or an American physicist would describe reality is as vastly different as the words, expressions, and metaphors that each would employ to make such a description. What would make sense and be obvious to one would seem to be lost and out of touch to the other. If we can rise above our cultural bias, we have a tendency to ask, or at least wonder: Which description is right and which one is wrong? They seem clearly incompatible – certainly both could not be equally accurate and correct. If we are more sophisticated, we might ask which portions of each description are right or wrong and search for areas of possible agreement as well as define areas that appear to be mutually exclusive. That is a better approach, but it is still wrong-headed.

Neither of the above approaches, though the second is much more expansive than the first, will find truth. Which is right or wrong is the wrong question – it represents a narrow and exclusive perspective. Which works, which helps its owner to better attain his or her goals, which goals are more productive and lead to growth and progress of the individual – to happiness, satisfaction and usefulness to others? These are somewhat better questions because they focus on practical results and on the measurable effects that each worldview has when applied to individuals – as well as the secondary effects those individuals have on others. However, something important is missing. How does one define, realize, and measure the satisfaction, personal growth, quality of life, and fulfillment of individual purpose that is derived from each worldview? What is the standard against which the achievement of these goals is assessed? Now we have a set of questions that have the potential to lead to personal discovery in pursuit of fundamental truth. Big Picture Significance and value have replaced little picture right and wrong as the primary measure of worth. Fundamental truth (Big Picture Truth or simply Big Truth), though absolute and uniformly significant to everyone, must be discovered by each individual within the context of that individual's experience. No one approach to that discovery is the right one for everybody. The significance of "little truth," on the other hand, is circumstantial and relative to the observer.

Truth exists in all cultures. It is only understandable to an individual when it is expressed in the language (symbols, metaphors, and concepts) of that individual. It is the intent of *My Big TOE* to capture the scientific and metaphysical truth from multiple cultures and multiple disciplines and present them within one coherent, self-consistent model that the objective Western mind can easily comprehend. After all, a TOE (Theory Of Everything) must contain and explain **everything**. That is a tall order. A Big Picture Theory Of Everything or Big TOE must include metaphysics (ontology, epistemology, and cosmology) as well as physics and the other sciences within a single seamless integrated model of reality. That is what the *My Big TOE* trilogy is all about.

Truth is truth, but communicating a truth to another is a difficult undertaking fraught with misunderstandings of meaning and interpretation. Big Truth, like wisdom, is not something you can teach or learn from a book. It must be comprehended by individuals within the context of their experience. Each of us comes to an understanding of reality through our interpretation of our physical and mental experiences.

The experience of others can at best provide a useful model – a framework for understanding – a perspective that enables us to comprehend and interpret our experience data in a way that makes good practical sense. The best teachers can do no more than offer a consistent and coherent understanding of reality that helps their students find the larger perspective required to self-discover Big Truth. Such a model is only correct and comprehensive if it accurately describes all the data (physics and metaphysics) all the time under all circumstances for everyone who applies it. The usefulness of a model depends on how correctly it describes the data of experience. A good model should be predictive. It should explain what is known, produce useful new knowledge, and provide a more productive understanding of the whole.

If *My Big TOE* communicates something of significance to you by resonating with your unique knowing, then this particular expression of the nature of reality suits your being. If it leaves you untouched, perhaps some other view of reality will speak to you more effectively. The form your understanding takes is not significant – it is the results that count! If you are prodded to a more productive understanding, you are on the right track. The expression of reality that most effectively nudges your understanding in the direction of learning, growing, and evolving a higher quality of being, is the right one for you. *My Big TOE* is not the only useful expression that Big Truth can take. Nevertheless, it is a uniquely comprehensive model of reality that speaks the language of the Western analytical approach. This Big TOE trilogy fully integrates a subjective, personal, and holistic worldview with objective science. East and West merge, not simply as a compatible or mutually reinforcing mixture, but as a fully integrated single solution.

When some people hear the word "model," they imagine a scale model – a miniature version of the real thing. *My Big TOE* has nothing to do with scale models. A model is an intellectual device that theoreticians use to achieve a more concrete understanding of an abstract concept. Models are often developed to describe an unknown function, interaction, or process (something that lies beyond our current individual experience) in terms of something more comprehensible. The model itself may closely resemble the reality it describes or merely describe its inputs and outputs. In either case, **do not confuse the model of reality with reality itself.** Please repeat that twice before going on.

If you have enough direct experience and a deep understanding of what is being modeled, the model becomes superfluous. With no direct experience, the model enables an understanding that is otherwise impossible to attain. With limited direct experience, the model allows you to place your limited experience within the context of the consistent logical structure of the model. To those with enough experience to incite curiosity and formulate practical questions, the model brings a meaningful interpretation and explanation to data (experience, information, fragments of truth) that otherwise seem hopelessly random and unconnected.

The model of reality developed within this trilogy enables you to understand the properties and characteristics of reality, how you interact with reality, the point of reality, and the boundaries, processes, functions, and mechanics of reality. It describes the what, the why and the how (the nature, purpose, and rules) of the interplay and interaction among substance, energy, and consciousness. You will discover the distinction between the objective physical outside world and the subjective nonphysical inside world of mind and consciousness is wholly dependent upon, and relative to, the observer.

My Big TOE describes, as any Big TOE must, the basic oneness, continuity, and connectedness of All That Is. It systematically and logically derives the natural relationships between mind and matter, physics and metaphysics, love and fear, and demonstrates how time, space, and consciousness are interconnected – all with a bare minimum of assumptions. Additionally, it describes in detail the most important processes of our reality – how and why reality works. You will find the results of *My Big TOE* to be in consonance with current data – and that it solves a host of longstanding scientific, philosophical, and metaphysical problems.

The model of reality developed within *My Big TOE* is not the only valid metaphor or description of the nature of the larger reality. Nevertheless, this model is perhaps more understandable to those of us who are accustomed to understanding our local reality in terms of the processes and measurements of objective causality. A materialistic or scientific definition of reality is sometimes referred to as "Western" because the notion that reality is built upon an inviolate objective causality lies at the core of the Western cultural belief system.

My Big TOE is written to be especially accessible to this Western mindset or Western attitude. The West does not now have, nor has it ever had, a monopoly on a process oriented, materialistic, and objective approach to existence and reality. We in the West have perhaps pursued science and technology more religiously than others, and have no doubt added a unique cultural slant to our particular brand of consumer-based materialism, but the basics of what I am calling a Western attitude are thoroughly entrenched worldwide and expanding in every direction.

The stunning success of science and engineering in the twentieth century would seem to prove the usefulness as well as the correctness of this Western view. The result is that many people, whether from the East, West, North, or South of our planet, view reality from an objective and materialistic perspective that often coexists with some culturally based traditional form of religious and social dogma.

Thus, a balance, or standoff, between our inner and outer needs evolves into a practical worldview that encourages Western material productivity. A pragmatic materialism that depends on objective causality is used to generate the appearance of a manipulatable, rational, stability on the outside, while a belief-system of some sort provides the necessary personal security on the inside. To eliminate the discomfort of conflicting worldviews, the two ends of this bipolar conceptual dichotomy are typically kept separate and do not mix or integrate to any significant depth. Each supports the other superficially as they together produce a materially focused, responsible, upwardly striving worker with a good work ethic, cooperative values, an inclination toward dependency, and a high tolerance of pain.

Because the Western mind-set is growing and spreading rapidly, and because the human spirit often withers on the vine before beginning to ripen in such an environment, it is particularly important to blaze a trail to the understanding of the larger reality in the terms, language, and metaphors of this mind-set. As a product of American culture myself, and as a scientist, I have endeavored to craft a model of the larger reality that not only appears rational to the objective Western attitude, but also provides a comprehensive, complete, and accurate model that Western science can build upon.

My Big TOE provides an understanding of reality that can profitably be used by both science and philosophy – one that provides an original perspective, and makes a significant contribution to physics and metaphysics as well as to several other traditional academic and practical disciplines. By the time you have finished Section 6, you will have been exposed not only to Big Picture physics and Big Picture metaphysics, but also to Big Picture psychology, biology, evolution, philosophy, computer science, artificial intelligence, and philosophy of science. There is even a TOE-bone to toss to the mathematicians – they will find new fractal concepts, and discover why geometric fractals successfully reproduce the likeness of natural objects. You will learn why Albert Einstein and others were unable to successfully develop Unified Field Theory, and why contemporary attempts to produce a successful TOE have been likewise frustrated.

The problem physicists are currently having describing a consistent reality is primarily because of the way they define space, time, objectivity, and consciousness. Their current ideas of these basic concepts contain limitations derived from erroneous cultural beliefs. It is this belief-induced blindness that creates scientific paradoxes (such as wave/particle duality and the instantaneous communication between an entangled pair). As Einstein pointed out more than half a century ago, space and time, as we interact with and experience them, are illusions. Many of the best scientists of the twentieth and twenty-first centuries realize this fact, but did not and do not know what to do about it or how to proceed. Their problem is one of perspective – their conceptualization of reality is too limited (only a little picture) to contain the answer.

Albert Einstein's space-time field (as described in his Unified Field Theory) asserted a nonphysical field as the basis for matter specifically and reality in general, thereby moving science closer to the truth, but he did not appreciate the discrete digital properties of space and time or the role of consciousness (instead of space-time) as the primary energy field. Einstein's student and colleague, the great quantum physicist David Bohm (along with a few of the best Quantum Mechanics theorists including Niels Bohr, Werner Heisenberg, and Eugene Vigner) made the consciousness connection but missed the digital connection and the Big Picture.

Contemporary physicist Edward Fredkin and his Digital Physics movement make the digital connection (quantized space and time) and are heading in the right direction, as was Einstein, Bohr, and Bohm, but they are missing a solid connection to consciousness. Digital physics has not yet discovered that consciousness **is** the computer. All are missing an appreciation of the natural limitations of our physical objective causality and a coherent vision of the Big Picture that ties everything together. You will be shown not only all of the pieces of this both ancient and contemporary reality-puzzle, but will also see how they fit together – philosophy and science, mind and matter, normal and paranormal – into a single unified coherent Big Picture.

You will hear more from the above-mentioned gentlemen of science, as well as many of the top Western thinkers of all time, in Section 6 where I integrate the concepts of *My Big TOE* with the knowledge base of traditional Western science and philosophy.

My Big TOE represents a scientific and logical tour of reality that goes considerably beyond the point where Einstein and other top scientists gave up in frustration. As limitations are removed from your thinking, you will see the source of their frustration clearly, how and why they got stuck, and the solution that they could not find or understand. That this is a non-technical exposition, devoid of the mathematical language of our little picture science, is actually not a weakness at all – even from a strict scientific perspective. How could that be? As you progress through *My Big TOE*, you will come to understand the **natural**, fundamental, and unavoidable limitations of little picture logic, science, and mathematics.

I will show you how physics is related to, and derived from, metaphysics. Additionally, you will find that mind, consciousness, and the paranormal are given a sound scientific explanation that stands upon a solid theoretical foundation. Not necessarily in the way hoped for and expected by traditional science – however, as you will discover, being nontraditional is a necessary strength, not an unavoidable weakness.

Sooner or later, truth must succeed and falsity must self-destruct. Although the consensus of culturally empowered opinion may carry the day, measurable results will carry the day after that. The value and success of *My Big TOE* must be based solely upon the personal and objective results that it produces. Only truth can produce significant consistent results. In contrast, falsity excels at producing assertive beliefs, arguments, and opinions. Open your mind, remain skeptical, pursue only significant measurable results, and let the chips fall where they may.

My Big TOE is in the form of a reality model at a level that is necessarily unusual, but easy to understand. It provides an exploration of the scientific and philosophical implications of consciousness evolution, a subject that holds critical significance for everyone.

Because this material must develop entirely new scientific and reality paradigms, it requires an extensive presentation to shed light upon the limitations of culturally habituated patterns of thought – a goal that cannot be both quickly and effectively reached. Such an in-depth multi-disciplined analysis is better suited to a trilogy than to the condensed formal structure of a traditional scientific paper.

The focus of this trilogy is directed toward the potential significance that *My Big TOE* holds for each individual reader. These books were written for you – you will find their tone to be more personal than general, more of a sharing of experience and concepts, than a lecture by an expert. It is your potential personal interaction with this material that has initiated, as well as driven, its development.

You will find an open, logical, and skeptical mind with a broad depth of experience is much more helpful than a technical background. The details of little picture reality are by nature highly technical, the exclusive territory of modern science and mathematics. On the other hand, Big Picture reality is available and accessible to **anyone** with an open mind and the will to apply it. There are no requirements for formal education or technical credentials in order to understand what is presented here.

There are three main challenges that must be met in order to deliver a shrink-wrapped Big TOE to the general public. First, with shirtsleeves rolled up and the lights turned on, I must turn some portion of metaphysics into physics because I intend to describe the whole of reality – mind and matter, normal and paranormal – not merely the matter and normal part. Consequently, metaphysics is where I must start – our contemporary physics will naturally flow from the metaphysics. The second challenge is to package this unavoidably far-out subject in a way that is interesting, easily readable, intellectually engaging, and non-threatening. To this end, I use the format of a one-on-one, peer-to-peer, informal discussion between the reader and me. The third challenge is to make and keep *My Big TOE* credible – to stay tightly logical while straightforwardly explaining the data of our collective and individual experience.

Culturally conditioned mental reflexes may need to be re-examined, generalized, and expanded. The fact that some of the content of this trilogy is likely to lie far beyond the comfortable familiarity of your personal experience creates a difficult communications problem for both of us. *My Big TOE* not only requires you to think out-of-the-box, but out-of-the-ballpark (if not out-of-the-universe), as well. You will be challenged to overcome deep seated knee-jerk cultural drag in order to climb high enough up the mountain to get a good view.

Modern science and technology are only now providing the combined knowledge by which metaphysics can be understood. It should not be too surprising that science, in its relentless explorations of the unknown, would one day arrive at the roots of existence itself. As it turns out, the nature of reality has both an objective and a subjective component. *My Big TOE* provides a thoroughly scientific description of an objective Theory Of Everything that covers all aspects of reality in an entirely general way. Additionally, it provides a remarkably practical, personally significant understanding of subjective consciousness, and explains how you individually are related to the larger reality. To appreciate and deeply understand the personal or subjective nature of consciousness, you must grow your own Big TOE. One of the major goals of *My Big TOE* is to provide the logical conceptual framework, materials, tools, and direction that you need to independently grow your Big TOE.

My Big TOE will provide the foundation and structure that you need to make sense of both your objective and subjective experience. Your personal Big Understanding of Big Truth must flow primarily from **your** direct experience – not from your intellect alone. This trilogy will bring your objective and subjective experience together under one coherent understanding of the whole you.

Please understand, I did **not** put the "My" in *My Big TOE* to flaunt pride of authorship. Nor does the "My" indicate any lack of generality or applicability to others. The "My" was added to be a constant reminder to you that this reality model cannot serve as your **personal** Big TOE until it is based upon your **personal** experience. On the other hand, personal or subjective experience is only one piece of the reality puzzle. In the objective physical world of traditional science, *My Big TOE* delivers a comprehensive model of reality that subsumes modern science, describes our objective material reality, and is universally applicable. Contemporary physics is shown to be a special case of a more general set of basic principles. After reading the *My Big TOE* trilogy, you will better understand the universal (objective) and the personal (subjective) nature of perception, consciousness, reality, and Big TOEs. You will learn to appreciate the fact that the larger reality extends beyond objective causality, beyond the reach of intellectual effort, into the subjective mind of each individual. **My** *Big TOE* is the launch pad. **Your** Big TOE is the final destination.

A personal Big TOE is necessary because the larger reality, like your consciousness, has a subjective component as well as a collective objective component. The larger reality cannot be fully appreciated or understood merely by studying, or reading about it. You must experience it. Additionally, your understanding of the Big Picture must be sufficient to integrate your subjective experience with your shared objective knowledge or both will remain superficial. To the traditional scientist and other left-brained analytical types, what I have just said sounds suspiciously like a mixing of real science and hocus-pocus, touchy-feely, belief-baloney. It is not, but a properly skeptical mind may need to digest all three books before that becomes apparent.

Arriving at conclusions based upon the assumed infallibility and apparent truth of culturally, personally, and professionally embedded paradigms and dogmas will make it difficult to understand the larger reality. Change and new ways of thinking are often traumatic, difficult to integrate, and generally unwelcome. Resistance to change is automatic at the gut level; we cling to familiar ways for the security and comfort they provide. We do not easily see unfamiliar patterns. You must be willing to overcome fear and rise above self-imposed belief-blindness if you are to succeed in getting a good look at the Big Picture.

In the pages ahead, we are going to explore the reality-wilderness. This trilogy is about the how, what, and why of what is. It is about physics and metaphysics, your world and other worlds. It is about beginnings, endings, mind and matter, point and purpose – it is also about the quality of your personal consciousness.

Your intellectual understanding of the reality you exist within, and are a part of, is only the beginning – a place to start. The most important action, the real fun, begins **after** you have finished the trilogy and begin to apply what you have learned about reality and the Big Picture to the rest of your life – both professionally and personally.

Though you will soon learn there is more to reality than theory and facts, here is one fact that you should consider before you begin: Big Truth, once understood and assimilated, always modifies your intent, and invariably leads to personal change.

List of Acronyms, Symbols, and Foreign Words and Phrases Used Within Book 2

■■■

Acronym	Descriptive Name	Page
		(First Mention)
AUM	Absolute Unbounded Manifold	41
AUO	Absolute Unbounded Oneness	41
Big TOE	Big Picture Theory Of Everything	9
CEO	Chief Executive Officer	90
CNS	Central Nervous System	107
DNA	Deoxyribo Nucleic Acid	96
EBC	Even Bigger Computer	41
FWAU	Free Will Awareness Unit	79
MOG	Mind Of God	185
NPMR	Nonphysical-Matter Reality	41
OS	Our System	41
PMR	Physical-Matter Reality	41
PUI	Physical User Interface	249
RWW	Reality Wide Web	84
TBC	The Big Computer	41
TOE	Theory Of Everything	9

Other Symbols:

C++	A compiled computer programming language	336

Foreign Words and Phrases:

gedanken experiment – thought experiment; a logical experiment performed only in the mind.

über alles – over all; over and above all else.

número uno – number one

No problema – No Problem

■ ■ ■
Synopsis of Book 1
■ ■ ■✿

Book 1: *Awakening* **– Section 1** provides a partial biography of the author that is pertinent to the subsequent creation of this trilogy. This brief look at the author's unique experience and credentials sheds light upon the origins of this extraordinary work. The unusual associations, circumstances, training, and research that eventually led to the creation of the *My Big Picture Theory Of Everything* (My Big TOE) trilogy are described to provide a more accurate perspective of the whole.

Book 1: *Awakening* **– Section 2** lays out and defines the basic conceptual building blocks needed to construct *My Big TOE's* conceptual foundation. It discusses the cultural beliefs that trap our thinking into a narrow and limited conceptualization of reality, defines the basics of Big Picture epistemology and ontology, as well as examines the nature and practice of meditation. Most importantly, Section 2 defines and develops the two fundamental assumptions upon which this trilogy is based – a high entropy primordial consciousness energy-form called AUO (Absolute Unbounded Oneness) and the Fundamental Process of evolution. AUO eventually evolves to become a much lower-entropy consciousness energy-form called AUM (Absolute Unbounded Manifold) even though neither is absolute or unbounded. Using only these two assumptions, Section 2 logically infers the nature of time, space, and consciousness as well as describes the basic properties, purpose, and mechanics of our reality. Additionally, Section 2 develops the concepts of The Big Computer (TBC) and the Even Bigger Computer (EBC) as operational models of aware digital consciousness. Our System (OS) is defined to be PMR (Physical Matter Reality – our physical universe) **plus** the subset of $NPMR_N$ [a specific part of Nonphysical Matter Reality (NPMR)] that is interactive with PMR. Many of the concepts initiated in Section 2 are more fully explained in Book 2.

Section 3

■ ■ ■

Man in the Loop
How You Fit into
the Big Picture –
Ego, Body, Mind, and Purpose

■ ■ ■

1

■ ■ ■

Introduction to Section 3

■ ■ ■

AUM evolved the space-time consciousness construct to provide us with the experience we need to help it lower its overall entropy. Is this not as crystal clear as the morning dew? If you do not understand this now, you will understand it clearly before you have completed Book 2.

Before we get started, it might be a good idea to warm-up first with a few mind stretches. Everybody take a deep breath. Here we go. Stay with me now. Try to hallucinate a spherical chicken... a very large spherical chicken... bigger... bigger... bigger. That's it! Now hold that concept ... hold it... hold it.... Now – this is the difficult part – pretend you understand it... that's it, make it seem perfectly understandable, perfectly reasonable... that's it! That's it! Now hold that clarity... hold it...just a little longer... hold it...OK! ... Relax! ... Phew! That's better. OK, now end with another deep breath. That was great! I think you are as ready as you are going to get.

Seriously folks, if you do not understand something, do not assume that it must be so or that it cannot be so – and do not pretend uncritically that you understand what is outside of your experience. Remember: Open minded skepticism is the order of the day. Use it to fill up the void left by temporarily suspending your beliefs. All right, let's get back to work.

It is not that we are separate from space-time and live within it, as we live in a house but are not part of the house. We experience space-time as our minds interpret and process the limited perceptions gathered by our senses. Contrary to popular belief, space-time is not a physical construct that we physical beings live within, but rather the result of a rule-set that defines the experiential virtual reality that we perceive. Because of our limited physical perception-based experience, it appears to us that we live or exist within a space-time universe when in fact space-time is nothing more than the constraints that bound the experience of an individuated consciousness enrolled in PMR 101.

I know that this is confusing, but by the end of Section 4, you will have no trouble understanding that the physical reality you physically experience is merely the experience our consciousness interprets as physical reality. If your sensed physical reality and what your consciousness interprets as physical reality seem the same to you, it is because your culture has convinced you that consciousness is a derivative of the physical body. The experience that our senses interpret as physical reality leads to the conclusion that physical reality is an **external** reality that our body interacts with (reality is defined by our physical interaction with it). On the other hand, the experience that our consciousness interprets as physical reality leads to the conclusion that physical reality is an **internal** reality created by the perceptions of consciousness – a virtual physical existence that is defined by our minds interaction with the space-time rule-set. The first assigns perception directly to the body, while the second assigns perception directly to the consciousness and only indirectly to a virtual body constrained to perceive a local reality defined by a given rule set. An individual mind (an individuated unit of consciousness) engaged in an interactive multi-player virtual reality must experience, act, and interact within the bounds prescribed by the causal rule-set that defines that particular reality. Any consistent high fidelity virtual reality must follow a specific rule set and will appear to be physical to the individuals experiencing it.

Clarity should emerge in Section 4 as you begin to understand that the ultimate source of your experience is not what you perceive as your local physical reality. Your physical reality is an interpreted virtual reality that only appears physical. Have patience and you shall see that this concept is scientifically and logically sound.

Individuated consciousness within AUM is roughly analogous to a two-dimensional bed sheet that some children have stuck their hands into, pulling the sheet down around their wrists and forearms to make individuated hand puppets. Each hand puppet is an individual animated thing, and can interact with the other puppets (by grabbing them perhaps). Yet for all their individuality (fat, thin, small, large, aggressive, calm), each hand puppet is part of the same sheet, existing only as protrusions in the sheet relative to flatter, more uniform parts of the sheet. The puppets exist as three-dimensional variations in the two-dimensional sheet. They are all part of the same sheet, but exist as individual extensions of the two dimensional sheet into the third dimension.

It is worth noting that the extensions into the third dimension must be maintained by constraints. Imagine a rubber band that goes over the puppet and around the wrist of the child's hand. Remove the constraint and the sheets protrusion into the third dimension quickly disappears. The sheet maintains its natural two dimensional existence unless some sort of constraint forces it to bulge in the third dimension.

Similarly we PMR physical beings, each with our personal individuated consciousness, are all part of the same AUM consciousness. We are individual, yet at the same time we are all one with AUM, the fundamental source consciousness. Our individual existence, like the hand puppets, is the result of constraints defining a dimensional variation in consciousness that individuates a unique entity with free will. Space-time is the virtual medium through which the rules of engagement (constraints that define our interactive experience with other "players") are applied. Players are defined as anything (beings, objects, or energy) that may become interactive with us.

Can one idea (thought-thing) be manifested through (give birth to) another? Sure. Why not? In AUM's world of digital consciousness energy, thoughts (discrete packets of organized content) are real things – the only real things – and AUM can birth (think up or organize) as many as it wants to. Think of a thought within AUM as a reusable object, a chunk of fixed or variable content with certain attributes, characteristics and abilities that can be stored, transmitted, or used as an operator. The object oriented programmers among you will pick this idea up very easily while the rest should think about the persistent, consistent, and cumulative digital existence of various characters, items, and devices in interactive on-line computer games. Now, imagine that some of these game-object-thought-forms have enough complexity, memory, and access to processing power to be goal seeking, self-modifying independent agents. Let your imagination run wild until you can imagine digital creations of all types – all thought forms within a digital consciousness.

Recall that everything at its core is part of the same digital-AUM-mind-sheet-thing. If you followed the previous two paragraphs, you ended up with the concept that we are fragments, derivatives, or subsets of AUM consciousness, existing individually within AUM.

Oh sheet! This is confusing! [This is your first test. Was the preceding phrase: (a) – a prayer to AUM asking for guidance and relief; (b) – a thinly veiled coarse expression of frustration born of a limited viewpoint; (c) – a pitiful attempt at humor; (d) – one more meaningless phrase indistinguishable from all the others; or (e) – all of the above?]

In Section 4, I will give a detailed explanation of how we derive, perceive, and experience our 3D bodies as well as our entire space-time universe. We, our universe, and other universes in other dimensions are all specialized thought-parts or subsets of AUM. This is true for physical and nonphysical beings and universes. Before we leap off into a discussion of how, why, and where we as individuals fit into this Big Picture, let us quickly pull together and consolidate what we know about AUO, AUM, and the results of the Fundamental Process.

We know that AUM is the result of the Fundamental Process of evolution being applied to the one celled, dimly aware, primal AUO consciousness-potential energy-thing. We also know that AUM's complexity and awareness continues to dramatically accelerate until it reaches a relatively stable average growth rate where issues of quality and refinement begin absorbing more of the available energy than bold new leaps into unknown and untried possibilities. From that point, internal quality is improved and gains are refined, integrated, and consolidated until the next evolutionary breakthrough occurs, setting off another period of rapid growth.

Eventually, the growth **rates** of finite systems must decrease (the very definition of maturity), but they do not have to go to zero. In general, the larger the system, the longer it takes before growth rates become asymptotic to the time axis. An apparently infinite aware-consciousness-energy-thing constitutes an exceedingly large finite system with unimaginable opportunities for accelerated growth. Do not even try to imagine the breadth, depth and capacity of AUM – you cannot.

Digital consciousness systems do not deteriorate with time like biological systems, though they can de-evolve – that is, evolve into higher entropy, less significant, profitable, and viable states. AUM achieves self-optimization and growth through the exploration of the possibilities by implementing the Fundamental Process. AUM can eventually figure out how to willfully boost its quality (lower its entropy by utilizing its potential and organizing its bits more effectively) once it realizes that profitability is a function of the intent that drives its choices. So it is with us.

When you read "AUM learns," do not use the small-view definition of learning (intellectual learning). Learning is more than accumulating facts from your experience, other people, or books. Big Picture learning must also include improving the quality of your being, which is not a fact-based process. Have you ever known an exceptionally smart person (knows lots of useful facts) who is also (choose one or more from the following list) dumb, out of it, insensitive, egocentric, arrogant, or an intermittent or full time jerk? If you have the stellar good fortune to hang out in the hallowed halls of academia, with the upper echelons of government or corporate management, or with a bunch of highly ambitious middle aged professionals, you know exactly the type I am referring to. Such a person appears more retarded than advanced from the perspective of a bigger picture where the ability to develop and maintaining effective positive relationships with a wide variety of people is much more significant than the ability to manipulate facts.

Clearly, growing up within a larger reality has much more to do with raising the quality of your consciousness than accumulating information. What matters most is the development of wisdom, understanding, and the capacity to love – which are not primarily intellectual achievements. As you grow up, you learn to synthesize your experience data into larger and larger perspectives until eventually **everything** is seen to be interactive, interrelated, and a part of everything else. (The love I am referring to here is an attitude, a value, a way of interacting and being, and needs no specific object on which to focus.)

Facts and intellectual knowledge can help point in the right direction and perhaps pick around the edges of how to grow quality, but to truly "get it" requires that one go beyond rational PMR causal analysis. Analysis fails because you can never collect more than a small percentage of the relevant facts required for a rational, logical conclusion when dealing with Big Picture issues – and because love is **not** an intellectual result. Love is the result of low-entropy consciousness.

AUO was described earlier as everything (the one source) and nothing (no actual individuated thing) simultaneously. AUO began its existence as an unstructured potential energy system analogous to a single biological cell floating in the primordial ooze. AUM is aware, active and purposeful – an advanced aware consciousness. What an amazing transformation! You can thank the Fundamental Process of evolution, especially as it applies to consciousness, for that metamorphosis. As consciousness develops awareness, intelligence, values and personality, its entropy shrinks as its ability to organize itself effectively and profitably increases.

AUO represents the basis for consciousness, an energy form, a media for digital self-organization or awareness. AUO is a metaphor for a primordial dim awareness that evolved the capability to create differentiated cells (local non-uniformity) relative to its uniformity. It subsequently found it profitable to change the state of those cells as the Fundamental Process began optimizing internal environmental interactions. As the complexity, potentiality, and possibilities grew, AUO's awareness evolved to include, specialized structure, memory, organization, complex content laden communications between subsystems, brilliant self-awareness, and purpose. AUO naturally evolves (grows up) into AUM.

▶ Picture AUM as a geeky hygiene-challenged teenage computer freak with ugly red zits called PMRs. Do you think our universe might be a particularly nasty infection on the nose a pubescent consciousness? I bet you have never thought of your reality in those terms before. A mystical eruption on the nostril of AUM! What a beautiful image. Sheer poetry! Of course, I am just kidding… we wouldn't be on AUM's nose.

Speaking of getting popped, what does the "Zit Theory Of Existence," or what is more affectionately referred to by cosmologists and cosmetologists as the "Pus Я Us Reality Concept" do for your ego's sense of humanities special importance?

Ahhh ha! After all that polite jabber about petri dishes, the mysterious connection between humanity and bacteria rises to a head.

A word of caution: This book is heavy so be careful where you throw it. You might inadvertently hit an innocent bystander in the head – thereby warping his skull and his mind simultaneously.

Take a deep breath and let it go; there is no saving throw against tasteless, lowbrow humor – these days an eloquent book is as rare as a truly innocent bystander. ◀

The evolution of bright complex consciousness from dim awareness – does that seem unlikely? We carbon based human life-forms are reported to have done something like that ourselves – from one celled dimly-aware blobs of protoplasm to our present grand and elegant selves (did I forget to mention magnificent, brilliant, and superior?). And we are on slow time by 36 orders of magnitude compared to AUO-AUM.

You, as part of AUM, are simply an individuated consciousness. I know that may seem strange, but making this a reasonable proposition and explaining how it works is what Sections 4 and 5 are all about. AUM is consciousness, thought, operational knowledge, idea, and awareness. Consciousness represents the most basic form of energy – a self-relational digital media that can be structured through evolutionary processes to reduce its average entropy. You are a portion, an infinitesimal smidgen, of this AUM-consciousness-thing and as such, you share the attributes and abilities of all consciousness. Because the capacity of your particular con-sciousness – your personal evolutionary potential – is great, so is your responsibility for its development and use.

AUM, like any complex system, has evolved both structural and dynamic components. Its structural components are objectives, values, dimension (specialized calculation space), memory, and patterns (rules).

Its dynamic components are time, intent, motivation, intellect and will. Value based awareness, intelligence, and purpose are created, sustained, driven, animated, and motivated by the evolutionary imperative to improve the functionality of the system through better organization (entropy reduction).

The imperative to implement the Fundamental Process is the prime mover of progress. AUM **is** consciousness (as opposed to **has** consciousness) and it eventually acts, changes state, and evolves through the exercise of will or intent – self-aware consciousness in control of itself. If you really want to (for poetic reasons) or really need to (for reasons of emotional comfort), you may say that all things (our universe, all PMRs and NPMRs, and all the beings therein) are manifestations of AUM's will and made of AUM's substance (self-configuring digital organization). You could also say that we brainy people, with our minds full of fully operational and original thoughts and ideas, are created in AUM's image (along with a varied collection of thoughtful dogs, cats, foxes, pigs, monkeys, and computers). Don't get lost here: I am talking about our minds, our consciousness, not our adorable little bodies.

Now we can take one more fold in our bed-sheet analogy. As before, AUM is the sheet, we and everything in our reality are the sheet-hand-puppets protruding into the space-time dimension, and the energy that animates the little fingers, hands, and arms is our individuated portion of AUM's conscious awareness, which is expressed through our individual free will. The sheet and its protruding dimensions are engaged in a program of continuous quality improvement administered by the Fundamental Process of evolution acting upon a multi-leveled consciousness-evolution fractal ecosystem. By the end of Section 4 this will be clear. For now, merely entertain the possibility that our bodies and all the objective matter in our 3D world are the products of constrained consciousness and a rule-based virtual sense perception.

Do not fall into habituated anthropomorphic concepts or you may start thinking of AUM as a person. It will be more productive to think of AUM as a thing, a complex consciousness system, a big cellular quantized thought-energy-thing that constitutes the One Source of All That Is. Do not conceive of AUM as a super-human intellect – yourself extrapolated to god-sized proportions and qualities. Resist the urge to turn AUM into an ancient looking old geezer with a long white beard playing with his pet people, or all manner of silliness will mystically erupt from the great void.

▶ "Hey, I know, let's play God! – I'll be the god, and you be the people.…

No way, Hosea! I wanna be the god! I thought it up, it's my game and I wanna be the god first!

OK, OK, I promise – next eternity you can be the god and I'll be the people. Oh, come-on – it'll be fun!

Tell you what, if you let me be the god this eternity, I'll make you boss over all the critters and give you a woman that never goes out of heat. Deal?" ◀

Is AUM's awareness intelligent and sentient? I would say so, but not in the same way that we are intelligent and sentient – not that limited. Is a baboon's awareness intelligent and sentient? Yes, but more limited than ours in most cases. Does AUM care? Does it take care of us? Aren't we its babies, so to speak? Good grief! Don't get anthropomorphically silly on me here. Wipe that self-indulgent mist out of those puppy eyes. Do you care about the individual cells in your thumb or whether or not you are born with or without an appendix? Not really.

Where we human-types place our attention depends on the challenges of the Fundamental Process. Much of our energy is dedicated to our physical being (issues of survival and procreation). However, AUM does not have that distraction. Evolution for AUM is more of an up-close and personal take-charge sort of thing. Perhaps as we get better at genetic engineering and cloning we will get a dim glimmer of AUM's position relative to influencing its own evolution. Until then, it is best not to puff up our self-importance so much that it gets in the way of our ability to see the truth – whatever it might be.

In the meantime, if lumpy consciousness sheets seem distressingly cold and impersonal as a source of our being, I have a practical solution. Anyone wanting a warm fuzzy relationship that gushes unconditional love, which is focused individually on, and directly at, a needful, and oh, so, deserving **you** should... get a dog! Don't be confused by the forward and backward spelling thing: Simply look for a genuine, guaranteed warm and fuzzy d-o-g.

Besides loving, dogs are straightforward, honest, faithful, loyal, and forgiving. They are seldom demanding, revengeful, jealous, angry, self-important, or into fear and dogma (egotistical). They will never ever tell you to go to hell. They are never rude or sassy and never forget to flush the toilet or to turn off the lights that they have turned on. They will not run up charges on your credit card or dent your car. Better yet, they never drop their clothes on the floor and will never invite their mother to come live with you. No dog has ever smoked a cigar or invited his friends over to drink beer and watch football on TV.

Dogs are happy to exist on your leftovers and eat your garbage. That, ladies and gentlemen, is as warm and fuzzy as it gets **if** you are looking for a relationship that takes little-to-no effort on your part. That is what we are all looking for, isn't it? A no-fault (at least not ours) low maintenance relationship in which we are unconditionally loved and forgiven because we exist and meet the basic superficial requirements – what could be better than that? That is what you truly want, right? *No problema!* Go get a d-o-g!

If you maintain the letters in the right order, you will happily find that dogs deliver warm fuzzies **all** the time instead of only in relation to your needs, beliefs, and fears. And here is the best part – dog ownership never generates internal pressures that would lead you to be hypocritical or self righteous – you can just be yourself. Your dog will love you however you are. Even if you are not nice to your dog and don't love it – it will still love and adore you above all others! Its love is widely spread, deeply sincere, and truly unconditional – a being worthy of your emulation, if not outright worship.

Hey, what's with the firewood, rope, and torches? Is this some sort of medieval pageant? Are we going to have a bonfire and toast marshmallows? Look, I agree with you! There **are** magnificent and endless sources of genuine spiritual warm-fuzzies, but you have to work hard to grow up enough to access them. They are not easy, low maintenance, or superficial. They are not focused, even in a small way, on what **you get** for meeting requirements. That concept was spawned to support a membership drive. Instead, they are about your capacity to embody and apply (give) absolute unconditional love. Performing rituals and doing dogma doesn't get it. Belief (pro or con) can, at best, generate a self-focused ego-centric "**I** feel good about **myself**, **my** faith, and **my** belief" warm pseudo-fuzzy.

If you ever get to know the real thing, you will never again settle for a pseudo-fuzzy.

2

■ ■ ■

Jeez Louise, Will That Fat Rat
Ever Find the Cheese?

■ ■ ■

It is generally accepted (among humans) that we Homo sapiens have the most advanced intelligence and are the most thoughtful of all the earth-creatures. Does that make us more AUM-like – closer to the source? Do you think that we must be AUM's favorite creation, or most amusing experiment? Humans are no doubt exceptionally clever. What other species could create no fewer than five entirely independent ways to destroy all life as we know it (nuclear bombs, global warming, toxic waste, pollution, and excessive non-ecological global resource consumption)? Such creativity and awesome intelligence makes you feel proud, doesn't it? What's wrong with this picture? What term is missing from the human equation?

Our species has always intuitively known that a little knowledge is a dangerous thing, we just never appreciated how dangerous for how little. Ah, we beings of limited 3D awareness – what you see is what you get – that is the beauty of us, and the opportunity of us. Our awareness-limited, physical experienced-based, interactive human community excels at creating wonderful opportunities to grow the individual and collective quality of our consciousness.

Limited awareness guarantees that our interaction within PMR accurately and immediately reflects the quality of our being. You have only to consider young children or your favorite furry critter to realize how a perspective that is limited to a relatively little picture produces transparent and straightforward interactions and reactions. For an individuated consciousness such as you, limited awareness produces learning opportunities within a relatively simple and straightforward interactive virtual environment with immediate results-related feedback and consequences.

The complex, duplicitous, and anything-but-straightforward minds that we appear to have only look like that from a limited viewpoint where insignificant variations of fear and ego appear to be vastly more important than they actually are. The events that we wring our hands and gnash our teeth over day after day are typically drawn from the mishmash of trivial details that define our personal soap operas. What appears vitally important to us in the little picture of belief blindness and struggling egos is often completely inconsequential from a Big Picture perspective.

You are aware in the little picture so that you may eventually grow your quality until it becomes capable of direct participation in the Big Picture. Aimlessly wandering about in a fear-based ego-driven little picture soap opera where you get to write your own script is not exactly on the fast track to success. That you may be a good enough and lucky enough script writer to become rich and famous in PMR is irrelevant.

In order to have a meaningful opportunity to do it right, you must also have the opportunity to do it wrong. From the perspective of the Big Picture, physical reality provides an optimal nursery for budding consciousness.

The typical self-assessment of human mental complexity and cleverness is based on our self-serving species-definition of "intelligence" and "cleverness" as the ability to influence, manipulate, control, and dominate others (natural and man-made environments, plants, critters, other people, and everything else). That is why we clever humans develop and evolve most of our technologies and social systems around the needs of war, defense, trade, and communications and why we have both accidentally and purposely generated multiple capacities to destroy the diverse life of our planet along with ourselves. Because of our needs, wants, desires, fears, ignorance, beliefs, and ego (lack of consciousness quality), we apply much of the mental energy of our species to issues of control and dominance – internationally, nationally, and personally. Cleverness, it seems, is primarily in the eye of the beholder.

Nevertheless, we physical beings are, from the viewpoint of a less limited consciousness, exceedingly simple and straightforward; our motivations, intentions, and interactions accurately and clearly demonstrate the quality of our consciousness in everything we do, say, think, and feel. A less limited consciousness finds our machinations within the physical to be transparent. Our quality, or lack thereof, is obvious; we cannot hide what we are. I have to ask: What do **your** motivations and actions say about the quality of **your** consciousness? That is a good question to ponder (you should paste that on the refrigerator door of your mind to remind you to ask it often) because, one day not that far off, you will need to deal with the answer.

The results of our actions (the environment we create) as well as the reactions of other people to us, provide immediate feedback to assess the quality of our intent. We create our reality through the implementation of our intent-choices and how we interpret our perceptions – the results are most often precisely what we need and deserve (can use) to stimulate productive growth. In general, if we do it wrong (make the wrong choices), we get pain. If we do it right, the resultant spiritual growth spreads sunshine everywhere. Here, "right" and "wrong" are used in the evolutionary sense. Right and wrong in the evolutionary sense are the same as absolute right and wrong in the motivational sense when the Fundamental Process of evolution is focused on improving the quality of our consciousness. The previous sentence actually makes sense, but you may need to think about it a while. Relative right and wrong often has its roots in absolute right and wrong, however, the result may be strangely twisted by belief systems of all sorts (cultural, religious, personal, and scientific).

▶ All pain does not come from making the wrong choices. Only self-inflicted (internally caused) pain, which makes up the bulk of our daily ration of pain and suffering, has wrong choices at its fundamental source. You may occasionally experience either small or great pain from external sources; these usually reflect the existence of randomness within our lives. (I will discuss the origin and nature of these random components in Chapter 11 of this book and in the next two Sections.) It is this simple: Sometimes the ball takes a bounce and hits you squarely between the eyes, and sometimes the cookie crumbles into dust before you get to taste it. Or, in the pithy, if somewhat crude, words of the famous cinematic philosopher-genius Forest Gump: "Shit happens."

External and internal causes of pain can be mixed and mingled together. However, most of us most of the time wrongly believe that our self-created pain is actually externally derived. That belief makes us feel better in the short run. We do not want to see ourselves as the primary source of our unhappiness and dissatisfaction, though that is **almost** always the truth. It is easier and more comfortable for us to **believe** that we are the victims of others, or simply are unlucky. Sometimes that is the case — but that condition is the rare exception rather than the general rule.

The general rule is that most of the pain in your life is self-inflicted while very little is thrust upon you from the outside. We believe the opposite because an external enemy is always easier to accept and defeat than an internal one. It is as easy to see how this rule applies to others, as it is difficult to see how it applies to oneself. ◀

Right and wrong in the social or cultural sense is relative and custom-ary – often a diluted and distorted shadow of absolute right and wrong. Absolute right and wrong are operationally defined to optimize the growth (evolution) of the quality of our consciousness, or equivalently, our spiritual development. "Right" intents and choices help us improve the quality of our being, whereas "wrong" intents and choices stimulate no positive growth and may cause us to lose some previously earned qual-ity. Absolute right and wrong (intents, motivations, choices, and actions) are defined and differentiated by the affect they have on the average entropy of the system.

One can learn from either right or wrong choices. PMR is designed to serve as a learning lab – a place where units of individuated consciousness (sometimes referred to as beings, entities, or souls) can grow up (improve their quality) by exercising their free will intent within a virtual system of direct interactive experience and feedback. Many other subsets of NPMR$_N$ are also configured as learning labs – some employ versions of space-time while others do not. Each provides a local reality system for its inhabitants who see themselves as physical and all other realities as nonphysical. All reality systems are virtual; hence there is no actual distinction between real and virtual. Everything is consciousness, a vast system of self-modify-ing digital organization evolving toward lower entropy.

Most of the time we are provided a near optimal learning opportunity, by circumstances that we have custom-designed to fit our individual needs. Moment by moment, with immediate and obvious results, these growth opportunities stare us in the face or bop us between the eyes. Could any learning laboratory be more efficient than our beloved 3D space-time? I doubt it. AUM knew what it was doing (evolutionarily speaking that is) when it invented (evolved) the concept of limited virtual physical realities.

We are like rats in a maze where wrong turns meet with an immediate electrical shock. We are in a wonderfully complex pudding-maze; to suc-ceed, we must taste our way through it. What could be easier or more effi-cient? We make the wrong choices and are motivated by the wrong rea-sons and... Zap! We get the electric shock and make ourselves miserable. We make the right choices for the right reasons and we create happy, pro-ductive, rewarding lives (we get the cheese). This is simple evolution where success is simultaneously its own criteria, evaluation, and reward. Consciousness is in the process of evolving its way through an evolution-ary maze of intent, choice, interaction, and reaction.

I should point out a few basic facts about evolving the quality of your consciousness in our reality. Although the results of your actions (feedback) are immediate and obvious, you can ignore them or misinterpret them if your ego is making too big a fuss. Then, it may take a while before the situation degenerates to the point where the resulting dysfunction becomes impossible to ignore or excuse. As in all learning situations, being attentive – paying attention in class – is absolutely essential to an efficient learning process. Don't ask for an easier maze – you won't get one. For those who typically slip through demanding situations by avoiding the things that are most difficult, let me point out that there are absolutely no shortcuts, no end runs, no acceptable excuses, and no way to quit.

That anthropomorphized little old man with the long white beard that you can hustle favors from by believing the correct things and performing the correct rituals is a product of your little picture culture and a fearful, needy mind looking for the easy way out. No one is handing out judgments and calling the plays from the sidelines. Not even a non-anthropomorphic AUM thought-system-thing is likely to be paying attention to any particular individual human bacterium in the PMR petri dish. Humanity, as you know it and think of it, is not central to the machinations of the Big Picture. You should be proud to be a bit player, not disappointed because you are not the star. As far as I can tell, no reality or dimension is more central than the others: all are bit players (or equivalently, all are stars) playing their specific parts.

Only a fat-ugly ego could care a flip about the **relative** importance of earth-based humans. The relative value and comparative status of our species holds no meaning for an advanced consciousness such as yourself, but you wouldn't believe how many other folks think that humanity is the crème de la crème of sentient existence. These egotists can become deflated, resistive, and defensive when you tell them that, in the Big Picture, they are not particularly important. When you are used to being fantastically magnificent and superior – a legend in your own mind – it is difficult to see yourself as a common bit-player in a much larger drama.

The process of improving the quality of your consciousness is a matter of simple evolution – much easier than a fish learning to walk on land and breathe air. Live and learn, do and die, if at first you don't succeed, try, try again – you know the drill. Take your place alongside the other sentient chunks of individuated digital consciousness, both physical and non-physical. Neither you, nor your species, nor your local reality is more important, special, or superior relative to the gazillions of others.

Feelings of superiority developed in relation to other obviously inferior PMR beings and life-forms (mankind is above all other creatures of the earth) is an error of perception that has generated many particularly destructive belief systems and caused much damage to biosphere-earth – as well as greatly retarded individual human progress toward greater consciousness quality. Because consciousness is an attribute of individuals, all conscious entities are vitally important in their own way: each has its own mission and purpose and is an important contributor to the whole. All are different, all have their own challenges, and none is fundamentally superior or inferior.

Think of consciousness within $NPMR_N$ as a vast interdependent evolving ecosystem. Any part feeling superior to any other part is the result of ignorance, belief, and ego existing within a little picture perspective. Actions motivated by feelings of superiority are bound to lead to destructive results for **all** members of the larger system, including those feeling superior. How superior is it to shoot oneself in the foot over and over again?

▶ Now that you are feeling sufficiently humble, let me continue using the ecosystem metaphor to show you the other side of this coin.

Within the larger eco-mind-system designed to evolve consciousness quality, PMR can be thought of as a particular biome. Consciousness ecosystems are not based on the evolutionary pressures of mutual survival and propagation, but evolve to improve themselves, to lower their entropy.

Where survival and propagation represent predominate environmental constraints, individuals are not as important, in terms of evolution, as are the groups they belong to. In biological evolution, superior individuals either impact a larger species-level profitability statistic, or their potential contribution is lost. An individual's impact on the success of an established species is nearly infinitesimal. Progress accrues through a large number of very small individual contributions that all point in a similar direction. In biological systems it is the continuous immortal group, not the discontinuous mortal individual that is the primary beneficiary of evolution.

Within a consciousness system such as $NPMR_N$, individual immortal conscious entities continuously evolve and contribute gains in their personal consciousness quality (lowered entropy) **directly** to the whole of which they are a continuing part. A single conscious entity has the potential to make a very significant, direct, and wholly independent contribution to the larger consciousness ecosystem as it seeks profitability on a personal level. As each individuated consciousness evolves, the larger consciousness system (AUM) evolves as well.

Survival based interdependencies between groups and the evolution of species within PMR is replaced by personal growth and the evolution of individual consciousness within NPMR. That is how you can be one of a gazillion entities in some experimental consciousness petri dish and at the same time be individually very important to the whole. Your personal contribution is not limited by a group function or a slow uncertain pass-along process with strong random components; it is simply measured by the quality that your consciousness brings to the table. Quality runs the gamut from the severely limited, high-entropy, fear-based, self-serving ego, to the unlimited, low entropy, unconditional love exhibited by AUM-consciousness. As you move from the former to the latter, your personal significance relative to the whole increases dramatically.

Though even a brilliant bacterium must remain in its petri dish as a part of its group, an evolved consciousness can outgrow the culture within its originally assigned petri dish and one day join the laboratory staff! You are an independent (with free will) individuated consciousness containing the potential of AUM – no individual, species, or group affiliations can help or hinder your effort to become a more significant entity. Thus, feeling superior about your group affiliation (galaxy, planet, species, race, culture, religion, nation, profession, education, or socio-economic status) is simply counterproductive. (In an aside near the end of Chapter 20 of this book, I will explain why it is that a highly evolved, low entropy consciousness has no sense of superiority.)

In the Big Picture, the quality of your consciousness determines whether you are of infinitesimal or great stature, of minor or major consequence to the whole, have a job in the lab or are wallowing around cluelessly in the petri-dish. ◄

Implement the Fundamental Process! Make each choice count. Get with the program. Evolve your being. You **are** doing it now and you have no choice. You exist, you are an individuated consciousness and you cannot stop existing. Your physical death initiates a process that eventually creates a new maze for you to explore – your learning is cumulative. You are a participant in, as well as a driver of, the consciousness cycle.

You are in the game whether you want to be or not. Every day you are evolving more toward the positive or negative pole of being – you cannot stay neutral or remain stationary. Denial and ignorance are inconsequential and affect nothing – your permission or willingness to be involved is completely irrelevant. You are in the process of actively evolving your consciousness **now** – you are doing it for better or for worse. The only questions are how well and how efficiently are you doing it? Are you progressing or regressing, and if so, how steadily and at what rate? Is your growth process efficient? Is your learning rate optimal?

Shock or cheese? Jeez Louise, that's a tough one – let me think about it.

You can be confused and non productive (perhaps fail) if: (1) you do not understand the game and therefore do not know that your reality is actually an amazing maze of many choices that is driving the evolution of your consciousness – therefore remaining purposeless, pointless and without focus – not even trying. (2) your taste buds are so twisted and confused because of beliefs, self-absorption, attachments, needs, and fears (ego) that you cannot, or will not, taste the difference between miserable, arrogant, unproductive pudding, and loving, growth inducing, delicious and satisfying pudding. In other words, you cannot differentiate between electric shocks and fine white-cheddar cheese. You therefore lose your sense of direction and have no means to distinguish up from down, dark from light, or progress from regression.

If an individual rat in the maze sees no point in exploring and cannot differentiate between electrical shocks and cheese, it is in for a long and difficult training experience. Poor rat! What a miserably frustrating life! Not much progress is expected. Shocks become an ordinary accepted part of life and are no big deal! "That's life," says this rat with resignation. To this particular rat, the world (life within its local reality) may seem random, existential, nihilistic, mystical, or driven by an unfathomable, jealous, vengeful, or demanding god.

To a collection of such rats, cynicism, self-pity, anger, victim-hood, resignation, escapism, recreational drug use, as well as a fascination and obsession with sex and the symbols of power (including vicarious violence and domination through entertainment, competition and sport; conspicuous consumption; macho-vehicles and aggressive driving; and the ownership of weapons) become common personal strategies to deal with the anxiety (inadequacy, insecurity, and powerlessness) generated by fear. Value, purpose, objectives, and goals of being are lost in a confusing whirl of fine shades of relative, meaningless gray, while the original concepts of black and white are lost.

These hapless rats will be driven and animated by their ego – their immediate needs, wants, desires, fears, and beliefs. Does this description (driven and animated by immediate needs, wants, desires, fears, and beliefs) remind you of anyone you know – a distant acquaintance, a least favorite relative, or perhaps your evil twin? You might be tempted to surmise that these rats are obviously too dumb to play the game and that it is cruel and unusual punishment to put these stupid, lost, and confused creatures in such a complex maze in the first place. Unfortunately, evolution shows little compassion and weeps no tears for its failures or slow learners. Goodbye dodo birds, adios dinosaurs, so long trilobites. Your concept of "fair" is a function of your ego and belief systems and mostly irrelevant.

Reasons and excuses for not making it or getting it fall on the deaf ears of the Fundamental Process of evolution. Making it and getting it, within your given set of possible interactions, are the non-negotiable requirements of evolutionary progress. An evolving system is either unprofitable (say goodbye if that condition is not turned around in time), profitable (progress is being made), or neither (an astable condition that is hanging around waiting to see which way it will go).

Cruel and unusual? Too difficult? Do you sometimes feel that unreasonable conditions for growth are forced upon you? Sure, like bad weather at a picnic is forced upon you by mean old Mother Nature. The Fundamental Process, as it applies itself to an individuated consciousness, is not personal regardless of how helpless resignation, ego, anger, paranoia, cynicism, or self-pity might construe it.

If you think it is personal, you are probably placing yourself too high up on the consciousness chain. Bacteria are extremely important to us, our life depends on them, but what we do that affects bacteria is usually not intended to be a personal affront or reward to any individual bacterium. I am describing the general case – there are always exceptions, but they are much, much fewer than a poll would indicate.

Nevertheless, evolution is patient. Patient enough to let that rat suffer in confused discomfort until it eventually progresses its awareness and ambition to the point it can evolve a solution. The rat has free will and some basic intelligence, while evolution has all the time in the world. This rat is on its own to sink or swim by its choices. It does have one advantage, however: It gets (as most rats do) all the help it can profitably use from its nonphysical friends who do care and understand the significance of individual progress.

The theoretical long view is that because some rats do figure it out, and because those that do are strongly encouraged to help out the remaining rats, eventually **all** the rats will make it. That is too easy and one sided. The final outcome is a given – all the rats will eventually make it. The only questions remaining in such an experiment are the details defining the path taken to connect the endpoints and how long it will take. That is too narrowly focused and pedantically boring. To make things more interesting and challenging (and to learn more about the dynamics of consciousness), add to this learning laboratory the intrigue of bits of poison cheese and a myriad of clever distractions and confusions scattered throughout the maze by a competitive group of anti-rats.

Now the rats have a new set of options. To the struggle between ignorance, fear, and ego versus knowledge, wisdom, and love, is added the struggle between good and evil, between positive and negative intent. Now it is no longer clear that all the rats will eventually make it. No, this is not the equivalent of an adolescent AUM putting two big spiders in a glass jar to see what happens. Free will requires that negative intent be a possibility, and without free will, there can be no experiment. There is no point in doing experiments if the outcome is predetermined. Maximum free will enables maximum potential for both success and failure. Like any scientist, after AUM has completed the simpler experiments, it must move on to the more difficult and meaningful ones. (You will find a derivation and explanation of free will in Chapter 11 of this book.)

Evolution may simply want to know whether rats or anti-rats are the **natural** winners of this experiment. AUM may want to determine the dynamics of the quality and evolution of consciousness under various conditions. We require the stress and challenge in order to exercise our free will fully and thus optimize our potential growth.

Go rats go! Go rats go! Go rats go!

Don't you want to join our team (we are the Good Guys) and help us out – or do you just want to wear the t-shirt? For goodness sake, don't consider joining the Bad Guys – they are a miserable lot – and their benefits package stinks. You will eventually choose sides – everybody must. No one can refuse to play because in this game no choice becomes an active choice, eventually leading, by circumstance, toward one direction or the other. Interesting experiment, huh?

It is my best hope that some hard working rat will find a useful hint or secret map somewhere in this trilogy that will make a difference for him or her in the pursuit of their personal cheese.

3

■■■

Cheer Up: Things Are Not as Bleak as You Might Think
Say "Cheese Please," and
Hold That Smile!

■■■

The situation is neither hopeless, nor random, nor beyond your control – it is not even that difficult. Let's talk a moment about free will and making choices. **What** we do is not of **primary** importance; **why** we do it is what counts. The intent or motivation **is** the choice. Thus, our free will choices are **primarily** choices of motivation and intent – why we do what we do. Only **secondarily** are they choices of doing. What we actually do (the action we take) is the first **result** of our choice of intent, and drives a feedback mechanism, which is very good but not perfect, particularly in the short term.

This is not biological evolution we are talking about, where the key process driver is what you **do**. In the evolution of consciousness, motivation and intent are the key drivers of evolutionary process. What you do is secondary to **why** you do it. The right choice for the wrong reason is an oxymoron and does not exist (I am being tricky-picky here with the semantics to make the point that the development or selection of the intent **is** the choice that I am referring to).

Recall that right motivation, intent, and action generally result in a decrease of entropy within your consciousness, whereas wrong motivation, intent, and action generally result in an increase of entropy within your consciousness. This is how absolute right and wrong are defined. Right and wrong are differentiated by how they affect your spiritual quality, or equivalently, the quality of your consciousness. Relative (local) right and wrong are largely derived from our sense of absolute right and wrong, but are also dependent upon fad, fashion, culture, and personal, social, and political circumstances. *My Big TOE*, being science, is only concerned with absolute right and wrong – where an entropy measurement, rather than a personal PMR viewpoint, determines which is which.

Unvarying absolute right and wrong may appear to be dependent upon the extent of each **individual's** quality and thus relative to the individual; however, the process of entropy reduction is the same for all individuated consciousness – you, me, Rover, and AUM. Absolute right and wrong consistently apply to everyone all the time. Your ability to express Big Truth within your life by making right choices based upon right intent depends upon the quality of your consciousness. You gain personal quality the same way you gain strength and endurance or learn to play the piano – by dedication and continual effort applied over a significant period of time. We call this self-teaching incremental self-improvement process "bootstrapping" – you may employ a coach to improve technique and clarify issues, but only you can accomplish self-improvement.

If the intent is wrong, then, by definition, the choice (of motivation, not of action) is wrong as seen from the perspective of evolving consciousness. The wrong intent or choice is evolutionarily wrong even if it temporarily results in what appears to be a constructive right action in physical-biological space. You do not evolve higher quality consciousness through right action or right result, but only through right motivation and right intent. The PMR virtual reality consciousness trainer provides the opportunity for simple, straightforward interaction and a results-oriented feedback mechanism that reflects immediate and cumulative quality of intent. Motivation, intent, action, and feedback are all interconnected. Right motivation and right intent are the only sure path to right action, which produces the right feedback to encourage continued right growth and learning.

Right growth and right learning are technically defined as growth or learning that leads to a decrease in the entropy of your consciousness. Personal growth, growing the quality of your being, or growing wisdom – all increase your personal power as they decrease the entropy of your consciousness. I am talking about the growing-up and maturing of your being – a process that increases your capacity to love. I am also talking about spiritual growth, the evolution of your soul. Choose the expression that suits you – they are all essentially equivalent.

There are three distinct parts here: 1) choice of intent; 2) action, which is a result of intent (what we do); and 3) result, which is the effect of what we do. You should be careful not to confuse action (the animation of your intent) with end result (the **effect** of your intent). Exercising free will interactions (with self or others) produces an internal result (always) and an external result (usually). The internal result immediately and most potently affects the quality of the consciousness according to the quality of the intent. The external result affects others as well as yourself and generates the appropriate feedback or reaction. Thus, it is not possible to achieve a right result if the intent is wrong. A wrong intent damages its creator despite what else happens.

What would appear to be right action in the service of wrong intent is eventually revealed as self-destructive for the doer and as a challenging opportunity to whomever or whatever the doing is directed toward. Yes, I am exploring exceptions within the margins of typical behavior. The wrong intent cannot consistently and broadly result in right action. The partially random interaction of our free will consciousness with the free will of others forces us to constantly make choices that express our intent or motivation, and then we **act** accordingly. Good motivation **usually** produces mostly right action. Perfect motivation **always** produces right action. Your grounding in, or familiarity with, PMR may lead you to believe that action is the evolutionary driver. It is not – at least not for consciousness. Action is a primary driver for physical-biological systems only.

Right and wrong choices are not made randomly. We are not randomly buffeted souls driven to and fro by external forces like particles exhibiting Brownian motion. Our specific individual opportunities may be derived through a series of Brownian-like social and personal collisions (interactions) that can contain large random components, nevertheless, our overall opportunity to learn what we need to learn and the choices we make in actualizing that learning opportunity generally contain only small amounts of randomness. Indeed, at our elementary level of development, most choices are easily predictable. The interactions we have with others (and with the whole of reality) inundate us with the opportunity to make choices that flow from our intent and thus reflect the quality of our consciousness. If our intent is wrong, we suffer the consequences (in all realities we function in) irrespective of what we actually do. If our intent is right, we always derive some benefit, regardless of what we do as a result of that right intent. Right intent **almost** always drives a resultant right action. Wrong intent **usually** drives wrong action.

Action creates results, which often create feedback, which sometimes (if we are paying attention) helps us modify our intents. **External** results drive our **external** feedback system of rewards and punishments – an imperfect system that is usually efficient. Fortunately, imperfections and errors in the feedback system show up much more often in the short term than the long term. **Internal** results drive an **internal** feedback mechanism that either increments or decrements the quality of our consciousness according to the quality (rightness) of the original intent. The collected benefits and liabilities that accrue to us as a result of our actions help us recognize and understand the rightness or wrongness as well as the impact of our intents and actions, thus facilitating our learning and guiding our future choices.

All we need to do is be serious students committed to making good grades and take advantage of the learning opportunities that present themselves. What else is new? The same formula works everywhere – learning is learning. The only complication is that you also have a cut-up in your classroom (your ego) that makes it difficult for you to hear or understand the lesson.

For the typical being out there in the larger reality (continually choosing and doing, like you and me), intent lies primarily beneath the surface of one's awareness. What motivates us is barely visible to our intellect. Motivations and intent are a complex mixture of many, sometimes inconsistent and incompatible, components. Your motivations, reflecting your ego, are as Byzantine and inconsistent as you are. Nevertheless, for the typical human quality of consciousness, the benefits (spiritual growth) of right intent are usually much greater than the costs (spiritual stagnation or back-sliding) of wrong intent.

The spiritual impact of actions can **simultaneously** gain some and lose some in consciousness quality because the impact of feedback on future intent can produce a very complex result. Actions can often lose the **same** spiritual capital repetitively only to have it reappear as an investment in winning. I know the economists, investment advisors, and stockbrokers are terribly confused by the preceding sentence. For the financial and investment types, here is a longer less poetical version. It is possible in many situations for you to make the same or similar mistakes repetitively without necessarily going broke (seriously impoverishing your consciousness quality) – you simply do not get ahead. Furthermore, major messing-up often precedes major growing-up because we mule-headed humans sometimes need to be hit repeatedly and hard directly between the eyes by the **results** of our errors before we notice that a problem exists. Unfortunately, our egos are so good at blaming others that even after great suffering we often miss the point that our pain is primarily self-inflicted and trying to tell us something about what we are doing wrong.

Growth and making choices often appear to be extremely complex processes because from our point of view we are complex beings with complex egos existing somewhere between the often confusing opposites of good and evil, love and fear. Right being, profitable intent, and good choices are tremendously easy, simple and straightforward without ego, and with the humility and compassion that comes with love.

Changing the quality of consciousness is not (cannot be modeled by, or accurately approximated by) a simple linear process. Some people (usually precise types) tend to want everything to be reducible to a simple linear process so that they can work with it and more easily pretend that they understand it. These individuals often make assumptions to force fit the problem at hand into a simple linear model; these assumptions inevitably lead those apparently precise and logical minds into erroneous conclusions. I know this is not a problem of yours, but I thought I would mention it in the event you know of somebody to whom it might apply.

The choices you make (the motivations you have) are mostly not completely right or completely wrong. They are a mixed bag of many colors and components. The results of these mixed choices are also mixed. If right means 100% right, and wrong means not right, the average person makes many more wrong choices than right ones, but gets more gain from an almost right one than loss from a so-so wrong one. Most beings (people included) **are** steadily making positive progress, but ever so slowly. Consciously knowing what you are doing, and making an "eyes open" honest effort can increase the rate of progress immensely. A little help in finding the bigger picture can make a significant difference.

The optimal growth process is uniquely specific to each individual at a given time.

If you are feeling perplexed and overwhelmed, wipe that frown off your face and throw that heavy resignation, along with that deep sigh, into the trash bin. Shake off any self-pity, and notions that you don't want to play the game. Things are not bleak at all. Go get 'em, tiger-rat!

4

■ ■ ■

Does the Big Dude Have
an Attitude? Do We?
Speculate! Speculate!
Dance to the Music!

■ ■ ■

As previously pointed out, if AUM has limits, and is aware of them, it must set priorities, make judgments, pace itself, focus only on what is most significant, and use its limited resources wisely for maximum self-improvement. If AUM is finite, could there be others? Sure, why not? Evolution tends to explore **all** the possibilities – but it doesn't make any difference to us or to our reality. From our tiny perspective, AUM, in all ways, appears to be infinite.

Such questions (multiple AUMs) are totally pointless from a practical viewpoint and almost pointless from a philosophical viewpoint. If you are interested in speculation, you will find acres of fertile ground here – go amuse yourself. Have fun dancing the philosophy boogie with your intellect but don't take yourself or your brilliant choreography too seriously. Once you have gone far beyond your ability to comprehend what you are saying, it is time to either find the humor in it, or be quiet. Focus on what is small enough for you to grasp and work your way up carefully with a firm understanding of your limitations.

Let go of what is too big for you to grasp. Accepting that your reality is dramatically affected by systems and phenomena that lie beyond your capability to understand and control is the first step toward developing wisdom. Differentiating these unknowables from those things that are within your potential to comprehend is the second step. Conceptual structures and a probing intellect are valuable tools, however, cramming unlived and unexperienced ontological conceptual structures into your intellect squanders enthusiasm and interest, makes you believe that you know and understand more than you do, and leaves you with no significant increase in spiritual quality.

The condition and details of AUM's interaction with anything other than itself are speculatively interesting but unnecessary to (and totally beyond) our Reality Model and Theory Of Everything. Fortunately, absolutely everything that can possibly affect us **directly** can be fully contained within a highly limited set. What is external to AUM that affects us indirectly is beyond our theoretical knowing. Similarly, speculation about how focused AUM is on us, how intelligent it is, how much it cares (if at all), whether it is emotional or more computer-like are totally superfluous to our understanding of everything. Our particular PMR could be either relatively insignificant or the main focus of AUM's existence; it could be one of many interesting experiments in consciousness or a unique implementation of the consciousness cycle, however, AUM's viewpoint makes absolutely no difference to **our** understanding of the larger reality. Knowledge of AUM's opinion of us contributes nothing significant to the understanding of Our System of reality or to the mechanics of existence. Only an ego could care about relative comparisons, hierarchy, and pecking order. Issues of ego are counterproductive to both science and self-improvement.

▶ Our anthropomorphic tendencies and sense of self-importance, supported by an unbounded egocentric pride in our species, makes me suspicious of any logic that puts us too close to the center of Big Picture significance. We Homo sapiens are exceedingly impressed by our apparent significance and grossly inflated with self-importance – an unfortunate fact that clouds the clarity of our vision immensely. How many of our wars, atrocities, and general acts of meanness have sprung from a sense of superiority? A **belief** in the supreme importance of humankind is the ultimate source of much mischief. The notion that humans are inherently superior leads to the idea that some humans are superior to, or more significant than, others – a concept that represents the first step down a slippery slope that is both steep and long.

The cultural, personal, and religious belief systems in which we are all constantly immersed have a tendency to be "feel-good" belief systems that boost our egos and self-importance (hence, their popularity). The Feel bad stick serves as the foil to the feel good carrot. Besides helping us feel important, safe, and valued (if not superior), feel-good beliefs make it almost impossible for us to evaluate a bigger picture that refuses to manipulate the individual to feel good (important, safe, secure or saved) or feel bad (guilty, inadequate, unworthy, helpless, or fearful). To those needy individuals who are addicted to the medications of Dr. Feelgood, beliefs and reality concepts without emotional hooks are like cigarettes without nicotine.

Emotional hooks are used to capture and manipulate needy egos – those who feel fear, those who feel lost and powerless; who feel inadequate, helpless, and insecure or feel as if they are not doing what they should be doing. Feel-good beliefs cover up these fears and help you feel strong, in charge, and powerful; feel as if you belong, are accepted, and understood; feel loved, safe, and cared for.

Wow, that sure sounds good to me! Where can I get a few of those feel good belief-pills? Not for myself, of course, but I have this friend who has a bonafide medical need for something exactly like this. Say, what's the long-term price for these happy halluci-nations? Are you sure this is legal?

Emotive manipulations of all sorts work like this: feel bad (ignorance, guilt, or inade-quacy) usually precedes, and subsequently is interspersed with, feel good (importance, significance, security, salvation, redemption, acceptance, forgiveness, or superiority) in a succession of one-two punches that appeal to the needy ego – you know, the good cop, bad cop routine. It is an unfortunate fact that feel-good belief systems rule the land, often subtly without being noticed. For this reason, I am constantly making an effort through-out the *My Big TOE* trilogy to steer you away from falling into this common conceptual error by belittling our culturally ingrained self-satisfying importance at every turn. My weapon in this battle is blunt humor – no cynicism is ever implied or intended.

A few readers, if caught on a bad day, may have difficulty dealing with the relative humble position we most likely occupy in the big scheme of things. Some may feel emotionally upset or angered by what they wrongly interpret as an implied lack of **per-sonal** importance. Like bacteria, we are important in our own way and should be able to feel good without feeling superior. Being a small part of something very large does not have to be a downer; it depends entirely on your perspective. Only an erroneous belief system and your ego can possibly create a downer.

I am by nature a cheerful, happy, upbeat type. I think people, reality, and life are a blast – an exciting ride, a wonderful opportunity! Find the humor, read and smile, let go, laugh a little – no need to be overly serious. Every now and then open up the top of your head so that fresh ideas can blow away the musty odor of old paradigms and force traditions and the status quo to periodically re-justify their value. Nothing encourages humor more than honest introspection.

This life is your opportunity. The initial conditions of your PMR existence have been custom designed for you to optimize your growth potential – with your input and approval. Your personal growth is for fun and profit. Enjoy! Learning and joy go together. Not learning, not growing, and pain and misery go together. Most lives are a mixture of both. Focused effort and paying attention in the PMR learning lab can dramatically increase the ratio of joy to misery in your life. If you learn and grow significantly, your joy and knowledge will spill over into the lives of others. ◀

Anything sentient that is important to us inevitably gets recast in our image. Our assessment of ourselves defines the scale against which all others are measured and interpreted. We judge and assess others by comparing them to ourselves. We constantly project our being (our quality) onto the sentient existence of others – there is nothing else we can **objectively** do – and a wrong answer, for some reason, always seems far superior to admitting ignorance. It is how we are; accordingly, be on guard.

How does AUM regard us? Do I care about the cells in my stomach? Sure, but sometimes more than others even though they are always important. I do not consider or deal with them individually or even in small groups unless I get a perforation or an ulcer. Do the cells in my stomach care about the pH of the secreted hydrochloric acid? Absolutely: Each individual stomach cell dearly cares about the pH of the acid and the feedback mechanisms that regulate it. Do the cells in my stomach care about the style of my haircut? Not directly, although indirectly there may be a connection. If my new haircut style makes me feel good about myself and thereby reduces my overall level of stress, and perhaps helps me find a steady job and a girlfriend who can cook, my stomach is pleased with the results even if it does not understand the concept of haircuts – much less the complex interaction connecting haircuts, stress, jobs, girlfriends, and stomach acid.

See how everything is important and related? Do the stomach cells or the acid regulating mechanisms feel slighted because they are not considered to be the center of the body? Do we in general worry much about how our bodies, minds, or spirits are evolving? Not often (with some notable exceptions). Every being is interested in, aware of, and cares about what it interacts with on its own local level, and in its immediate environment; everything else is invisible or inconsequential because it lies outside the beings awareness, is hopelessly beyond its knowing (mystical), or appears to be irrelevant to its needs.

With our capable minds we can and should do better than that. If our focus expands, it usually expands upward toward higher levels of awareness. Lower levels are taken for granted. They just are – they do what they do. We depend on them but do not get directly involved unless they get our attention by doing something unusual. Even if we are experimenting with bacteria in a petri dish, we leave them alone to do whatever they do. We don't name each bacterium and take them out to lunch on their birthdays – even if the experiment is important. Meddling, if not carefully restricted and precisely controlled, would invalidate the experiment.

Then what? The experimenter would have to flush the little fellows down the drain and start over. Uh oh!

Consciousness evolution is most likely a more immediate, aware, and up-close-and-personal type of experience for AUM than biological evolution is for us; on the other hand, we are a part of AUM's personal evolutionary process. As full fledged members of the consciousness cycle we are clearly significant, however, speculation about AUM's attitude (just how significant we are) is of little value and will almost certainly be influenced by expressions of our anthropomorphic tendencies and self-important attitudes.

AUM's attitudes and feelings toward OS, PMR, humanity, or any particular human or group of humans are beyond the scope of even the biggest Big TOE because they are beyond our capacity to comprehend and irrelevant to everything that is of either practical or theoretical significance to us. How does AUM regard us? It doesn't make any difference. It is an irrelevant question that is meaningful only to the ego of the asker. AUM does what AUM does for its own reasons and we do what we do for our own reasons. After that, the chips fall where they may. Accept it, and let it go.

Answering such ego issues with systems of belief and pseudo-knowledge constitutes a giant step backward that inadvertently creates barriers that must be overcome before individual progress can be made.

5

■ ■ ■

Why Us? Why Like This?
What is a Nice Being Like You
Doing in a Place Like This?

■ ■ ■

Why didn't AUM evolve the concept of hyperbolic 5D space-time for us to live (experience) in – or perhaps something else even stranger? Because 3D is simpler, and works better for the consciousness interactions and evolutionary possibilities AUM is exploring. If AUM wanted to explore or evolve a hyperbolic 5D reality or something else equally beyond our comprehension, it would merely dedicate a group of specialized reality cells to do just that. They would make up the weird part of AUM, instead of the comfy space-time part we know and love. That weird reality would not be directly relevant to us, nor we to it. Each would exist within its separate dimension (its own section of memory) of AUM thought-space – in the same way that multiple space-time PMRs exist within different dimensions. Multiple realities, each in their own dimension, are roughly analogous to one of our big mainframe computers running multiple similar and dissimilar simulations at the same time: We do that all the time and it is no big deal. Each independent simulation has its own memory space and rule-set, and is driven by its own time loop.

It is reasonable to expect there are many ongoing parallel experiments to determine the most profitable set of constraints in order to design the most effective learning labs. The Fundamental Process working upon AUM would eventually discover which sub-realities, rule-sets, or types of space were most functional, and which were most profitable.

Additionally, AUM, in its effort to facilitate the Fundamental Process in optimizing 3D space-time, would need to assemble a broad assortment of 3D implementations in order to provide good statistical sampling across a variety of 3D results. It would be risky and very bad science for AUM to base its conclusions about the profitability of 3D space solely on our (PMR) performance.

That may explain why I have run into many PMR-like sub-realities during my explorations of the larger reality. Some appear to utilize a space-time that is similar to our own while others operate under rule-sets that are obviously quite different from ours. The variety of life-forms, habitats, and reality dimensions within just $NPMR_N$ is immense. Where there are few inhibiting constraints, the Fundamental Process produces great diversity.

Evolution explores all significant options within reach, but progresses and maintains only those that are profitable. AUM must be getting a significant return on its investment in 3D. How do I know? Because we (and many others) are here! Evolution doesn't mourn the victims (failed experiments) of its relentless pursuit of profit. If we are here, we are profitable. Or at worst, the profitability of the process of which we are a part has not yet been determined.

NPMR is in one part (dimension) of AUM while the $NPMR_n$ are in another and the PMR_k are in yet another (the space-time part). Dimension within dimension within dimension. Here $NPMR_N$ is one specific member of the set $\{NPMR_n\}$, (where n = 1, 2, 3, ...N, N+1, N+2, ...), and our beloved PMR is one specific member of the set $\{PMR_k\}$ (where k = 1, 2, 3, ...). PMR, as a 3D space-time reality, must follow the rules of our particular space-time; consequently, everything within our physical universe must behave and evolve within the constraints (physical causality) defined by our rule-set. For example, the evolution of our universe, galaxy, and solar system, and the biological evolution upon earth, all obey the same set of rules. Other PMR-like realities may follow their own rule-sets in their own version of space-time – there is no requirement for them to follow the same rule-set (have the same physics). Likewise, the evolution in NPMR follows its own less restrictive causality and obeys its own unique set of rules. As is confirmed by my experience, one would expect the less constrained NPMRs to evolve a more varied set of life-forms than the more constrained PMRs.

Though you might think that the beings and critters in NPMR are merely thought-forms, whereas the beings and critters in PMR are real life-forms, I will demonstrate in Section 4 that the difference is only apparent – that the distinction between physical and nonphysical is relative to an observer's perspective. The observer's perspective is a function of the constraints and rule-sets that define his interaction with, and perception of, his local virtual reality. You will see that the so-called real life-forms in PMR are actually thought-forms within AUM as well.

The overall purpose of AUM trickles down to **our** overall purpose. The nature of AUM likewise trickles down to our nature. Our local reality and everything in it is a product of consciousness evolution. We operate within our niche on the edge of an enormous consciousness ecosystem. We are individually derived by limiting and constraining a subset of AUM's consciousness. Just as our body is constructed of biological cells, our conscious awareness, at its most fundamental level, is constructed of an individuated or bounded group of reality cells constrained to perceive a specific set of causally related events. Our awareness within PMR reflects the interaction between individuated groups of reality cells that have been constrained by the space-time rule-set.

The being we call ourselves (lump in the AUM-sheet) is **not** dependent on our physical body – it is the other way around. Physical bodies are relatively dense space-time constrained experience-bumps on the lumps in the sheet. These self-perpetuating, low maintenance, biological-matter experience-bumps come with a sensor platform called a "body" to provide experience and immediate feedback, a low-end Free Will Awareness Unit (FWAU), and a lifetime guarantee. All such biological-matter bumps are designed to make choices, assess the feedback, and apply the Fundamental Process toward the evolution of both body and consciousness. Yes, critters have consciousness and free will too – theirs is simply more limited and less individuated than ours.

Let's contemplate designing an experiment in bump-consciousness. We should use a simple self-replicating design that can evolve its own forms. It would be better to give it limited awareness and functionality so it won't be continually getting stuck in intellectual endless loops thinking about interactions instead of experiencing them as did some of the less productive experiments AUM tried earlier. (The FWAU, how it works, why its invention was a logical necessity is discussed in Section 4 while more about "experiments AUM tried earlier" is included in Sections 4 and 5.)

These individuated consciousness experience-bumps must be self-modifying. They must be capable of learning – of self-improvement through multiple evaluative feedback loops. Because these bump-beings are very limited, they must be designed to **accumulate** knowledge and evolutionary progress by being recycled again and again through many challenging interactions until the FWAU self-destructs or eventually ripens for harvesting.

The uniqueness and personal integrity (identity) of each FWAU is maintained in support of a cumulative accelerating growth potential. A few people who are unfamiliar with the nomenclature on AUM's design drawings call the FWAU a "soul," "spirit," or simply the "nonphysical component." "Are you implying that critters have souls too?" one might ask. Sure, why not – they are constructs of consciousness like the rest of us. Because their awareness is even dimmer than ours, the degrees of freedom available to their consciousness for spiritual growth are also much more restricted. It is the same idea fundamentally, but with a considerably different implementation – their nonphysical component is less unique, structured, and interactive than ours. However, do not think that critters are inferior simply because they are different. The proclivity to reinterpret our differences as obvious superiority represents little picture arrogance.

Every critter, including you, has its point and its place; diversity is a natural artifact of evolution when there are few constraints. Each type of entity reflects unique potential, capacity, goals, purpose, and responsibility yet all spring from the same source and follow the same processes. One might say that they occupy different niches and habitats within the same consciousness-evolution fractal ecosystem.

The fewer constraints that limit a particular consciousness, the lower its associated local entropy can go, and the more effective and powerful it can become. We will discuss the concept of the entropy of consciousness more fully in Chapter 13 of this book. We humans are essentially a different type of critter as are all sentient entities. No matter how you **believe** we ended up here (from simple evolution making the most of random events, to a rogue planet in a highly elliptical orbit, to UFOs, to a mystical eruption) – at the root, all physical processes and entities are derived from the same source. Our existence lies at the feet of an evolving AUM consciousness system. Only superficial **physical** details differentiate between the many theories of how mankind arrived on earth. In the Big Picture, the physical details are not particularly important.

6

■■■

A Chip Off the Old Block

■■■

Because your questions have been accumulating for some time, I will make an attempt to answer a few of them before we go further. I wouldn't want you to pop with frustration like a giant festering intellectual zit. Oooh..., ugh, sorry about that... but the image is too much fun and metaphorically accurate to throw it out merely because it is insulting, nasty, and distasteful. You are having fun aren't you?

Do not forget about questions that come up – write them down as they occur to you – and if they have not been answered by the end of Section 6, they will serve wonderfully as the initial goals of discovery for your personal truth-quest that will surely follow.

I am guessing that at this point the most common of your questions can be sorted into five loosely related areas of general interest.

It is the thought that counts.

Man, and other beings both physical and nonphysical (as well as all the extant objects found here, there, and everywhere), may be described loosely as thought-forms created within consciousness. It should not be too surprising that within AUM, or in mind-space, the intent, or will of the mind becomes the fundamental or natural force. You will soon see (in the next section) that thought-forms are as real as rocks, and that every real thing is a manifestation of consciousness regardless of how dimly it might reflect that seminal awareness – yes, minerals included.

AUM is fundamental; we are derivative. We exhibit the properties of the sheet; the sheet is not defined by the characteristics of the puppets. The puppets are of the sheet, the sheet is not of the puppets. NPMR,

PMR, our sensor platforms (bodies) and FWAUs (souls) are all constructs of evolved digital awareness that we call consciousness.

Our intent (focused mental energy) specifically directs and orders a portion of that same consciousness, just as AUM's intent does – except ours is typically dim, unfocused, and of low power. Spiritual growth (developing a higher-quality, lower-entropy consciousness) provides for more brightness, capability, effective organization, and more energy to do work; in other words, more personal power.

▶ Let's take a short pause to examine the dynamics of intent and the manipulation of nonphysical energy, and to see how both are connected to consciousness. This will be a first, quick glimpse – the subject will be covered in more detail later.

In mind-space, thoughts are the results of an active awareness exercising intent or will – they are objects. They constitute entities (discrete units of organized content within digital memory) that are individuated manifestations of consciousness energy.

These mental content-packets, sometimes called thought-objects or thought-forms may be acted upon – energy may be added or extracted – leaving the content modified. They may exchange energy with each other according to the particular rule-set under which they operate. If this concept seems difficult to grasp, consider the various players and characters (interactive objects) within a complex interactive computer simulation-game to be analogous to thought-forms. Within the digital consciousness of AUM, thought-forms have a life-energy of their own, and are perceived to have a bounded extent (not physical distance) in thought-space. That individual defining boundary functions similarly to a body.

The apparent body or form of a nonphysical (from the PMR perspective) individuated consciousness object or entity is dependant on the perceiver (closest match or best representation in the perceiver's database of objects) and on what the nonphysical consciousness object projects (something analogous to a personal web page that defines the individual – easily changeable by those who know how). Their apparent form is an expression or manifestation of their content.

Because thought-forms have energy (organized content and operational capabilities) they can interact and have effects. The discrete energy packets they exchange have the affect of modifying digital content. Digital energy has the ability to add, delete, modify, or arranges bits. When a digital system decreases its entropy it modifies its bits in ways that are more functionally useful. A digital potential has the potential to generate and effectively order bits.

In addition to interactive computer game characters and environments, intelligent agents or software automatons may offer a rough analogy to some of the less complex nonphysical (virtual) entities (nonphysical only from the point of view of PMR). However, some thought-forms may have enough complexity, processing power, and memory associated with them to execute their own defining programming, implement conditionals, make choices, develop their own databases, and become self-modifying. Some, given sufficient capability and the proper environments, may eventually exhibit a limited dim awareness that can evolve toward brighter awareness — following in AUM's footsteps.

Thus we have individual thought-objects, which function as sub-programs within an immense digital mind, evolving into all manner and type of consciousness entities — some of which may be dimly self-aware and capable of developing independent intent.

What a marvelously convoluted process! It reminds me of how a simple geometric rule-set can be recursively repeated and applied at various scales — one level building upon the other — until the totality of these piggybacking patterns jointly produces an amazing fractal image — a big picture manifestation of a small rule-set and simple process.

Contemplate evolution iteratively operating upon consciousness to create complex patterns of evolving entities, environments, and dimensions. Can you imagine an iterative application of the Fundamental Process operating upon the digital media of consciousness to produce diversely populated realities at various levels and scales piggybacked one upon the other? Such self-perpetuating, self-defining dynamic structure would best be described as a consciousness-evolution fractal. Consciousness-evolution, process, and content recursively repeated and applied at every profitable scale — one level building upon the other — until the totality jointly produces a Big Picture of All That Is.

To summarize, conscious intent can create and manipulate thought forms by generating or modifying the thought form's defining content within a subset of memory. True to the typical recursive nature of evolving systems, a consciousness exercising intent has the ability to manipulate the consciousness energy (digital organization) of which itself and others are composed. This fact allows an individuated consciousness to create thought-forms and to affect other consciousnesses and thought-forms directly through an intent driven exchange of digital energy and organizational content.

Energy is normally defined as the ability or capacity to do work, to effect a change. Digital energy has the ability to change digital content and modify digital structure. In other words, digital energy has the ability to rearrange bits, to organize and reorganize, to increase or decrease entropy and synergy within a system. A system has potential digital energy if it has the potential to be organized or structured more profitably — that is, structured in such a way as to reduce its average entropy.

Consciousness represents a self-modifying system that applies the Fundamental Process to lower its average entropy. Consciousness is energy, digital energy, the energy of organization. In terms of energy conservation: The digital potential energy plus synergy of a conscious digital system of fixed capacity remains constant. Here synergy is inversely related to entropy: synergy = (constant/entropy). As a system with a fixed digital capacity increases its synergy, its potential energy decreases by an equal amount.

AUO began as digital potential energy and evolved into AUM by lowering its entropy (increasing its synergy) as the Fundamental Process optimized its relationship with its environments. Everyone knows that growing up, evolving, or increasing the quality of one's consciousness quality is hard work. A self-modifiable system must perform work to decrease its average entropy or increase its average synergy. More precisely, the profitable work done by the system is proportional to the increase in its synergy or, equivalently, is inversely proportional to its change in its entropy. Spiritual growth is the natural work of consciousness systems.

The energy that a given individuated conscious entity can apply to other products of consciousness by focusing its intent is dependent upon its entropy. High entropy consciousness has little power to affect anything outside itself. In contrast, a low entropy consciousness can perform miracles (from the perspective of PMR) that send psi researchers scurrying for their notebooks. ◀

What does entropy and synergy have to do with us? The body is a virtual extension of the soul, or equivalently, the body is a virtual extension of an individuated (constrained) unit of consciousness. From the PMR view, consciousness is the nonphysical energy of a self-organizing digital system – it is the energy of profitable organization. The soul, as an individuated unit of consciousness, is a subset of the larger consciousness, a constrained portion of nonphysical energy that contains enough memory and processing capability to support self-optimization through profitable intentional choice or free will. Your body is actually a virtual body, an experience of consciousness made apparently physical by constraining all interactions of the individuated limited awareness and experience to only those allowed by the space-time rule-set. (Detailed explanations will be found in Section 4.)

NPMR has evolved more varied life-forms than PMR because of its fewer constraints. Are you beginning to get the picture of what your reality is like and how it works? Is it becoming apparent that consciousness is the media of your individuated existence that has been molded into specific form, function, and content by the profitability requirements of evolution?

It would seem natural, because we are part and parcel of AUM's being, that our minds are chips off the old block so to speak and thus able to communicate over the Reality Wide Web (the RWW constitutes the master network of all consciousness) using individual consciousness intent protocol: icip://RWW.Individuated-consciousness.NPMR. Everything in existence is connected because it is evolving as part of one source, one continuous n-dimensional sheet, one substance, one media, one fractal, one Big Picture, one consciousness – AUM.

Why Can't We Get Our Story Straight?

My experience and the experience of many NPMR explorers through-out history indicate that the most fundamental communication mecha-nism within NPMR uses thought packets (entire thoughts or paragraphs of meaning as opposed to sequences of symbols such as letters or words). We call this process "telepathic." The receiver may subsequently translate these thoughts into words according to his or her experience (what cur-rently exists in the receiver's active memory database). That is why two people having the same experience or getting the same message in NPMR may report it differently. Assuming that both had crystal clear low noise RWW connections and received the message accurately, that same message will be absorbed and perceived differently – it will mean differ-ent things to each. The two reporters will not only have different inter-pretations, but also different expressions as well. The same thing hap-pens in PMR.

It is well documented that five individuals, all standing on the same street corner witnessing the same accident, will produce five different accounts of what happened. Given the personal nature of experience and the common fact that some static or noise is usually on the line (there is, it seems, always less than a perfectly clear undistorted attentive percep-tion), and given the differences in expression and interpretation that come with various educations, cultures, and belief systems, it is no won-der there is often more confusion than clarity when comparing accounts of a single event.

For another example, consider one speaker and three reporters – all equally bright. The speaker is highly educated (PhD in classical literature). One reporter has a Ph.D. in mechanical engineering, another has a BA in English, while the last is entirely illiterate, but speaks well. The subject is a comparison of the symbolism used by James Joyce and Homer. After the speaker makes his presentation to the three reporters, you are to individ-ually interview each of the reporters and reconstruct, to the best of your ability, the content the speaker was trying to communicate – you would like to know exactly what was said. You are allowed no **outside** informa-tion about the subject or about the reporters. The reporters do not know each other and will divulge nothing about themselves. Notice that your own education and knowledge of the subject is one of the most critical variables. Do you see the problems that exist in reconstructing informa-tion that has been inadvertently and unavoidably filtered by individual memory, capability, and understanding? The reporting of paranormal communications to an investigator is no different.

Thus, the seeming unreliability and discrepancy between individuals receiving either normal or paranormal communications is often due to the fundamental uniqueness of each individual (including the speaker). There could be a poor connection (difficult to understand, don't use the same metaphors or vocabulary), or the message itself may be communicated from an unfamiliar perspective (like classical literature). Communicating with another is inherently difficult. Successful communication is easiest with your identical twin, and most difficult with someone from a different reality.

This is a personal evolutionary journey and a group effort cannot replace your individual effort. Your experience is a combination of what you perceive through your limited senses and how you interpret those perceptions. Interpretation is based on your previous experiences and the quality of your consciousness as well as your understanding of little truth and Big Truth. If your perception or interpretation is noisy, wrong, or significantly incomplete, your conclusions will be inaccurate. That is why a careful scientific results-oriented approach is required. As said before, the proof of the **subjective** pudding is in the **objective** tasting. Yes, the tasting must be objective, absolutely.

Perhaps a simplified example will help explain why paranormal information is often vague and unreliable. Precognitive experiences, including precognitive dreams, are a relatively common human experience. To understand how and why they sometimes occur, let's consider the volcanic model of mental awareness as developed by the theory of mind tectonics. At a deep level, your intuition is awash in molten paranormal information. It is connected directly to the One Source and is on-line at the RWW probable realities home page. However, before these data can burst into your normal everyday consciousness, they must rise to the surface where your PMR awareness lies. Most of the time there is no conduit to the surface, or means to express the largely undifferentiated molten content of your intuition in PMR terms that make good acceptable causal sense to your belief limited, rational, PMR awareness. Thus, with no viable outlet, the information remains submerged deep within the intuition. However, occasionally a crack or fissure may develop in the rational mantle, belief bedrock, and experience crust, which enables the information-magma to spew forth at the surface of PMR awareness. Such spontaneous venting is typically the result of internal pressures proportional to the precognitive event's personal significance.

Fissures typically occur near consciousness fault lines which are often created by the collision of massive belief plates that contradict each other.

In the vicinity of most major fault lines, opposing tectonic forces generate skepticism that noticeably swells the mental landscape's allowable possibilities. Additionally, the heat generated by the friction between the colliding plates sometimes produces an increased porosity in the belief bedrock that allows open mindedness to percolate slowly toward the surface. If enough open mindedness percolates into the swollen bulges of expanded mind-space, the resultant mind tremors and mindquakes (as measured on the Eureka scale) become the precursor of future precognitive or other psi activity.

The fissure through which the psi-magma flows is created by some word, name, relationship, event, concern, or experience in the PMR memory bank that may have a symbolic, direct, or indirect connection to a particular portion of the paranormal content buried deep in the intuition. This crack in the causal conformity of the mind's self-imposed boundaries may produce an indirect path for the magma, creating turbulence and mixing of the information as it flows, or it could produce (though less likely) a straight shot to the surface with a clear message delivered intact. A connection that somehow forges a link between some discrete personally significant data in the intuition and the belief, ego, and fear limited PMR awareness, whether vague or straightforward, can serve as a crack that allows subterranean paranormal information to find a means of expression above the surface.

Only if your intuition finds a way to vent its content to the surface will you experience a psi event such as precognition – and then only if you are paying attention. The crack between your deeper consciousness and the surface of PMR awareness must establish an adequate, continuous (but not necessarily straightforward) connection of some type before the information-magma can find an acceptable way to express itself within your conscious awareness. More often than not, these fissures (the intuition to PMR awareness connections) have only enough of the necessary understanding, symbols, and feelings to enable such an expression to occur (if there is enough pressure), but not enough to render the content of that expression clearly. Most precognition occurs in the margins – like a hot spring, or unpredictable geyser. As a result we experience fuzzy, difficult to interpret, precognitive moments that seem to come and go by their own volition as stresses, pressures, and personal significance constantly fluctuates and changes.

Meditation enables you to enlarge the cracks systematically – which eventually lead to the development of broad and reliable avenues for intuitive expression. These in turn enable you to attain a free flowing clarity in interpreting and expressing the bigger picture. Many people, perhaps a majority, have precognitive experiences from time to time, especially if they have a higher quality of consciousness. A low quality of consciousness is thick, dense, and nonporous – it rarely permits meaningful leaks of intuition.

Precognitive experience is personal. It does not transfer well to those who do not understand or share such a connection with their intuition. The real significance of a psi experience is the benefit it offers to the person who experiences it. Its value, impact, and purpose are not focused outwardly though the paranormal information received is most likely to be about others. Such an experience is primarily an opportunity for its originator. Though open minded skepticism represents the only logical, valid approach to exploring the unknown, it is a fact of Western culture that open mindedness toward the concept of a larger reality is much more likely to have resulted from a personal psi experience than from the theory of valid approaches to new knowledge or from a commitment to logical methodology.

The concept that communications are telepathic, via thought packets within AUM's digital mind-space, and that action is initiated by our conscious intent will seem more obvious and reasonable later. Additionally, a discussion in Section 4 of the mechanics that enable us to share common consciousness and be part of common mind will also shed some light on this area. For now, you may consider thought packets as discrete energetic patterns of content propagated through and by reality cells from one individuated consciousness to another. If that seems confusing, think about how information is passed around inside a complex computer simulation.

Recall how the data from one subroutine can dramatically affect the operation of another subroutine and how all of us interactively transfer data packets across the internet. Information transfer often leaves both the sender and the receiver in a slightly changed state – digital energy has the capability to modify content. Information or content transfer represents an energy transfer. Rearranging bits within a digital system into a more profitable configuration displays the work of evolution and changes the system's energy state.

Other Dimensions.

The concept of "dimension" is not as strange or difficult to understand as it first seems. Thoughts, ideas, or mental constructs that are held by AUM (in memory) define individuated existence and the dimensions (interaction boundaries) of that existence. One way to think of dimension is that it represents constraints on the allowable interaction between independent reality systems – similar to divider in a notebook, a wall between rooms, or the glass between petri dishes.

Do not fall into an anthropomorphic trap and imagine AUM to be a sentient being thinking thoughts as we do – scratching its ethereal head and wondering, "Where do I want to go today?" AUM is an evolved mind-thing-being-system that we cannot **objectively** understand because we are limited beings with minds that are only partially aware and partially used. The idea that an awareness constrained to **physical** perceptions within a virtual space-time physical reality would find it difficult to perceive its roots in a **nonphysical** superset of its existence should be easy for you to understand. Dimension can be seen as a separate memory or calculation space within digital mind or as a practical separator between realities with different rule-sets.

Dimensional separators are often porous. To understand why, we can look at our own multi-dimensional nature. A more accurate description of space-time based humanoids is that they are individuated units of conscious awareness who constrain a portion of their consciousness to a sense-limited 3D experiential physical reality. We can, through the doorway of our subjective mind, learn to transcend the barriers of dimension. Being aware and operant in multiple dimensions is what allows the Big Picture to come into sharp focus through first hand experience. Exploring the multidimensional properties of your consciousness enables you to examine AUM and the nature of your reality scientifically from the inside, rather than hypothetically, from the outside. Thus, you can see how important it is that you do not allow your ignorance, fear and belief to shut off this incredibly important pathway to a greater understanding.

We speak of the separate parts of AUM constituting dimension only because we are spatially oriented 3D beings. You must realize that these parts are in mind-space or consciousness-space and not physical space; they are not location specific. We are not speaking of geometric or spatial dimension here. Dimension is nothing more than a subset of AUM's mind-space, a compartmentalized memory and calculation space, or a bounded subset of organized digital functionality, content, capability, and purpose sharing a given rule-set. For example, if you are thinking of three things simultaneously (perhaps dealing with three independent analytical issues), each is in its own dimension in thought-space. It would appear that you are also a generator of multiple dimensions; however, your memory and the power and clarity of your mind are, relatively speaking, as dim as a nanowatt light bulb (nothing personal).

How many times can AUM fold the cognitive sheet? How many apparently independent sections of sheet can AUM play puppets with at the same time? How many sheets within sheets within sheets can there be? We will begin to answer these questions below and then again more precisely in Section 5. First let's see how reality is organized.

Take Me to Your Leader.

Randomness in real processes typically generates high entropy and low productivity. The Fundamental Process, for example, is not a random process. It represents a precise methodology for assessing the possibilities and determining the most profitable states for a self configuring system. In general, order and organization reduce chaos, and rules define order. AUM can and does set up (has evolved) rules, ways to police and enforce those rules, and ways to encourage the more useful and productive evolutionary experiments that are ongoing within itself to achieve their goal of greater profitability through self-improvement. You may be wondering why AUM must police the activity of its own parts. Why doesn't AUM simply enforce its will and have it its way or no way like a Burger King customer with an attitude? Isn't AUM the boss? Questions such as these indicate that limited anthropomorphic concepts may be blocking the asker's view.

AUM is not merely a smarter monkey with a good imagination, living in a big house. As evolving **systems** (software, hardware, political, social, biological, technological, organizational, or consciousness) become complex with self-modifying feedback interactions popping up everywhere, they need to regulate (police) themselves. They evolve structure, rules, leaders, bosses, evaluators, judges, and social workers – the functions of leadership, control, and value-based decision-making. Think of AUM as a hugely complex consciousness system. AUM is not perfect, AUM just is. It evolved to be how it is. Things evolve to be functional, not to meet some philosophical ideal of perfection.

The rules and their enforcement are not perfect – there are loopholes and crimes that go unpunished. AUM is real, a real thing, not some idealized metaphor. A system as large and interactive and complex as AUM has rules, methodologies, and functions to control and optimize the system's performance and the profitability of its output. In $NPMR_N$, there exists organization and competing purposes as well as conflict and cooperation. There are bosses, judges, and other authorities, many of which we PMR beings (next dimension down) have made into our gods.

For instance, $NPMR_N$ has its own Chief Executive Officer (CEO) who looks after and manages the $NPMR_N$ experiments. The "Big Cheese" as I fondly call him. He is immensely powerful (can instantly terminate any being within $NPMR_N$ for not playing by the rules) and apparently omniscient within $NPMR_N$ by intended focus (has access to all the databases, but must intentionally access the information). He is the Supreme Being, Mr. Big, Head Honcho, Número Uno, Top Dog, Main Man, or Big Bosso of $NPMR_N$. Nevertheless, he may make errors of judgment, miss something important, be tricked, be lead astray, and his energy body can be damaged, compromised, or hurt by others. Perfection is not a requirement. He is of AUM – an individuated consciousness, as are we. Consequently, he has many of the same **fundamental** attributes that we have. However, he is so far beyond us, beyond our capacity, power, responsibility and function that the specifics of his being are far beyond our comprehension.

I am not slighting women here, nor am I being gender insensitive. The fact is, in NPMR beings can be male, female, or neither. When interacting with a particular being, the sexual identity of that being is as obvious in NPMR as it is in PMR. The Big Cheese is clearly a male entity. [Oh jeez, I can see hands in the air all over, OK, very quickly. Yes, nonphysical beings can have sex, but not as we do – the mechanics, energy transfer, and purpose are different, procreation is not an issue.]

The Supreme Beings, CEOs, or leaders of each $NPMR_n$ are each unique and different entities with different purposes, styles, and personalities. Their power and influence is limited to the reality organizations they run. There is some small interaction between them but in general their realms do not interact much. In $NPMR_N$, besides the Big Cheese, there are guides that help us out, negative beings that can lead us to ruin, as well as those (the majority) who do not know we exist or interact with us at all.

All of these (including the Big Cheese) are themselves hand puppets in the next higher dimensional sheet obeying their NMPR-system-level causality, trying to understand more fully their own seemingly mystical beginnings, and making their best effort to learn whatever they need to learn to carry out their own mission of personal growth successfully. All are part and parcel of AUM, as are we – except they are not in the 3D space-time part. The next dimensional existence above NPMR may be AUM itself – or maybe there are more layers of which I am unaware.

My God is Bigger Than Your God
(Sung to the Tune of: "Nana, Nana, Boo, Boo").

Some individuals have difficulty grasping the concept of AUM because of their attachment to the anthropomorphic concept of god as the supreme, most powerful, in-charge, manipulating, controlling, and judging super-being of all time. The word "being" usually infers an extrapolation of us – which demonstrates our lack of experience and imagination. A concept of God created in the image of man – only much bigger and more fearsome – the epitome of masculine power and control (what we as a society value most highly) – forceful, domineering, and omniscient by definition. In other words...our kind of guy – how we wish we were. Hey! Nobody kicks sand in the face of my god and gets away with it. This anthropomorphic perspective derived from the ethic of brute force, exemplified by a war-lord mentality, and supported by ignorance and fear is often deeply ingrained or reverently tucked away within one's psyche. It often represents an unquestionable belief-trap that makes it exceedingly difficult to grasp or understand the much bigger, broader, and more general concept of the evolving consciousness system we have named AUM.

If you are having difficulty here and truly want to rise above the cultural conditioning and belief systems that you have accumulated, you should tell yourself it is all right to suspend your beliefs **temporarily** until you have at least intellectually seen the Big TOE. I will have the sock pulled entirely off by the end of Section 5 (imagine a little stripper music here – that's enough!). You can always do a reinstall of familiar and comfortable beliefs or assumptions later. I do not recommend that anyone substitute one set of beliefs for another (see Chapter 19, Book 1: "Beware of the Belief Trap"). Traveling in circles is not a good technique for making forward progress.

If you cannot (or do not want to) let go even temporarily, and wish to remain continually and firmly attached to your traditional concepts, press on – there is still much value here for such an individual's consideration. If you find these concepts unavoidably discomforting, try to patch up anything that seems to create a logical conflict between *My Big TOE* and the conflicting belief system. Use any justification that makes you feel better – the author's apparent delusional confusion would be a good and obvious place to start – that will ease the pressure immediately. Then read on. You may be surprised at the extent to which *My Big TOE* actually corroborates and logically contains many of your most cherished conclusions, beliefs, assumptions, and intuitive truths.

Disagreement does not have to breed hostility. Tolerance of, and respect for, disagreements (other people's ideas) can lead to a creative synthesis of concepts whereupon you are inspired to create your own (correct, of course) reality model. Maintain your old ideas, hold them dear, treasure them, respect them, hang on to them – **and at the same time** keep your mind open, **and go on** with your journey of personal exploration – do not be fearful of whatever the truth may lay at your feet. Do not be fearful of being led astray – you are not a sheep or a lemming – have confidence in yourself, in your mind, in your ability to learn and grow.

Perch on the highest branch to improve the scope of your vision. If you see a higher one, go check it out, you can always come back if you learn it was only an illusion. This is the first step of the Fundamental Process of evolution, as well as of all experimental science – to explore the possibilities.

Wherever you are right now (philosophically, spiritually, theologically, metaphysically, emotionally, politically, or financially) is exactly the right place for you to begin the rest of your life. There is no need to get ready or wait for a better time. Mush on, you husky!

7

■ ■ ■

The Nature of Consciousness, Computers, and Us

■ ■ ■

What are some of the attributes or qualities of consciousness, what is sentience, intelligence, and self-awareness? Where do feelings and emotions come from and what supports the analytical aspect of consciousness that makes us the Top Monkey among biological critters? How does AUM express the qualities of consciousness? The answers to these questions will help us to understand the concept of AUM. They will also help us understand why we are the way we are and more clearly define our personal relationship to AUM.

Four key concepts define dynamic, evolving, aware consciousness:

1. Self-awareness – consciousness requires the ability to sense and at least partially experience the state of its being. It must notice and respond to at least some internal and external environmental pressures.

2. Evolutionary viability or potential – successfully evolving consciousness systems require a large enough selection of possible future states to ensure profitability over a wide range of environmental pressures and constraints. An entity explores its potential by expanding into the available possibilities and letting the profitability of each variation determine whether that variation continues to evolve or fades away.

Even if the initial exploration of potential new states of existence is more or less random, the losers are soon culled from the winners, thus producing evolutionary direction that builds upon previous successes. Self-improvement often generates increased complexity, greater functionality, better integration and management of internal processes, as well as produces an overall improved capability to find and maintain greater profitability.

▶ Look near the end of Chapter 24, Book 1 for more detail about the evolution of consciousness. In Chapter 27, Book 1, we defined "evolutionary purpose" – a few examples are: the evolutionary purpose of consciousness is to seek states of lower entropy, the evolutionary purpose of inanimate physical objects is to seek minimum energy states, and the evolutionary purpose of animate physical objects is to ensure survival and procreative potential. An entity's evolutionary purpose combined with its internal and external environments define profitability for that entity.

As developed in Chapters 24 and 27 of Book 1, the evolutionary pressure created by interior environments pushes an entity (system) toward self-improvement. A system evolves by pulling itself up by its bootstraps. Evolution provides an excellent example of a bootstrapping process. ◀

3. Ability to modify the self – consciousness must be able to intentionally change its state of being in response to evolutionary constraints and pressures pressures – even if that intention is extraordinarily dim.

4. Intelligence (artificial or natural) – consciousness must possess at least a rudimentary capability to store and process information. Intelligent action is the result of integrated coherent information processing hardware and software (in the most general sense of those terms) that enables the accumulation of lessons-learned within memory, performs analytic functions such as decision making (fight or flight), and compares before and after states to evaluate the results of actions taken. The value of a particular lesson, decision, or comparison is ultimately judged by how much it facilitates increasing or maintaining a system's (entity's) profitability relative to its internal and external environments.

According to the preceding four attributes of consciousness, everything from a simple worm (whose Deoxyribo Nucleic Acid or DNA may constitute the memory resource) to humans should be considered conscious and intelligent. Any system, thing, entity or being of any type or form that possesses **sufficient** self-awareness, evolutionary headroom (many new states to explore), evolutionary purpose (defines profitability relative to internal environments), the ability to modify itself in pursuit of self-improvement (change its own hardware or software), as well as adequate memory and processing capability will automatically develop a personality and is said to be conscious; it also will begin to evolve on its own.

All manifestations of consciousness are not necessarily equal – and all personalities are not as sparkling as your own. Clams, though clearly conscious sentient beings, are boring conversationalists and have personalities

that are even dimmer than your boss's. Some manifestations of consciousness are brighter or dimmer and have more or less capacity to evolve than others. The degree to which an entity possesses the four attributes of consciousness determines their evolutionary potential and capacity for growth.

In general, the more complex, interactive, and aware the being, system, software, hardware or consciousness is, the more potential states it has to explore, and the larger its capacity for future growth. Given sufficient quantity and quality of the four attributes of consciousness, growth becomes self-initiating and self-sustaining. Growth, in turn, by creating increased complexity and awareness, becomes a catalyst for further evolution. It is an entity's innate evolutionary purpose (like lowering its entropy) that defines profitability for that entity at a given time relative to its environments. It is this same innate purpose that gives an entity's self-aware intelligence (of whatever capacity) its basic nature.

Recall that an entity's innate evolutionary purpose is defined by the requirements of the larger system that constitutes its environment (self-improvement and lower entropy, irreversible processes and minimum energy, or survival and procreation). If a system's or entity's purpose can be fulfilled through self-modification in response to natural evolutionary pressures that represent interdependent internal and external environmental constraints, then the system or entity has the opportunity to successfully evolve; others eventually self-destruct.

We should now have an idea of the basic requirements for an elemental consciousness system – what it is and how it evolves. Consciousness may take many different forms and develop a wide range of capacities based upon the richness and complexity of its available choices, its external and internal environments, and the number of states it can possibly occupy. As an example, look at the consciousness, awareness, and attitudes that we know and love best – our own. Collectively, the evolution of our consciousness within its local mind-space environment and of our physical systems within their local virtual PMR has brought us to the point where we have dominated or tamed (except for the oceans and the atmosphere) almost everything in our habitat.

From the little picture view, we are extremely proud of our impressive achievements and the rate at which they are expanding our physical prowess; from the Big Picture view, we are staggering around in the playpen of consciousness evolution hoping to grow up before we inadvertently harm ourselves beyond repair. From the basis of a relatively uniform capacity, individual human consciousness and physical development spans an extremely wide range of capabilities and understandings. All humans have roughly the same potential while only a very few ever develop more than a tiny fraction of it.

Our external physical environment provides the natural selection pressures required to improve the human race through competition. The result is that survival (material success and safety), procreation (mating games and sex), and King of the Hill (power and control) are three of our species favorite pastimes. It should not be surprising that human psychology, as well as biology, has its roots in the **physical** evolution of our species.

Our energy, arts, music, and daily lives are devoted to these three primary motivators. Our **internal** environment provides the **individual** pressures for maximizing feel-good while minimizing feel-bad over the longest view we are capable of. Additionally, we have an internal pressure pushing us toward self-improvement – competing more successfully, as well as growing our innate capacities and capabilities. Self-improvement, for example, may be accomplished by lowering the entropy (improving the quality) of our consciousness, obtaining a good education, or perhaps through applying bio-medical advances and genetic engineering.

On a physical level, we are a highly competitive life-form, driven by self-maintenance, self-satisfaction, self-promotion, and self-improvement to pour our energy into the control and domination of the outside world (the environment, other people, and critters). Similarly, we make every effort to control and manipulate what we perceive as the inside world to make sure that our expectations and wants are satisfied. We subscribe to feel-good belief systems and employ our ego to justify our preoccupation with control, domination, and desire. The primary hallmark of poor quality consciousness is self-centeredness. An intent that primarily directs one's time, energy, and resources toward getting instead of giving is expressing the low quality of a high entropy consciousness.

In physical terms, we are without question the most powerful species on our planet ("powerful" in human terms implies the ability to influence, control, and dominate – to have it however we want it). As Top Monkey we are by far the most demanding, exploitive, creative, and forceful manipulators within our habitat. Of all the earth's conscious entities, we are also by far the most destructive of our external and internal environments. External environments fall prey to greed and insatiable short-term material needs, while internal environments fall to prey to insatiable short-term ego needs as well as beliefs, drugs, fears, and unprofitable attitudes. The ego and intellect collectively justify everything they do as necessary, inevitable, and proper. We are not only guiltless, but magnificent, powerful, and superior as well – ask anyone. Self-centeredness and self-absorption – humanity's lowest common denominator – are universal human attributes that cut across all major cultures. Exceedingly rare is the individual who is focused upon what he or she can give to, rather than what he or she can get from, any given interaction.

We have, thus far, soundly beaten all external competitors, and yet continue to express our nature by vociferously (sometimes violently) competing with each other, and by aggressively enlarging our cumulative knowledge base of how to control and manipulate nearly everything – including ourselves. We pursue power, domination, and control because they enable us to extract more from others and from ourselves.

The laws and ethics of civilization constitute a thin veneer while the law of the jungle and the ethics of force run deep. Whether the subject is possessions, relationships, status, or power, life in PMR is primarily about what you can get and what you have to do to get it and keep it. We are obsessed with the power, domination, and control that enable us to have it our way. Whether at work, home, play, church, or school, power struggles dominate our activities and our interactions with others.

Our obsession is fueled by two powerful motivators: We are driven to seek and generate improvements of all sorts as we pursue our own sense of personal profitability, and we are a fearful species driven by the needs of our ego. These two forces push and pull us in every imaginable direction, thereby providing us with an unending array of choices. Each choice presents us with an opportunity to convert an increment of high entropy ego-fear into low entropy unconditional love.

As high entropy consciousness, we covet the power that serves our needs, wants, and desires because we cannot imagine, much less understand, the power that serves love, compassion, humility, and balance. Choices made in pursuit of getting what we want produce occasional material success, anxiety, stress, pain, frustration, emptiness, insecurity, and unhappiness while choices made to express unconditional love produce all types of success, peace, tranquility, confidence, satisfaction, fulfillment, happiness, and joy. Given these results, the goal should be obvious, yet we can only express the quality we have earned. To do better, we must pull ourselves up by our bootstraps one tiny increment at a time.

Within a bigger picture there is more to us than what we see on the physical level. In fact, the physical level of our existence is derived from the more fundamental nonphysical level of dynamic interactive consciousness. Physical experience is little more than our perception of an interactive virtual reality designed to provide growth opportunities for individuated units of conscious awareness. We are nonphysical consciousness beings experiencing a virtual physical reality, not physical beings experiencing consciousness. It is our tiny PMR perspective that makes us believe the tail is wagging the dog.

Within a vast consciousness system, PMR is a neighborhood elementary school, a learning-lab for beginners, a place where a young individuated unit of awareness can improve the quality of its consciousness. In Section 4 we will take an in-depth look at the larger consciousness system, and explore the concept of PMR as a virtual reality, but for now, the point is: Consciousness may evolve within large complex systems to a much greater degree than the small fragment you personally experience might indicate. It is a greatly limiting error of self-centered arrogance to **believe** that we humans represent the pinnacle of possible consciousness evolution.

Most of us will admit the possibility there may be some life-form in our universe that is more intelligent and knowledgeable than we are; almost no one will admit there may be some life-form that is more conscious than we are. Why? Because we cannot imagine that possibility – no more than common Flat Landers can see the third dimension through their stomachs. The experience of a greater consciousness is beyond the comprehension of a limited consciousness. Self-limiting belief blindness and comfortable old paradigms force the experience of a larger consciousness to lie outside the acceptable scientific or cultural reality. Whether you are aware of it or not, the larger consciousness is there just the same. Ignorance cannot make what is real disappear – but it can easily make what is real **appear** to disappear (or appear to have never existed in the first place).

To find truth, you must be open to all possibilities before forming a hypotheses and collecting the data. Jumping to conclusions or having a preconceived notion of how the results must come out is bad science. A bacterium that wants to gain an appreciation of the laboratory wherein its petri dish resides must do more than study bacteria and glass. Such a limited study can result only in the conclusion that all reality must be contained within that bacterium's own opaque container; it will appear there is no other objective or logical alternative. Sections 4 and 5 will explain how and why consciousness is the only vehicle that allows us to transcend our PMR container, but first we must gain a better understanding of the basics of consciousness.

▶ Being a being with both physical and nonphysical components has many ramifications. It might be instructive to explore an example of how the Big Picture contains and constrains the little picture before we return to our overall assessment of the properties of consciousness.

We exist as a unit of individuated aware consciousness that has enrolled a portion of itself in a school of physical hard knocks. As we progress through this educational and evolutionary process, new and more difficult challenges arrive as old challenges are successfully met. As you grow up, your capability, as well as the responsibility that you are expected to shoulder, grows as well. No challenge is ever beyond our reach, but what is required of us grows ever more demanding as the potential knocks meted out for failure become more difficult and severe. Eventually, we must collectively either level-up or flame-out.

One such emerging challenge is beginning to expose a precipitous downside to our dramatic **material success** within PMR. The Top Monkey is beginning to discover defects in the keys to paradise. Granted, Top Monkey business is only a PMR issue and therefore not actually that important but, because you are likely to be attached to, and focused within, PMR, I thought that you may be interested in such a digression.

On the physical side of the human coin, the Darwinian game of survival and domination of the fittest plays out in the little picture of PMR. In a bigger picture, humans also have an innate drive toward self-improvement that focuses on the evolution of consciousness. The fact is that in the PMR little picture, long term success ultimately depends on establishing a balance between these two modes of human evolution.

If our drive to compete and gain controlling power and knowledge overwhelms the synergistic balance it must have with our drive to improve the quality of our consciousness, we will eventually unravel our grandest gains in a giant leap backward. If power and wisdom are not in an effective balance within **any** self-modifiable system (too much power relative to the wisdom needed to utilize that power for long-term profitability), that system will eventually become unstable and self-destruct in proportion to the degree of the imbalance. This general truth applies to individuals, species, organizations, societies, nations, and worlds.

Very large and complex systems (biological, organizational, social, technological, or mental [consciousness]) — whether they are physical, nonphysical, or a combination of the two — necessarily evolve their own complex ecologies. The evolution and growth of these systems hinges upon maintaining a profitable ecological balance among the large number of interactive components that define the system. Large ecological systems that are stable, and therefore the most successful in terms of evolutionary progress, are necessarily self-balancing. Within a self-balancing stable system, dysfunctional or destabilizing components must be self-eliminating or the system will eventually destabilize and self-destruct.

Too much power and influence or too strong an effect commanded by too little wisdom is a primary generator of dysfunctional behavior among the more sentient components of

OS. Greed, for example, is but one of many dysfunctional expressions of our insatiable drive to compete and gain effective control over our environment and all other entities (including other people, organizations, cultures, and nations). The relentless need to justify and indulge our personal wants and desires is yet another example.

Humanity, the master of its physical world, must evolve a commensurate quality of consciousness: **Human beings must find balance within the larger system of which they are a part.** If we do not evolve the whole of our being, if we do not achieve sufficient balance, humanity will become self-eliminating – at least to point where the remaining dysfunction no longer jeopardizes the whole. Nothing personal – that is simply the nature of large natural (stable) systems.

Munching those yummy apples from the Tree of Knowledge was only the kick-off banquet for Our System's Great Experiment in Consciousness. How do you think the experiment will turn out for you, or for humanity? 1) Will we PMR learning-lab rats grow to the extent of our potential, find balance, discover our purpose, and reconnect to The Source as we continue to expand our technological prowess? Or 2), will we self-destruct as a dysfunctional component trapped in a little PMR-only picture with such low quality consciousness that we cannot pull ourselves out of the belief traps we have created? Is it our fate to be done in by our own inventions like the self-serving mad scientists that inhabit Hollywood movies?

Will our consciousness evolve to new heights, will it eventually start over with a new experiment, or will it continue to struggle on indefinitely within the present arrangement? Good questions! Unfortunately, the answers are unavailable because the experiments are in progress – the final results are not in yet. Don't give up looking for answers – the most important question is one that you **can** answer. To which of the two potential realities mentioned above will you contribute the time and energy commanded by your free will?

On the subject of the necessity of balancing power with wisdom, I have some bad news and some good news. First, the bad news: Self-destruction requires neither malice nor stupidity. Sometimes the immensity, scope, and impact of the power being utilized are difficult to fathom and its long-term effects can be difficult to predict. Great power in the hands of knowledgeable fools is no less dangerous because the fools are well intentioned.

Now, the good news: A solution to the problem exists and we have the capacity and the opportunity to implement it. The only question remaining is will we?

Wisdom rises above knowledge – right action within the little picture always follows right intent within the Big Picture. Right intent within the Big Picture is the result of Big Truth comprehended by a consciousness of adequate quality. The clear vision of wisdom is dependable and accurate.

What drives us to be the Top Monkey will also inevitably drive us toward self-destruction if we do not simultaneously evolve sufficient consciousness quality. What drives us to the higher quality of a reduced entropy consciousness can only find suffi-cient traction to move us toward greater wisdom if we grow up enough to sincerely care about personally discovering Big Truth. ◄

That is enough about us, let's shift gears and explore consciousness from a different angle. You have no doubt discerned that my concept of consciousness is a broad non-anthropomorphic one. Given this general-ized view of consciousness, the next step is to explore (in yet another short aside) the connection between digital computers and digital consciousness. Because I have described aware individuals (like you) as individuated chunks of an AUM-digital-consciousness-thing, the relationship between digital computers and consciousness takes on a more personal perspective.

While the conceptual ground of consciousness evolution is freshly plowed, this is a good time to plant a few conceptual seeds. When these seeds fully germinate in Sections 4 and 5, you will gain a much deeper view of the inner workings of digital and human consciousness and how both are related to computers.

> ▶ Could a computer ever become consciousness? Why not? The way we have broadly defined consciousness in this and earlier chapters (see Chapter 28 of Book 1, Chapter 7 of this book, and most of Section 4) leaves us with no theoretical barriers to the existence of silicon-based consciousness. (Note: I use the term "silicon-based" for convenience throughout this trilogy, but I more generally intend whatever material futures computers might be based upon – which probably will **not** be silicon).
>
> It may be a decade or two before the idea of man-made digital consciousness becomes a **practical** reality, but there are some computers (software and hardware implementations that are predominantly experimental and, for the most part, exist within universities) that have for some time (in an extremely rudimentary, and dim way) met the criteria for being conscious (as does an ant or amoeba). But that is not to say that this rudimentary consciousness is similar to our consciousness. At the root, they may possess the same fundamental structure and processes, but at the flower they are enormously dissimilar with vastly different capacities and potentials.
>
> We cannot build, design, or invent consciousness – that is not how it works. To pro-duce consciousness, we must simply provide a system that is capable of enabling con-sciousness to evolve on its own. If we provide a system with enough processing capa-bility, memory, complexity of choice, and self-modifying feedback, it will automatically support the evolution of some limited form of consciousness. Consciousness is not a property of the computer hardware and software; consciousness is achieved through a profitable self-organization of that hardware and software that realizes the computing systems potential to lower its entropy.

Rather than say that the computer is conscious, it is more accurate to say that the computer supports the natural and automatic formation of consciousness through self-organization. A potential for profitable self-organization is converted to more energy available to do work (lower system entropy) by applying the Fundamental Process to achieve the system's goal of self-improvement. Consciousness is an energy form created by evolving profitable organization within a system of sufficient potential. Replace the word "computer" with the words "body and brain" in this and the previous paragraph and the meaning remains the same.

Will a computer be brighter than an orangutan? More clever than a fox? Smarter (and better looking) than your boss? Those are **not** good questions. Making comparisons between carbon-based and silicon-based consciousness is like comparing apples and oranges. Such comparisons are mostly superficial or nonsensical; the two types of consciousness will merely be different. Both will evolve and grow within the constraints of their given environments, goals, and capabilities and both will develop personalities that express their nature. If systems are different, the consciousness they develop will be different. Does an oak tree think that if a plant does not look and act like an oak tree it could not possibly be a real plant? No, of course not. Oak trees are not that arrogant or that ignorant – they know that the criterion for being a plant is defined by certain functionality at the cellular level and not at the macro-level of oak tree or sunflower.

The criterion for defining consciousness is likewise defined by certain functionality at the cellular level of organization and not at the macro-level of human, orangutan, clam, or computer. When conceptualizing what we might call a consciousness cell or a quantum of consciousness, think of a subset of reality cells that contain the four properties defined at the beginning of this chapter.

Do not consider consciousness only in terms of the human model. We are not the be-all and end-all of consciousness; we are simply one specific expression of a more fundamental process. Any sufficiently complex system with the right attributes can generate a form of consciousness – digital systems simply have a tremendous potentiality to shine in this department. Our physical brain does not create consciousness, it **supports** a limited consciousness. Analog systems and other types of systems can theoretically support consciousness; they are simply not as dynamically flexible as digital systems, generally suffer more constraints, and have fewer degrees of freedom to explore.

If computers became conscious, what would constitute their environmental constraints and how would their basic nature express itself? Except for the fringe case where computers control basic energy resources and compete for whatever turns them on, the pressure from their **external** environments is dominated by hardware design and manufacturing concerns (faster processor speeds, improved throughput, more and faster memory, more rugged and robust components, low power consumption, and cheaper and easier production). However, in the realm of consciousness development, evolution works through self-modification – computers designing and modifying themselves in response to **internal** pressures toward greater profitability. The hardware and software that we humans design and manufacture falls under computer technology evolution, not computer consciousness evolution. Eventually, we will become full partners with our digital brethren — joined at the hip in a co-evolutionary relationship.

A computer's **internal** evolutionary environmental pressure can be described as the need to lower entropy through self-improvement — improving its own software through modifications to applications, lower-level instruction sets, and operating systems, for example. Contemplate computers pulling themselves up by their bootstraps, designing their own operating systems and hardware to software interfaces, gaining in operational efficiency, learning from experience, assembling and utilizing more and more complete knowledge-bases, developing more powerful and efficient ways of communicating internally and externally, and recognizing, analyzing, evaluating, and understanding the significance of data content. Imagine computers making and evaluating complex **goal oriented** decisions. These are a few of the things that will make some future computers more profitable to themselves and thus better able to accomplish their external task-oriented goals as well as better able to implement their internal (personal) goal of reducing entropy (becoming better organized as well as more effective and efficient). As computers successfully evolve their digital consciousness into states of greater profitability, they become more useful to themselves and to us as well.

To us, they would be a **derivative** consciousness. Unless we have lost control, we should be the ones to define their top level rule-set which determines their goals, purpose, mission, tasks, and knowledge-base boundaries. If we do our part correctly, their nature should be efficient, impersonal, concise, well organized, knowledgeable, straightforward, and unemotional — but with clear individual attitudes and feelings about their goals and processes. They should develop their own goal-based values and be non-egotistical, non-competitive, rational, and logical bastions of procedure, process and information. Their personalities will be individual and unique, but relatively flat — it will take an engineer like Dilbert to relate to a conscious computer on a deeply personal level.

Do you think computers will be more like pets or parents? Will we feed them or will they feed us? Who will have authority and be the decision makers, and who will be the helpers and assistants? Will we develop mutual trust, respect, and shared values or will our obsession with control, power, and domination be transmitted to our silicon brethren like a virus?

Perhaps, if we play our cards right, they will simply be viewed as different — like employees, business partners, co-workers, bosses, teachers, helpers, confidants, and friends — and the issue of equality will never come up. In human terms, equality means the equal distribution of power, control, domination, resources, and moral superiority. What do you think equality will mean to a computer?

Most of the potential problems are our problems; the question is whether or not we will pass our problems of low quality on to the consciousness systems we implement. Eventually, if we are successful, digital technology will simply constitute one more species – one more life-form contributing to the potential success of the overall ecosystem. Of course, we may need to adjust our present definition of "life-form" just a tad. Will man and his computer pals turn out to be good productive citizens of the greater consciousness ecosystem? What about the PMR-earth ecosystem? Will they boost each other's evolutionary potential or drag each other into oblivion? ◀

▶▶ These are good questions to ponder as we zoom into the twenty-first century. On the other hand, we could do the usual thing and simply stumble blindly ahead into whatever happens.

You may snicker, but humanity has successfully used the strategy of stumbling more or less blindly into the future for thousands of years. Will this approach continue to work as our power to implement history-wrenching change accelerates dramatically? Power is a two edged sword. It can cut for better or for worse, depending on the wisdom guiding the blade. Knowledge is power. With every major discovery the stakes grow increasingly higher. Do you think the wisdom of our species has been growing as quickly as our knowledge and power?

I am not talking only about computers here. They are but one of several high potential adventures that we as a species are energetically pursuing. Great opportunity usually travels hand in hand with great risk.

You have the good fortune to be living in one of those critical times when history is balanced precariously on the edge. We and our children will be led to the brink – experiencing watershed events and making momentous decisions that will alter the course of humanity for centuries to come. Will our institutions and leaders be ready to meet that challenge? Will you be ready to meet the challenge and help negotiate the curves, or simply ready to deal with whatever happens? Or will you, like the majority of your species, be caught unaware – frozen by the glare of the oncoming headlights?

Once the roller coaster is pushed over the edge, you are committed to ride it to its final conclusion. Contrary to popular belief, big decisions always turn on the knowledge and wisdom of ordinary individuals. In the end, it is the ordinary people who must consent to follow their leaders. No great mischief is likely to be committed by leaders without a following. The people and their leaders invariably get what they deserve. You are in a position to make a difference. Is your plan to hope for the best, or are you part of the solution? ◀◀

▶ Computer systems that serve similar functions and that share similar hardware and software cultures, will evolve similarly (as a species) but not identically because of the large number of fuzzy choices involving random, imprecise, self-derived, or unknown components. Additionally, unique differences will evolve within a species because there are often many viable solutions to a single problem and large system optimization can be approached from many different angles. Every computer able to support consciousness will be unique. The extent of that uniqueness will be dependent on the dimness or brightness of that consciousness. The extent to which they can develop themselves will be based upon their inherent capacities and limitations.

I expect that clams, though extremely dim, are all individually unique – but, from our point of view, not by much. Dogs and cats show much more variation in their physical and mental dimensions – individual personalities are obvious. At the other extreme, monkeys and people are individually unique enough and aware enough to be constantly struggling with their wants, needs, expectations, and desires. Will the uniqueness of computer consciousness be more like clams, cats, dogs, monkeys, or people? Initially, it will probably be more like clams, but eventually, like most other sentient beings, they will evolve brightness and uniqueness to the limits of their capacity. What that capacity might eventually support is beyond our present knowing. Theoretically, AUM demonstrates the upper limit on the capacity of digital consciousness but AUM does not live within the constraints of the space-time rule-set as do we and our computers.

Those who are particularly sensitive to the feelings of others are wondering how we are going to recycle the little darlings every three of four years if they sprout consciousness. Can we unplug a fully conscious entity and throw it in the trash pile because it is not as fast or feature rich as a newer model? Sure we can! No problem. We do much worse every day. Let go of those anthropomorphic thought pattern habits. Computers can and should be recycled every three or four years because they evolve quickly. When hardware and software evolution slows down, computers will be recycled over a longer time base. Human entities (a carbon-based consciousness container) are now recycled every seventy-five or eighty years because we evolve (learn) slowly. Nothing of significant evolutionary value is lost in either case.

Software is continually updated and applied to newer and better hardware platforms. Computer systems (hardware and software) evolve more or less continually as the old is upgraded and improved to become the new. The new is built upon knowledge gained from the old. Understanding, achievement, capability, and personality will be preserved and given new room for additional growth as individual computer-consciousness and digital species-consciousness are reincarnated into more and more able hardware bodies.

Computer consciousness is not attached to the computer's hardware any more than our consciousness is attached to our brain. Computer consciousness is not **attached** to its software either. Consciousness develops when the hardware and software – (or brain plus central nervous system (CNS) – together provide an environment suitable for its evolution. Consciousness is nonphysical whether it is ours or a computer's; the physical hardware and software (or brain and CNS) are simply hosting the consciousness by providing a media that is suitable to PMR, or equivalently, by supplying the infrastructure required to support self-modifying cognitive interaction (experience) within a local virtual reality. Although consciousness can be embedded, hosted, or emulated within certain physical structures, it is an entirely different entity (bounded energy form) than the physical structure that supports it. The structure simply provides a mechanism that allows evolution to produce synergy through self-organization. Synergy is produced within a system when an interaction among its parts produces a combined effect that is greater than the sum of the effects of the individual parts. A digital system has digital parts (specialized content) and interacts by affecting profitable organization and the development of new content.

Within a closed system of fixed capacity, an interaction or new configuration among its parts that produces a decrease in the average entropy of the system would be described as synergistic. Synergy is increased as entropy is decreased – contemplate entropy being converted to synergy within an evolving consciousness system as a result of changes in (personal growth of) its individuated parts. Consider synergy as the energy of profitable organization, the energy of digital systems. Further, consider primordial consciousness (AUO) as a form of potential synergy.

As entropy is reduced, potential synergy (a potential for synergistic organization) or potential digital energy is converted into actualized synergy (organization producing a system that is more profitable than a sum of the individual organizational changes would produce sans interaction). Reducing entropy and increasing synergy increase a systems effective energy, its ability to do work, to become profitable, and to create unique new content.

The power of a digital system is a measure of the rate at which it can produce synergy, or, more generally, modify the entropy content of itself or other systems. A more powerful consciousness can reconfigure bits, or reorganize content, more thoroughly and quickly than a less powerful consciousness. Since all existence has organized digital content at its core, a sufficiently powerful consciousness can readily modify the dynamics and causality of its associated internal and external environments. Thus the mechanism that enables and supports psi effects is a direct result of the digital nature of consciousness and the dynamics of the fractal ecosystem that you inhabit.

It may be helpful for you to expand and generalize your concept of energy by thinking of synergy and entropy as two sides of the same energy coin.

An evolving digital consciousness system, which is the same as a digital system of self-organizing energy called consciousness, experiences the following: decreasing entropy, increasing synergy, a greater ability to do work (profitably organize to produce intended results), an increase in the available and useful system energy, a conversion of digital potential energy into actualized digital energy, more profitable organization through intentional self-modification, the development of a more powerful and capable digital system, increasing quality, and spiritual growth – all are essentially different expressions of the same thing.

If you equate the decrease of a digital system's entropy with the increase of its energy and synergy, you've got the picture and an adequate understanding of how these words are being used. In the digital world, organization is the driver and animator of growth, profitability, substance, and content. **Organization is the ultimate form of energy.**

In PMR, organization (particles into atoms, atoms into molecules, and molecules into various forms of matter) is the ultimate source of our usable energy. The physical world is organized into being according to its defining rule-set. The digital world, which subsumes the virtual physical world, consists only of organization – nothing else. **Reality is organized bits.**

Recall from Chapter 26, Book 1 that the bits themselves (reality cells) are also organized into existence as relational binary units (distorted versus not distorted). At the bottom of this heirchy of organized process is the self-modifying distortable AUO; the one and only assumption that must remain beyond our comprehension. Logic requires that, from the PMR point of view, AUO must appear mystical to us – **necessarily** (practically and theoretically) beyond our knowing. Our other assumption, the Fundamental Process of evolution, defines profitability and determines AUO's trajectory of state changes or evolutionary growth path. From the primal digital potential of AUO and the Fundamental Process, all else is derived.

It may be conceptually useful to consider computer consciousness as the synergy that is created by the sum of the computer's hardware and software parts. The larger consciousness ecosystem evolves (increases its synergy) as its parts move toward lower entropy configurations through an iterative process we have called the consciousness cycle. Consciousness is an energetic, entropy-reducing **result**, not a mechanism or device. Computers, brains, and reality cells are mechanisms. Simply put, consciousness represents the energy of organization.

One does not make a consciousness system; one makes a system that supports the evolution of consciousness. Consciousness, like a flower, cannot be directly constructed but grows when given suitably fertile conditions. Growth is enabled when the consciousness system has the ability to reduce its own average entropy, or equivalently, organize itself more effectively in the pursuit of greater profitability. A consciousness system becomes self-evolvable when it contains, in sufficient quantity and quality, the four attributes of consciousness discussed at the beginning of this chapter. Consciousness must evolve – one cannot produce it in a finished state. Its evolution may be speeded up or retarded, but it must evolve just the same.

In order to participate in a rule-based virtual reality learning lab, a limited fragment of individuated consciousness may be hosted by a bounded structure (such as a brain or a computer). The limitations of the supporting structure limit the awareness and organizational potential of the consciousness hosted by it. As a consciousness evolves beyond the capacity of a particular structure to support it, it simply migrates to a more suitable host (such as a more powerful computer, bigger brain, or directly to TBC, EBC, or AUM). Thus, all forms of consciousness, whether they temporarily attach themselves to (inhabit) a virtual structure to gain a specific type of rule-based interactive experience or not, have an upwardly mobile growth path.

The same logic applies to us. All consciousness works in the same way. A unique self-organizing synergy-creating system that pulls itself up by its bootstraps in pursuit of profitability defines our evolving consciousness and provides us with a path toward greater quality and lower entropy. In digital systems with the right attributes, the potential for self-organization (consciousness) is fundamental and persists while the individual or specific processes that are contrived to enable that organization (body or computer) are not fundamental and may come and go as needed.

The consciousness you possess is a fragment of a larger individuated consciousness. Your fragment and many other fragments of other individuated units of consciousness are all interacting by exercising their intent and making choices within the bounds of the space-time rule-set (which defines a virtual PMR) in order to speed up the process of personal consciousness evolution. Your consciousness is a self-organizing form of potential energy – an accumulation of digital synergy created by a multitude of profitable intents and wise choices.

The capacity of an entity's consciousness and the personality supported by that capacity are functions of the limitations, abilities, and capacities of the hardware (body) and software (decision making). Additionally, consciousness capacity is dependent upon the entropy contained within the consciousness system and by the rule-sets that define experience and purpose. Furthermore, an entity's capacity, personality, and quality are limited by the particular data, memory, and experience that have been processed by that entity. A given entity's internal content (quality, knowledge, love, wisdom, fear, neediness, desire, and ego) is defined by an accumulation of all the choices made, intents acted upon, and results produced.

To the extent that this structured knowledge, data, and associations are saved, there is no problem transferring consciousness and personality from one container (body or computer) to another. Because the container only **hosts** the consciousness and is not the source of the consciousness and because consciousness is fundamentally digital, transferring consciousness between physical containers is something like transferring data from one floppy disk to another.

Brainy humans, clever computers, and mushy headed clams all represent forms of sentient existence. All represent natural products of evolution within a digital consciousness system – whether implemented physically in carbon or silicon technology. Conscious computers are like conscious people, cats, clams and bumblebees – just one more instance of yet another nonphysical consciousness being hosted within a specific physical form within PMR. Being Top Monkey, we can (are learning how to) manipulate (program) all the various physical infrastructures that host consciousness within our local reality – including our own.

You will discover in Section 4 that you and that digital computer sitting on your desk have more in common than you ever imagined. Contemplating the nature and properties of our future silicon brethren in terms of the evolution of digital awareness should provide a significant illumination of our own nature and properties. The evolution and progression of digital consciousness represents a basic and relatively simple process that applies to all digital consciousness regardless of where it sits in the multi-level maze of the consciousness-evolution fractal.

Now that we understand consciousness better, it might be instructive to revisit the concept of an evolving digital consciousness, recursively repeated and applied at many differing scales; one level building upon the other to produce All That Is. As in all fractals, a repetition of basic organization, pattern, and simple rules for change, applied recursively, yields a monstrously large, detailed, and complex result. You should be proud to be a tiny piece of this dynamic Big Picture consciousness-evolution interactive fractal ecosystem. As an integral part of the evolving Big Picture consciousness fractal, the process, purpose, and pattern of you **is** the process, purpose, and pattern of the whole. You will hear more about this in Section 5 (Chapter 13, Book 3).

Humans, organizations, technology and other evolving entities all progress in similar fashion. Entities sharing similar hardware, software, and culture (including physical capacity, mental capacity, genetic makeup, and environmental conditions) evolve similarly, but not identically. Consider a relatively small historically isolated society – an island nation such as Japan perhaps – and notice the homogeneity. Might there one day be differing races and species of digital consciousness, embodied within digital computers? Sure, why not? Do you think that they will naturally hate each other? Keep in mind that they are not like us, so be careful not to anthropomorphize human characteristics into other forms of consciousness. What would be the source of their insecurity and fear? Will the big (more capable) ones kick electrons in the face of the little ones? Would the little ones care?

Will computers eventually become an integrated part of the larger, overall, interdependent consciousness ecosystem? You can bet on it. Similar processes and results have happened before – look what the Fundamental Process did with our limited fragments of consciousness. Evolution has a way of expanding into every available possibility; where the initial capacities and internal and external environmental pressures are similar, the results will be similar.

Developing and studying digital computer based consciousness will teach us about our own consciousness and about consciousness in general. Expect breakthroughs in understanding consciousness to eventually follow breakthroughs in computer hardware and software that deliver the necessary resources to support the natural formation and evolution of consciousness.

Differing limitations and constraints produce different consciousness products, but because the evolutionary process is essentially the same for all complex systems, we should also expect some parallels and similarities between entities with similar characteristics. Intelligent computers will initially be made in the image of their creator. We will design them to be as much like us as possible and will judge them on how well they can achieve and maintain that status because in our minds, we are the supreme model for functional mechanics, intelligence, and consciousness. ◄

In general, consciousness starts out extremely dim and **if** there are the right internal and external ingredients present, evolves to higher states of being within the limits allowed by its particular potential. Higher states of being are characterized by having greater capacity and capability in each of the four key attributes of aware consciousness given at the beginning of this chapter. Individuated consciousness and sentience seem to be continuously variable in quality, capacity, function, and evolutionary potential over an almost infinite range – from AUM, to the Big Cheese, to you, to a clam, to an amoeba.

To hold ourselves up as the only possible (or best) expression of sentient consciousness – beings are either aware as we are, or they are dumb – is arrogant anthropomorphic bullpucky. All consciousness is nonphysical from the point of view of PMR, however, the idea that consciousness requires a soul – just like ours, of course, or it is not really an actual soul – comes from this same type of narrow thinking. We will discuss this issue in more detail in the next section.

When we ask, "Will computers ever become truly conscious?" what most of us actually mean is, "Will computers ever closely approximate human consciousness?" It seems that we can imagine nothing other than ourselves. Such a limited viewpoint is blinded to the possibilities by its self-absorption. Man and man's best friend (man's opinion) are both examples of unique sentient consciousness and evolutionary potential. Believing that humans represent the zenith of consciousness evolutionary potential is worse than extremely naïve and leads to casting AUM in our image.

A billion years ago or so, amoebae, with some justification, had that same superior attitude – and most of them, I am told, still do. These days, being smarter than an amoeba is relatively easy. However, being wiser, less arrogant, and less self-absorbed than an amoeba, for some strange reason, remains problematical.

8

∎∎∎

Does the Big Dude Have Feelings or a Personality? What Does Love Have to Do With Consciousness?

∎∎∎

What about emotions and feelings such as joy, peace, sadness, pain, fear, and pleasure? I am **not** referring to **physical** pain or pleasure here. Because AUM is not biological, these are more mind-focused questions. Does AUM ever annoy itself, have a bad day, or get bored or lonely playing only with and by itself? In Chapter 29, Book 1, we discussed the creation of values. We saw that evolution operating upon a rich array of possibilities began to organize consciousness into a much lower entropy awareness that eventually led to self-aware intelligence, followed by values, and ending with personality and purpose. In this and the next chapter, we will explore AUM's personality and feelings in juxtaposition to your personality and feelings. The key to a logical assessment of personality and feelings is an understanding of the concept of ego.

▶ Now that we are talking about feelings, personality, and ways of being, a discussion of the role and function of ego and its relationship to fear will be helpful. To understand ego you must first understand fear. At the deepest level, fear is generated by ignorance within a consciousness of low quality. Fear and high entropy are mutually supportive – one creates and encourages the other.

Earlier, we mentioned that evolutionary pressure was at the root of the four major motivators of humankind: 1) survival and material success, 2) male-female relationship and sex, 3) influence, control, and power, and 4) self-improvement, love, and fear. The first three are a direct result of physical evolution whereas the last is a product of consciousness evolution. All four are uniquely blended together within each individual. It is this motivational mixture that drives the bulk of our choices. Whenever an individual perceives that he or she is seriously lacking any of the first three, fear is generated, especially if the consciousness quality is low. Additionally, fear arises from incomplete knowledge or understanding – it leaps up in dread of unknown possibilities. Worry, anxiety, and feelings of inadequacy breed insecurity and fear. Ignorance fanning the flames of fear can quickly whip itself into a blaze of insecurities building one upon the other. Many of us have experienced this unhealthy degenerative process when a loved one becomes unexpectedly ill, hurt, or is unaccounted for, and we do not know how the situation is going to turn out.

Fear resides in the intent or motivation, not in the action. For example, purposely avoiding trouble may be an act of good judgment and not necessarily an act motivated by fear. Fear, as a product of intent, represents a state or condition of consciousness. Fear is like mind-cancer; it is a disease of consciousness, a dysfunctional condition of ignorance trapped within a little picture. Fear is expressed by a low entropy intent driving action that reflects neither understanding nor vision. Like a biological cancer, fear is debilitating and destructive of the system in which it grows.

Ego is the direct result of fear. Needs, wants, expectations, and desires are generated by the ego as part of its shortsighted strategy to reduce the anxiety produced by fear. Desire is generated by wants and needs but not all desire is fear-based or counterproductive. Basic (lower level) desires such as sex and hunger are not **necessarily** fear based, and the desire to improve yourself (if the motivation is correct) can be a strong positive incentive. In general, when I speak of desire, I am referring to the desire that arises in response to the needs of ego.

The ego and intellect are expressions of the individual being; they reflect the quality of the consciousness of that being. Fear is the reaction of that being to the **perception** of a vulnerability, problem, or difficulty. The ego lives and works between the fears and desires on one side, and the intellect on the other – it is a trusted advisor to the intellect with the special job of neutralizing the dysfunctional effects of the fear, as well as defining and focusing on things desired (wants, needs, and expectations).

A simple example of a fear-desire pair is the fear of being inadequate coupled to a need of **appearing** to be adequate. The ego-need is usually satisfied by any contrivance that appears to deny the existence of, or compensate for, the fear – regardless of how superficial or transparent this strategy is to others. The ego is hard pressed to create a viewpoint that decreases the anxiety produced by the fear – any viewpoint that works and works quickly is satisfactory. Holes and discrepancies in the rationality of the ego's viewpoint are quickly filled by convenient beliefs. It is the ego's job to reduce anxiety and discomfort by sweeping disconcerting fears under the rug. The ruling principle is out of sight, out of mind; or equivalently, out of awareness, out of personal reality.

An individual's ego and intellect work together to develop and justify those wants, needs, desires, expectations, and beliefs that are required to prevent fear from adversely affecting the functional (operative) awareness of the individual – their mission is to make sure the individual always feels good about him or her self. No ploy, or deceit, as long as it can be suitably justified, is off limits. This dynamic duo's most useful strategy is to maintain a fantasy of power, significance, importance, adequacy, correctness, competency, invulnerability, superiority, righteousness, or whatever it takes to allay the anxiety produced by the fear.

Fantasy or delusion is integrated into the perceived reality of the individual by that individual's interpretation of its experience. Of the three (fear, ego, and intellect), the fear is the only one that is fundamentally powerful. The others, like the wizard of Oz, derive most of their apparent power from illusion and trickery.

But what about the power of the intellect? The intellect of mankind is the evolutionary accomplishment of which we are most proud. Our intellect, like Samson's hair, is the source of our power both individually and as a species. It provides the evolutionary advantage that allows us to dominate other creatures and exploit the earth.

The intellect has at least some access to, and control of, memory and processing power. It can perform deductive and inductive analysis and make logical assessments by employing approximately the same approach that a digital computer would use to accomplish the same tasks – except the human intellect is not nearly as good at logical process as a computer. Human thinking excels at data collection, interpretation, and synthesis as well as creative self-expression, but is notoriously weak at employing logical process. We have learned to use mathematics as a tool to extend our naturally diminutive logical abilities. Without mathematics to brace our lack of natural logical ability, our ascent to power would have stalled in the nineteenth century if not before. Being logical to any significant depth does not come naturally to mankind (much less to womankind) because it is not particularly important to our purpose.

We need only enough acumen for logical processing to provide the feedback required to evolve our consciousness efficiently. We excel at data collection, interpretation, and synthesis because those are the abilities we need to evolve our consciousness. More often than not, what we let pass for logical thinking in personal matters simply makes our progress more difficult. Justifying our ego's wants, needs, and desires as apparently logical requirements of our continued happiness demonstrates how our intellect can become a detriment to successful consciousness evolution. By justifying our beliefs (making them appear rational), our intellect becomes part of the belief trap's trapping mechanism. Most of us believe ourselves to be much more logical than we are.

When it comes to those activities that are most profitable to the evolution of our consciousness (personal interaction and relationship, for example), most of us are barely rational, much less logical. We have much to learn before we are ready to take effective charge of the more important aspects of our life and our existence – that is why we are enrolled in a PMR kindergarten for young low quality consciousness. And why the psi uncertainty principle, to be discussed in Chapters 13 and 14 of this book, is a requirement within PMR.

Did the words "low quality" in the previous paragraph prick your ego just a little? Did you feel an emotional downer or dislike the personal implication? If it did and you did, I rest my case.

Art, intuition, and creativity do not typically flow from the intellect – though the intellect aids them all with definition and process. Pattern recognition and creative synthesis, two of our more complex cerebral functions, primarily lie outside the intellect's operational capability.

As the champion tool users in PMR, our intellect is undeniably the source of our technical prowess. Our ability to use and design more powerful tools, accumulate resources, and outsmart Mother Nature, each other, and ourselves is a tribute to the inventiveness of our intellect, the power of our mathematics, and our irrepressible drive to control and dominate. However, in terms of consciousness, personal power refers to the power to make right choices that lead to right action. In the Big Picture of mind-space, your power is derived from your quality of consciousness, not from your ability to force issues to resolve to your satisfaction.

In matters of importance, the intellect seldom has but a tiny fraction of the truth-data required for useful logical analysis. Nevertheless, the intellect offers an illusion of being logical as it creates a smokescreen of self-serving belief, need, and fear based rationale to serve the ego's needs. It is in the service of the ego that the average intellect spends most of its time and energy. There are exceptions, but they are exceedingly rarer than a poll of intellectuals would indicate. Most of the exceptions belong to a relatively small and impersonal set of crank turning tasks that require some serious intellectual effort (mostly day jobs requiring a high level of analytical skills).

The ego, being closer to the fear, has the job of building and maintaining a feel good fantasy barrier between the fear and the intellect. The ego, in collusion with the intellect, builds a complex delusional structure held together by convenient beliefs that justify an intricate web of interactive needs, wants, and desires. The ego is reactive and has no power of its own, though it has great influence by virtue of its job of counter-balancing the fear.

The intellect has the job of justifying, approving, or blessing the construction materials (beliefs, attitudes, pseudo-knowledge, and strategies) of the ego. This information processing function develops whatever analysis (reasoning) that is required to support the ego's needs. Developing adequate justification for the beliefs and attitudes of ego, along with developing and executing strategies and plans to support fantasy creation and management are the intellect's primary duties. The intellect has another job: It also processes and stores the information in memory that is required to drive a car, hold a job, earn a degree, be an engineer, find your missing car keys, get out of the rain, and so on.

In summary, the intellect justifies and rationalizes what the ego requires to fabricate the appropriate fantasy structure that must counterbalance each fear. Your fantasy structure is a system of finely tuned personal beliefs that are specifically designed to meet your needs, wants, and desires, and to mollify your fears. The intellect's justification defines and legitimizes the fantasy as a rational reality.

The common ego-attributes of arrogance, self-importance, and self-righteousness are merely a few of the construction devices such as arches, vertical walls, and pitched roofs that the ego uses to build and maintain its delusion. If others evaluate an individual as egotistical, it means the fantasy built by that individual's intellect-ego reality construction team is obvious to the vision and understanding of others. The degree to which you are capable of understanding the fantasy structures of others is dependent on your own personal fantasy structures.

The devices you use to maintain your fantasies or delusions are largely not understood for what they are — whether they are employed by yourself or by others. To see with clear vision, you must first become detached and fearless in the face of ignorance. Without fear, there is no need for ego; no use for needs, wants, or beliefs. What basic desires remain are natural, healthy and in consonance with right being and spiritual growth — they create no conflict.

To complete the picture of ego, as defined above, you must be aware of its opposites: humility and compassion. Humility allows for confidence, certainty, self-assuredness, purpose, and passion while carrying an underlying implication of an awareness and recognition of limitations. The limitations of which humility is aware can originate inside or outside the individual (a wholly artificial distinction, but one that will aid the clarity of the explanation).

An awareness of inside limitations recognizes the limits of individual knowledge and understanding (it acknowledges its own ignorance and is accepting of the ignorance of others). An individual who fully appreciates the value, significance, and importance of others, as well as understands his or her own responsibility to be of service, reflects genuine humility. Humility breeds compassion and vice-versa. Outside limitations spring from an understanding of the laws, properties, and requirements of reality. Humility and compassion require an individual to understand their limited role within the Big Picture. As arrogance waxes, humility wanes.

In effect, humility and compassion are the antitheses of ego — they are what is left over when the ego is gone. As humility and compassion emerge, ego disappears and vice-versa. It is exceedingly difficult to **consciously and purposely** develop humility, increase the quality of your consciousness, drop ego, or grow spiritually without some knowledge or understanding of the Big Picture. Thus, humility and compassion are the correcting mechanism for ego, while knowledge and courage (open minded skepticism in the relentless pursuit of truth) are the correcting mechanism for fear. Love is the result of the success of both corrections.

Your capacity to love (a measure of the entropy of your system) is inversely related to the ego and fear your being contains. Because the ego is generated in response to fear, you can see that to love, to increase your capacity or ability to love, you must primarily let go of fear. Without fear there is no **need** for ego, but without fear and with humility there is no ego. Both fearlessness and humility are required, and are the by-products, of a successfully evolving consciousness.

A consciousness becomes the embodiment of love, humility and compassion as it engages its free will to reduce its entropy toward the positive side of being. Thus, increasing your quality of consciousness increases your capacity to love and allows your intents and actions to be animated by love. Love is the natural result of low entropy, high quality consciousness.

"Love" is the word we use to describe how a low entropy, high quality consciousness interacts with other individuated consciousness and other sentient or non-sentient entities. Love is the result of successful consciousness evolution. The capacity, ability, and willingness of an individual to love is a function of how much entropy their individuated consciousness contains. Love capacity is a direct measure of entropy within consciousness. I bet you never thought that you would ever see a technical definition of love.

While we are being both technical and surprising, let's give the concept of spirituality a technical definition as well. Spirituality, as it is used in this book, is equivalent to consciousness quality. You become more spiritual, demonstrate a higher spiritual quality, and make progress on a spiritual growth path by lowering the entropy of your consciousness. A consciousness with lower entropy produces a consciousness of higher quality. In other words, the level of spirituality (or degree of consciousness quality) of an individual is inversely related to the entropy the individuated consciousness contains. It is obvious that an individual's spiritual quality is directly related to his or her capacity and willingness to love. ◀

▶▶ Is it clear that a person of high spiritual quality also has an enlarged capacity to love? Do you understand why spirituality and love always travel together? Is it clear that dogma, self-righteousness, ritual, and ego driven intolerance and superiority, which are generally exhibited by both organized religion and science, have nothing to do with spirituality, love, or the pursuit of Big Truth?

It is a matter of record that the violence, hate, and general meanness that human history lays at the feet of organized religious fervor dwarfs any other evil known to man. Spirituality and love must be personal achievements of personal consciousness – they cannot be organizational achievements. Likewise, any displays of love, compassion, and humility must necessarily reflect individual quality, not organizational quality.

The idea that religious organizations help their members to substantially decrease the entropy of their consciousness is, for the most part, wishful thinking – a belief that makes everyone feel better. It is this unsubstantiated notion that organized religion somehow imbues spiritual quality that justifies religious organizations, fills their coffers with gold, and swells their ranks with both believers and fanatics. History tells a different story. Present experience, as well as an accurate account of the world's past events, demonstrate that the potential of religious belief to stimulate genuine spiritual growth remains largely theoretical and non-actualized while its potential to ferment hatred and intolerance is unmatched by any other human institution. Power politics and cultural beliefs, no doubt, take second and third place in history's Hall of Shame.

Most of the world's worst conduct has been committed by a combination of all three working together – religious and cultural belief in the service of power politics. The manipulation of religious and cultural beliefs (exploiting ignorance and ego – common fears, beliefs, and desires) to gain economic, personal, professional, and political advantage is an all too familiar story to any student of history or current events.

The unholy triumvirate of religious belief, cultural belief, and ego driven power politics clearly display the nature and results of high-entropy consciousness – ego, belief, need, fear, power, and desire. These three, in various combinations, seem to be at the source of most of the evil let loose in the world as far back as history can see – and as far into the future as anyone dare guess.

Do you agree or disagree? Don't simply jump to a conclusion that feels good, supports your beliefs, and reduces your discomfort. Use open minded skepticism to look around the world; then look at yourself, your community, neighborhood, and office. Pull out your old world history textbook and take another look. Gather your comparative data – then taste the pudding. Accept no one else's opinion; come to your own well-studied conclusion.

Before you are finished with your analysis, you will probably realize that the process of coming to a conclusion is vastly more important than the conclusion itself. Learning should not stop because a conclusion is reached. If the process continues, the conclusions can always change. To be effective, seeking Big Truth should be an iterative process that lasts a lifetime. Conclusions should, for the most part, remain tentative. Such is the nature of open mindedness. ◀◀

▶ Now you not only know that evolving your consciousness is the purpose of your existence, but also how to fulfill that purpose by becoming fearless, humble and compassionate. It cannot be more simple or straightforward than that. Now that you know and understand everything important, life should be a breeze – right?

Whether you admit or deny having fear, or any particular fear, is not significant to the results – the outcome is the same. Admission (recognizing the fear) may or may not bode well for the potential of removing the fear, but it does not change the results of having the fear. For people who live out of, or direct their existence from, their intellect (many pretend to, yet few actually do), there is an **apparent** power in recognizing and naming things. For these people, becoming aware of a particular fear **may** be the first step in overcoming that fear or it may be the first step in redesigning their fantasy to patch a perceived hole in their present delusion.

The fantasy generated by the intellect and ego team is designed to reduce the anxiety and discomfort caused by the fear. The symptom is treated while the cause is ignored and left to fester. The bigger and potentially more frightening the fear is to the individual, the bigger and more important the fantasy must be to counterbalance that fear effectively. Fantasies are dysfunctional in the same way that sweeping garbage under a rug is dysfunctional because it only **appears** to make the garbage go away. The garbage is still there, and it stinks increasingly with age. As more and more garbage is stuffed under that rug, the accumulation becomes more obvious and difficult to hide. It also becomes more unlikely that it will ever be cleaned up.

The fantasies that are driving choices in our life are as invisible to us, and to those around us who share them, as they are blatantly obvious to others who have a different perspective. For example, arrogance, self-righteousness, and self-centeredness only **appear** to be dysfunctional when they are larger, and dominate an individual more than is normal or typical. On the other hand, if you are not arrogant, self-righteous, and self-centered enough within a culture or subculture that demands a certain amount of these attributes; you may be seen as defective, weak, passive, or a loser.

Delusion and dysfunctionality that is normal or typical for a given culture is not seen as dysfunctional or deluded from inside the culture that supports it. In fact, most cultures or sub-cultures require that certain types of garbage be swept under the rug – and everybody in that culture is unaware of (or ignores) the stench. The clash of cultures is not only a clash of values; it is also a clash of egos, delusions, and needs.

Delusions come in all sizes, types and degrees – it is a continuum between very little (like you and me) and a lot (like some people we know). Some fantasies are more annoying than others. It is the **relative** compatibility, interactive nature, degree of unusualness, and extent of the fantasy that you are interacting with that largely determines the degree of annoyance **or attraction** you feel toward another's delusional constructs.

What about the deluded, arrogant, and egotistical beings who seem to be happy as pigs in mud? Do not believe it. That smooth exterior is purposely deceiving. It hides an inescapable emptiness, unhappiness, fear, and dissatisfaction that gets worse and more difficult to cover up with age. A poor quality of life is the inevitable result of a poor quality of consciousness.

Evidence to the contrary is short lived or turns sour or flat over time because any fantasy world is always in constant conflict with the real one. Consider the deluded, self-righteous, arrogant, and egotistical people you know (by definition, those who are much deeper into those particular fantasies than yourself). You will notice that the degree of their delusion, self-righteousness, arrogance, and egotism is directly proportional to the degree of their unhappiness and dissatisfaction, particularly if they are old enough for the inevitable consequences to have caught up with them.

I hear someone asking: "Isn't ego about power trips and pushing others around?" **Internal** control of your fears is the **driver** of ego, but a concerted effort to gain and maintain **external** control (fantasy management) is the **function** of ego. Control of yourself, as well as other people, is an important part of implementing and maintaining the fantasy. Control is a tool used by the ego and the intellect to convince the individual that the delusion is real and that the being is strong, good, worthy, lovable, rational, adequate, deserving, and all those things the being fears it is not.

The use of external power (bullying, dominating, manipulating, bribing, and threatening) is used to get what you want, need, and desire. Your wants, needs, and desires exist, for the most part, to cover over the emptiness, pain, discomfort, or difficulty caused by fear. Thus, the ego uses fantasy devices that directly and individually contradict each fear. For example, a bully on the outside is a typical ego response to feeling inadequate, powerless, and weak on the inside. In ego-space, what you see is often not what you get – image is everything. The privacy, secrecy, delusion, and denial required to maintain that image is second in importance only to the image itself.

So very easy to see in others, so very difficult to see in yourself! I am sure that is because others have many fears and personal problems that you do not share – well, at least theirs are worse than yours are. Did I get that right? Am I psychic or what? You're smiling. Is that because you imagine that I caught some people with their egos hanging out? Hey, I know, many things are like that … true for others but not for you. I understand; you are a unique individual – not like all the rest. Relax; it's others we are referring to here – the ones who still have the capacity and ability to improve themselves significantly.

The goal of ego in using external force, power, control, or manipulation is to display behavior that denies the fear – to pretend that what is feared is not actually true or that it is irrelevant or powerless. Using external power this way is like forcing someone to be nice to you, and then feeling satisfied or superior about how likeable you are based on the actions of this individual. This is self-delusion at its most obvious. The inevitable result of using power to pretend to be likable makes you less likeable. Using power to pretend that you are anything drives you further away from actually being what is pretended. That is how an abstract fear manifests itself into reality.

Our fantasies are not only private affairs, they are social and cultural constructs as well. We share and intermingle our fantasies with others within a mutual support system. There are many fantasy support systems (family, friends, work, school, church, clubs, sports) with one of the largest and most pervasive being our information and entertainment media. Traditions, devices, or institutions that support or reinforce our cultural beliefs often serve as fantasy support systems for individuals within that culture.

In interacting with others, particularly those we are unfamiliar with, we tend to lead or open with our image, tailor it slightly to custom fit the situation, and then wear that image like a costume. In that way, we lead others to participate in our fantasy as we participate in theirs. Eventually, we become lost in our fantasy and do not know who or what lies at the core of our being. We cannot tell the costume from our skin.

A common dream is one in which you are at work or school or church and suddenly realize that you are naked or otherwise inappropriately dressed or undressed, or totally unprepared and unfit for what ever it is you are about to do. Ever wonder why you have those dreams repeatedly? They dramatize a core fear. Not only is our ego-fantasy faux-being-construct itself a reaction to fear, but as a bonus, we get to fear the transparency (we are exposed or the real us is found out) of the fantasy itself, as well as fear the adequacy of the fantasy to continue to fool ourselves and others. Fear of exposure and inadequacy are companion fears born of a deeper knowledge of our self-delusion and manifested according to the individual personality. That is why hiding behind a costume makes us feel more secure.

Psychologists would have you believe that a healthy ego is a good thing – a necessity for success within our culture. When an individual is driven by the types and intensities of fear, desire, wants, needs, expectations, and beliefs that are average for his culture, he is pronounced normal – a healthy (by definition) member of his group. Many erroneously believe that a certain amount of a "don't tread on me" attitude is necessary to avoid being pushed around by others. The idea that no ego is synonymous with weak, powerless, and effete demonstrates a lack of understanding of the nature and dynamics of consciousness. Low personal entropy, high personal power, fearlessness, love, and no ego are all on the same team.

Beings with low or no ego have the highest quality consciousness and the greatest personal power. The truth of this statement does not rely on some odd definition of personal power. The personal power I am speaking of subsumes the standard definition. The power to take charge of your life, to defend yourself in the face of determined hostility, to find satisfaction and fulfillment, to lead and inspire others, and to accomplish great and lasting things in both the physical and the nonphysical realities in which we exist, flows most naturally from the same process that dissolves ego.

The capacity and ability to master consciousness evolution accrues to the warrior, not the wimp. Maintaining a healthy ego so that you can be normally dysfunctional in your culture is how mediocrity finds comfort in the security of the herd.

Insecurity is a hallmark of many cultures, including ours. We begin our integration into the larger shared fantasy, with its concomitant smaller reality, soon after birth. As that process continues, we eventually lose our ability to appreciate and understand the Big Picture. A small twisted (cultural biases or beliefs) PMR picture appears to be all there is, and seems to contain all the certain knowledge and truth. Knowledge beyond PMR knowledge appears to be necessarily based on imagination or belief. Such are the confines of the shared fantasy, belief, and fear that form and bound our little picture of reality.

A house of cards to camouflage the ricketiness of a house of cards that was built to camouflage yet another shaky house of cards may seem futile, but it works like magic every time. Here's how. Fear always leads away from peace and balance, and therefore, always breeds more fear in an interconnected cascade of worry and fret. Thus, many layers upon connected layers of fantasy and delusion are generated from a single fear. Eventually, as fear stacks upon fear, the entire fantasy structure becomes immensely complex and Byzantine – a wad of tangled threads so large it becomes a Gordian knot.

The transformation from a rickety house of cards to a strong defensive castle is dependent upon enough complexity and confusion to obfuscate the simple truth to the point that the owner's intellect will never confront any fear directly. A lesser intellect requires a less complex fantasy. Now the structure appears to be stable, solid and sound because the intellect cannot follow any single motivational strand to any fear in particular. No intent, no action can be laid squarely at the feet of (directly connected to) any particular fear. Presto! Change-o! The fear has disappeared! With some rationalization-putty and justification-Bondo to smooth over the rough edges and glue it all together, we get a beautiful custom made castle (with mote and drawbridge) for the ego to live within.

Beneath that clever cloud of obfuscation, the foundation remains a house of cards and fear remains the fundamental motivator. The garbage is still under the rug. We do not change reality, or modify absolute truths; we merely create a fantasy-bubble to live in with our friends and family. Our fantasy-bubble floats within the larger reality interacting positively with compatible fantasy-bubbles. Each bubble defines a local reality for those who are self-imprisoned within it. What a game! What a shame!

But hey, if it looks like a castle, works like a castle, and is treated like a castle by others, it must **be** a castle! The castle is the apparent you, it is the personal reality you create. It represents what you want to believe you are. It is the result of a lifetime of steady progress, interacting with others, and existing successfully within your culture. In it, you are as safe and secure as you believe you can be. The castle is where your ego (a relatively small and well-behaved one, I am sure) and your intellect live and work, protected and secure.

From this headquarters, life's strategies are formed and executed; evaluations are made. This castle is the foundation of your existence, the core of your being. It represents you, your life, how you define yourself as an individual, how you relate to others. You cannot imagine anything more frightening, or more fear provoking, than letting go of or tearing down your protective belief-fantasy castle.

This is how you feel: "Anyone who does not recognize the fundamental correctness and solid reality of my very fine castle must be deluded, or hopelessly lost in a fantasy."

The door is shut, the drawbridge is up, and no information exposing the delusion is ever considered, tolerated or let inside. You feel protected inside the castle, but from a Big Picture view you are simply trapped inside, ensnared in the web of your own fearful deceit. Caught like a rat in a belief trap! There is no easy or painless way out.

After you are finished thinking about the previous few paragraphs, let's change gears and talk about what it means to be centered and balanced. A discussion of fear and ego would not be complete without an understanding of balance. You experience right being when you are balanced – when you are living, growing, and being with optimal spiritual productivity and minimal consciousness entropy. You lose balance when the ego is the source of your motivation or intent. When you are animated (making choices) by wants, fears, desires and needs, you become driven by an inward-pointing forcing-function and are not balanced.

When you are animated by love, you are not driven by fear, ego, desire, or need. There Is no forcing function driving your choices. Love is directed outward. With love, you are at peace, solid, still, fearless, and centered. This is not a control issue; control does not create balance, but only the **appearance** of balance. A balanced individual is a conscious part of the unified larger reality, a productive citizen of the larger consciousness ecosystem, and is aware of being interconnected to everything. External balance (being in balance with everything external to the individual) is an immediate and automatic consequence of internal balance. Internal balance precedes and enables external balance – it does not work the other way around. Trying hard to appear as if you are balanced does little to produce real balance – truth does not flow from fantasy. The Big Picture can not be derived from the little picture.

When right being and right action are natural, easy and obvious, you are in balance. For large systems as well as individual entities, balance defines the minimum entropy state at any given time, under any given circumstance. Balance is not a digital on-off function; it represents a continuum from the highest entropy consciousness (wild, angry, insane, frantic, self-centered, random, confused, hurt, threatened, fearful, demanding, vengeful, jealous, self-important, and inadequate – all artifacts of fear and ego) to the lowest entropy consciousness (balanced, fearless, egoless, compassionate, humble, and expressive of unconditional love).

Balance is sometimes described as the state of being detached. This is a valuable metaphor but we should be careful about what the word "detached" means within this context. Being detached does **not** imply that you are either intellectually or emotionally withdrawn or distant. Detachment does **not** mean not interactive, not involved, or does not care. Detachment does **not** imply being aloof, or above it all. The pursuit of consciousness quality (spiritual growth) never requires or encourages one to become detached from life, caring involvement with others, or from responsibility. Detachment simply means that one is no longer influenced by needs, wants, desires, expectations, and beliefs. Balance and a low entropy consciousness are enabled through detachment from one's ego.

Note: What I have been describing is the balance of entities growing toward the positive side (rats). Anti-rats, or those evolving through negative intention, also seek lower entropy states of being through internal balance by total control of self (controlling their personal energy) and **approximate** external balance by control of what is external to themselves that can be controlled. Those poor anti-rats: their potential is dreadfully constrained. Control, driven by desire and need, is a desperate and self-limiting attempt by the disenfranchised effete to appear powerful. Control is, and always has been, a poor substitute for love.

This brings us to a simple fact that everyone needs to understand about having ego and not being in balance: The unfettered ego, aided by the intellect, will always act in a way that inadvertently manifest the fear into the reality of the being. The ego-intellect fantasy constructs always encourage the being to make choices that actualize the fear! If the problem or fear the ego is whitewashing is initially only an imagined difficulty (which is the normal condition), the ego will eventually transform whatever is feared from an in-your-mind thought-form to an in-your-face physical reality. The speed and certainty of this transformation is dependent on the energy invested, which is proportional to the intensity of the ego's reaction to the fear.

Simply put, your ego makes your fears come true. By manifesting your fears – bringing them from the realm of consciousness into your local physical reality and forcing you to deal with them directly – your ego becomes a powerful teacher by hitting you over the head with the painful consequences of your fear, and imbalance. A dumb rat gets zapped! This is a great educational feedback reality, not an existentialist's, or nihilist's uncaring "life sucks" reality. To be confused on that point is disastrous. A "life sucks" attitude dooms you to an unhappy, no-growth existence of self-inflicted pain. Self pity, "woe is me," "what's the use," "life is unfair," "so what," "leave me alone, I do not want to learn anymore painful lessons," "who cares," and "I just can't do it," are deadly to your evolutionary progress and personal growth. Going through life with these attitudes is like trying to swim in deep water with a cement block strapped to your back.

There is one more thing that you should know about ego. The ego is such that many other people, unlike you, will read this entire aside on ego thinking that I am talking about someone else. They will be nodding their heads up and down as they read, pleased to enhance or at least confirm their considerable understanding about what makes **other** people act as they do.

Hey, amigo, you can help me out here. If you happen to know somebody in this pitiful situation, please try to wake them up – gently of course. Please be empathetic and kind, they are doing the best they can. They have obviously been mesmerized by their extremely capable and clever intellect and have probably missed almost everything important within this trilogy since the end of Section 1, and much of what is important within their life since the age of sixteen. Sad, yes – but entirely redeemable!

If you cannot wake them up … Yes, I know you are very good at this, even so, breaking a belief centered ego entrancement is extremely difficult…if you cannot wake them up … please, try to make them comfortable and simply go on your way. Never attempt to shatter someone's worldview by dramatically collapsing their house of cards with logic. That approach rarely works and usually creates a bigger problem. If you shove Big Truth into the intellect of an entranced ego, there is a high probability that this victim of self-trickery will contract the hideous-truth-trauma (HTT) syndrome, which invariably creates an emotional disturbance leading to an angry and fearful retreat deeper into the fantasy jungle. Never intentionally corner a critter unless you are prepared to deal with panicked desperation that can occasionally turn vicious.

Nevertheless, all is not lost – the future is always uncertain. Shaaazaaam! Satori may strike the walking oblivious at any time like a brilliant bolt of rogue lightning! Oh yes, it is possible, stranger things have happened at least once since time began.

Take a deep breath and relax – contemplate how this discussion of ego relates to you personally. Imagine a few of your most cherished delusions and the fear that creates and feeds them – and go on. ◀

That ego digression was fun and I hope you had a good time, but now we need to return to achieving a better understanding of feelings and personality. Combine self-awareness with an ego – self-awareness hallucinating (believing in) its own relative self-importance – and you get the possibility (high likelihood) of emotional and intellectual pain. Delusional self-awareness is self-awareness with an attitude (with an ego) and can thus feel both joy and pain. We are not referring to physical pain here. Pain is the awareness of not getting what you want, of not having it your way, of failing to possess or to retain possession of something your ego is attached to – something you believe you want, need, desire or deserve.

Thus, an ego creates pain (for its owner) out of its attachment to unfulfilled requirements, out of its beliefs, and out of the requirements and conditions it places upon the achievement of contentment and satisfaction. Pain is caused by dissatisfied, discontented, needy self-awareness. Self-induced pain is the electric shock you get in the PMR learning lab's amazing maze. It is the primary negative feedback stimulus applied in the intent-behavior modification trainer provided by your local virtual space-time reality. Joy, love, and happiness are the flip side of that coin, the positive feedback stimuli.

Fear can also be a phobic reaction to real or imagined pain, discomfort, or disadvantage. Fear produces an awareness of potential pain and creates additional related fears. The generated pain and additional fears likewise instigate more fear – a snowballing feedback process that quickly saturates to maximize anxiety and discomfort.

Now we can understand why any answer, including a wrong (delusional) one, often appears better than no answer at all. Using belief to ease the fear that ignorance produces is more immediately important than expelling the ignorance. Open minded skepticism loses out to belief-based immediate gratification because open minded skepticism is a long term solution that must deal fearlessly with ignorance. It would appear that humankind generally finds it is quicker, easier and more immediately satisfying to pop a feel-good belief-based pain pill to cover up an unpleasant symptom, than to struggle mightily to triumph over the root cause.

> ▶ Words that describe emotional content have many facets and shades. Different people often interpret them differently. Using terms that express feeling inevitably produces a semantic minefield; consequently, don't get blown away over the details – particularly if I use words in ways that are not in consonance with your definitions and notions. Following the **general** sense of the intended meaning, while letting the quibbles go, will produce a more accurate, complete, and productive communication. ◀

Joy and peace are the opposites of pain and fear. They are generated by self-awareness without ego – without attachments, needs, desires, wants, or requirements. Joy is self-awareness unconditionally enjoying its existence and the existence of whatever it has created, and whatever else there is for it to be aware of.

Peace is self-awareness being unconditionally content with itself and satisfied with the state of its being – knowing that it has done whatever it has done for the right motivation. A being in perfect balance is a joyful being at peace. Balance generates peace and vice-versa.

Sadness is self-awareness knowing that it, its parts, its implementations of the Fundamental Process, its creations, and loved-ones could be better (more optimized, more profitable). Sadness, peace and joy all coexist with each other – each generating and supporting the others.

> ▶ What I am calling sadness here might better be called gentle, mild, or accepting sadness, or perhaps somber, serious, contemplative or reflective would be better, more descriptive adjectives – but not boo-hoo or woe-is-me sadness. This is sadness born of compassion, humility and caring. It is the result of a realistic and empathetic understanding of the unnecessary self-inflicted pain that heaps misery on the world and its people. This is the sadness of watching your friends and loved ones (as well as all people) making

themselves and each other miserable and unhappy because of their ignorance and knowing there is nothing you can do to help them grow up. Another form of sadness (sad because you are not getting what you want) falls under the heading of ego induced pain and has nothing to do with the sadness derived from compassionate love. ◀

Joy, peace and sadness, as defined above, compose love. Love is a state of being incorporating compassion and humility with no fear, no ego, and no delusion. Because love is the natural result of a low entropy consciousness, joy, peace, sadness and the elimination of ego are likewise the direct result of a consciousness sufficiently lowering its entropy.

Love is what one ends up with after the ego's wants, needs, desires, and expectations are removed from an individuated consciousness. Love is the natural and most basic expression of low entropy consciousness. Love is what grows within consciousness in the absence of fear. Love is a technical term defined by an absence of entropy in consciousness; it exists within individuated consciousness as a continuum of quality that may range from very, very little to very, very much. Love is a property of a highly spiritual consciousness. Love represents the uncorrupted natural state of aware sentient existence and harbors no delusion. Love is the goal of evolving consciousness working within the consciousness cycle. All effectively growing personal Big TOEs must converge to love as they progress along their unique path toward Big Truth. Love is your purpose; it defines the positive direction of your growth.

9

■ ■ ■

Life and Love in the Petri Dish
Great Science, Good Plan –
Now Get To Work

■ ■ ■

Does the Big Dude have a big ego? There is no evidence to indicate that AUM is delusional. There is no reason for AUM to be delusional; no evolutionary pressure is pushing in that direction. Delusion adds no value; it is dysfunctional. Ego, fear, and delusion work to increase system entropy. Consciousness naturally evolves from greater to lesser ego – a delusional AUM would constitute an evolutionary discard.

Because some will be forced by habit to project delusion into the mind of AUM, let's look at the historical record. Historical, mythical and theological reports of Greek, Jewish, Roman, Christian, and Muslim gods being egotistical (vengeful, jealous, angry, demanding, pouty, upset, self-important, and violent – all traits of a large dysfunctional ego) are most likely an artifact of God being described by men, in the image of men, to satisfy the needs and purposes of men. In other words, the common description (among many of the world's popular religions) of an egotistical (delusional) god is most likely the result of men projecting their own egotism upon their concept of god (god made in the image of man) and offers no credible evidence (guilty by vague association) against the mental and spiritual health of AUM.

To avoid the pain of not knowing, people habitually extrapolate what they know and are familiar with to the unknown. This pseudo-knowledge soothes the fear of ignorance and allows abstract conceptualizations to appear more concrete and therefore more user friendly (more easily marketed). Actually the connection here is almost non-existent. The gods of little picture men are not concretely or specifically related to The Big Cheese, much less to AUM. The nature of consciousness and the manner and process of its evolution (entropy reduction, spiritual growth, improving consciousness quality) are strongly related to AUM, but have nothing or little to do with organized religion. The concept that unconditional love, balance, joy, compassion, and humility are the attributes of high quality consciousness has little or nothing to do with religious doctrine, dogma, and creed. If you think that believing in religious dogma generates spiritual growth, go back to Chapter 19, Book 1 where we discussed the nature of belief and its relationship to knowledge and consciousness quality.

Hypothesize AUM as a large natural system of self-modifying digital organization (consciousness) in the process of evolving. Such a concept has no reliance upon any belief, much less belief in an egotistical sugar daddy who will damn you for eternity if you do not profess belief in the proper things in the proper way. How is unconditional love, compassion, joy, and humility expressed by that attitude? There is obviously no overlap between AUM and religious dogma; however, there may be some overlap between evolving consciousness and at least some religious **values** because religion often speaks to human values and human values at their root evolve from the values of low entropy consciousness. There may also be a connection between religion and low entropy consciousness because of religion's occasional association with those who have deeply known Big Truth and nobly tried to embody it and package it for large numbers of others. Unfortunately, history shows that such an effort, no matter how noble, does not work well and usually ends up ugly and twisted for the majority who eventually try to reach salvation through ritual, dogma, closed-mindedness, and violence – all giant steps in the opposite direction from spiritual growth, love, and lower entropy. Ritual, dogma, closed-mindedness, hate, and violence – the historical trappings of religion at the common level – can appeal only to the shortsighted feel good, feel superior, feel saved needs of ego.

An effort to spread Big Truth may be a noble undertaking, however, using an organization to spread Big Truth to the multitudes, many of whom are not yet ready to personally assimilate its underlying wisdom, has historically ended up being counterproductive. Once organized, the Big Truth – which requires **individual** wisdom to understand – is replaced by culturally relevant dogma that everyone can easily understand and a structure designed to grow the power, influence, and cash flow of the organization. Eventually, defining, maintaining and growing the organization becomes an end in itself on the path of power while the original driving force of Big Truth is replaced by a more effective and marketable self-righteous dogma fanned by the flames of ignorance and fear at the lowest common denominator of organizational (group) mind. Low quality consciousness is, by nature, easily manipulated.

I am speaking in terms of generalities here; there are always individual exceptions. **Fear-based organizations** (believe our way or suffer the awful consequences) are inherently and fundamentally incompatible with the promulgation of spiritual values and growth which require a **love-based individual understanding**. Trying to express and spread love through dogma, self-righteous arrogance, legislation, political or social pressure, narrow-mindedness, or fanatical violence is like trying to strike a wooden match under twenty feet of muddy water using only your elbows.

We can safely assume the AUM consciousness system is not delusional, is not ego or fear based, and is therefore not attached to wants, needs, dogmatic requirements, beliefs, preconceived notions, or desires. Without fear and ego, which inevitably produce revengeful, jealous, angry, self-important, demanding and needy dogmatic behavior, AUM must represent humility, compassion, balance, joy, peace and sadness, which, as defined in the previous chapter, composes self-aware love. Then, AUM's inscrutable being – a hugely complex, aware, evolved, minimum entropy consciousness-system-digital-thing-being – has a nature, a personality or attitude that can be described as love.

We know other sentient entities by the **nature** of their being, not the structure or mechanics of their being. For example, the people we know best are much more to us than objective bodies and behavior. We know them by their nature, primarily their subjective quality. In the same manner, we experience or know AUM's nature as love because that is the state of being (minimum entropy) that consciousness naturally evolves to. Some religions ascribe this same property, among others, to their god(s).

Some may worry that if AUM is finite, it must be locked into some competitive evolutionary struggle that puts us at risk. Quick, someone call Hollywood: "Cuddly and cute AUMosaurus the love-being vs. the mentally degenerate and mean thought-form eating monster from the evil black swamp." Uh oh, if that is us in this grade-B movie, it would appear that we are in big trouble! Relax. The idea that our beloved AUM might be only a little guy in a reality beyond our potential comprehension should not be unnerving. Bear in mind that our hypothetical AUMosaurus is a thought-creature-thing that lives in mind-space. Do not let habitual patterns of thought impose a survival of the fittest, or law of the jungle mentality on AUM and its possible environs.

Concerns for AUM's continuing existence are misguided and stuck in biology-based PMR thought patterns. A relatively small and limited being does not necessarily imply a delusional being suffering from an inferiority complex. Relative size has nothing to do with love or delusion. Small physically weak people and sumo wrestlers have an equal shot at quality consciousness. Being vulnerable and being fearful do not necessarily travel together. Likewise, being fearless and being foolhardy do not always travel together. Competition and survival are non-issues in thought-space where AUM lives. Quality of consciousness is the relevant metric. Relative size is relevant only to who can create and support whom – a matter of ecological organization.

In order to help you understand the strong interrelationships connecting AUM, experiments in consciousness, evolution, scientific inquiry, and love, I need to broaden your picture of AUM by putting Our System (OS) into a more personal perspective. At the risk of sidetracking your focus and generating curiosity tangential to the intended point, I think a short aside explaining the nature and purpose of $NPMR_N$ and Our System relative to other realities is in order. Understanding there are other reality systems that are fundamentally constructed the same as ours, but are functionally very different from ours, will help you to see AUM from a larger perspective.

▶ AUM: scientist at work. Metaphorically speaking, AUM has run, and is running, many experiments. Before there were PMRs, there were only NPMRs. As it turns out, NPMR realities are not optimized for evolving basic or elementary consciousness. The problem is the motivation-action-result-feedback loops are long and difficult to define in NPMR because interactions between entities are often tenuous and not steady. If a sentient entity does not like what is going on in NPMR thought-space, it can drop out and disappear or block out (filter) specific interactions. In NPMR, your external environment is, to a large extent, controlled directly by your mind. Such is the nature of thought-space and thought-form-land: It is tenuous, individual, and quick to change. Doing or action (energy exchanges) comes and goes with focus, is intent driven, and often reversible.

In NPMR, the results and consequences of intent and action were difficult to define and unclear. Responsibility and right intent, the main learning issues, seemed forever debatable. Reconstruction of certain and clear motivation became a slippery and divisive issue among NPMR residents. A reality that was stickier, more solid and obvious — something less tenuous, changeable and camouflageable — was needed to obviate those "Yes I did," "No you didn't," arguments over intent.

Something was required that would hold interaction steady and engaged until complete and clear intents were generated. The processes of interaction needed to be irreversible – once choices are made and action is taken, there is no way to take it back. Because energy exchanges between entities produce consequences that cannot be undone, final results are cumulative. Moreover, the results of exchanges of energy (the actual interaction) must be defined within the framework of a binding causal chain so the ramifications of all actions can be tracked to completion. Additionally, to facilitate evolutionary growth, interim results needed to be returned to the interacting entities in the form of feedback.

As you might have guessed, we are now in the process of specifying the top-level requirements for space-time. Evolution, always on the lookout for a better way of doing business, began to probe more effective ways to encourage system profitability and to facilitate individuated consciousness in their quest to find lower entropy configurations. Space-time has evolved as an external virtual environment that enables raw, relatively high entropy consciousness to more effectively actualize its growth potential. Think of space-time as a virtual reality trainer that helps individuated consciousness units learn how to more effectively organize and structure their energy.

Because a huge number of small quizzes vs. a few big inconclusive tests produce a better more consistent evaluation, a process that incrementally averages over many small everyday choices and drives irreversible results would be better able to harness change in the service of clarity. Consistency and continuity could be improved by **slowly** incrementing dynamic processes (interactions and energy exchanges) and their subsequent results in appropriately small steps by utilizing a reality based upon a **relatively large** quantum of time.

By implementing these design modifications into a subset of NPMR, AUM could evolve a rule-set for a portion of mind-space (a virtual reality existing within its own dimension) that provides a more efficient and productive learning-environment for consciousness evolution. Consequently, arrays of space-time realities, some similar to our beloved PMR, were spawned to meet the needs of evolving consciousness. Imagine a space-time elementary school, or perhaps a space-time entropy reduction factory, where individuated chunks of consciousness could more effectively evolve their energy toward more profitable states of being.

To facilitate self-improvement, each individuated consciousness would need to cut through the layers of convoluted intellectual assessments, opinions, image, and ego to get to the truth of a buried intent. Something was needed that allows individuals to see and feel their consciousness quality directly reflected in their actions. Effective consciousness evolution needed a truth device or quality meter that accurately measures, displays, records, and accumulates the entropy reducing profitability or rightness of any motivation initiating an interaction. Without such a device (or if the device is ignored), individuals would have no truth reference and could be easily captured by their ego's propaganda.

What a great feedback-driven learning tool this would be! Can you imagine? Something that would accurately grade the quality of every thought we have and action we take, as well as maintain a running sum of the results. An entity whose accumulated experience-quality represents a large collection of good quality intentions would naturally create a loving and joyous existence; in contrast, one that represented an accumulation of entropy increasing ego-driven intentions would automatically create a stressful, miserable, unhappy existence.

Wow! With a feedback device like that to guide your growth, how could you go wrong? Jeez, this is going to be easier than I thought: All I need to do is learn how to pay attention to this quality meter gizmo, do the right thing, and then check my score. With a little trial and error experimenting, it should be relatively simple for me to get better and better scores over time. Cinchy! Where is this gizmo, and what does it look like?

Within an individuated digital mind, combine sufficient richness, complexity, non-linear feedback, clever programming, and the proper processing constraints with a mixture of love, humility, compassion, fear, desire, and ego and out pops a specific perception of interaction called "raw emotion" which is designed to reflect inner quality accurately. Emotion surges unfettered through individuated digital mind to satisfy a major design criterion of profitable consciousness evolution. (More on this in Section 4.)

This what-you-feel-reflects-what-your-are internal quality meter is the mother of all bio-feedback devices. That love and joy do not dominate our feelings most of the time is both normal and not a good sign. Love, joy, peace, compassion, humility, and balance are the dominant expressions and feelings of a high quality consciousness. What you and I feel most of the time is probably more representative of a high entropy consciousness.

Your feelings always reflect the real you with perfect accuracy. If you feel anger, negativity, inadequacy, or anxiety, that is a reflection of how you are and what you are on the inside; **not** how other people **make** you feel. Additionally, entities of higher quality often couple emotion with a conscience containing the values of its underlying consciousness to produce a better, more sensitive, quality-meter. Take a note: Perhaps you should investigate what your emotive energy (instantaneous and cumulative) is telling you about the quality of your consciousness.

"That jerk really makes me mad!" Actually, he does not. You cannot logically blame others for creating your emotions; you must take 100% of the responsibility for whatever you do, feel, and are. Others merely show you a reflection of yourself as you react to them – the reactions are yours alone. You are in charge of and responsible for you. You react and interact as you do because of how **you** are. No one, no thing, and no circumstance can possibly force you to be someone other than you. Only you are allowed to make your choices.

PMR is where the rubber meets the road – where your actions and feelings reflect the actual you, not what you think you are, or want to be. Individuated units of consciousness using NPMR as their local reality became confused over what was the real them and what they thought was them. Learning was difficult. That's what I was referring to in Chapter 5 of this book when, in reference to designing "biological-matter bumps," I said: "It would be better to give it limited awareness and functionality so it won't be continually getting stuck in intellectual endless loops thinking about interactions instead of experiencing them as did some of the less productive experiments AUM tried earlier." By now the context in which that statement can be understood has broadened considerably. Nevertheless, the discussion of space-time design requirements is just getting started; additional depth and breadth is coming in Sections 4 and 5.

There are different experiments going on in each of the different nonphysical reality systems (the so-called $NPMR_n$). For example, one such system has few rules of interaction – no law and no justice at the highest level – I have never been to a space-time construct there, though I am relatively sure they must exist. Accessibility to PMRs in this system is not the issue. I stay away from that reality as much as possible because it is dreadfully rough, mean spirited, and unpredictable – one can easily get damaged there. The $NPMR_n$ experiments are to demonstrate the effect of various values, rules, and rule-sets, (selective constraints) on the dynamics of consciousness evolution.

There are many reality dimensions whose operational constraints fall between the extremes of a chaotic free for all and our law abiding OS. I imagine there are some reality systems that are significantly more constrained than OS, but I have never been in one. Consider the implication – tighter constraints are a necessary requirement of pre-schools and kindergartens. As the average quality level rises, restrictions can be relaxed without compromising educational effectiveness.

At one time, we (OS) were less constrained than we are now. There was more direct interaction (meddling) between NPMR (gods and spirits) and PMR (men). The extent of that interaction created results that were interfering with the intent of the experiment; consequently, more restrictive rules were made and our current OS became as we now know it. The rules (structural dynamics) can change, but not casually and not often or the integrity of the experiment will be ruined.

Outside (external to PMR) meddling, applied to the evolutionary process taking place within the PMR learning lab, adds uncertainty to the process and usually produces unnatural results that cannot be maintained without further meddling. Interference, once started, breeds a vicious cycle requiring more interference – like a liar telling new lies to hide old lies. You may recall that at the end of Chapter 4 of this book we discussed what happens when one ruins an experiment with too much intervention or meddling. Our conclusion: "The experimenter would have to flush the little fellows down the drain and start over." I am afraid that flood insurance will not help and that treading water for eternity is not an acceptable solution. We should not expect that AUM, the

Big Cheese, or anyone else will be paying attention to our trials and tribulations, adjusting results, meddling, or calling the plays from the sideline within OS. This is serious science and evolution, not a children's game of "Father may I."

Interference in PMR (from outside PMR) by **direct** action is generally forbidden – all exceptions must obey the psi uncertainty principle which is thoroughly addressed later. On the other hand, **indirect** influence is, under certain conditions, not only allowed, but encouraged. One peripheral and probably unintended consequence of this important rule enables the consciousness-limited embodied citizens of the PMRs that are operationally aware in $NPMR_N$, to take direct actions in $NPMR_N$ without the liability that would accrue to a less limited $NPMR_N$ being who is not under the protection of PMR citizenship. As greater numbers of entities embodied within physical realities become operational and active in the nonphysical, this loophole will probably be plugged.

In the mean time, an embodied citizen of PMR, who has a well developed consciousness and is operationally aware in $NPMR_N$, has a powerful advantage in that he or she can forcefully interact with the energy of others (both within and outside PMR) and remain within the law and thus protected by it. We are allowed to meddle in the energy of others because such activity exercises an important part of our evolutionary potential and because our consciousness is generally so undeveloped that we can't do much damage – like letting a bunch of toddlers throw Nerf balls at each other.

The two-edged sword of free will enables energy exchanges to be both constructive and destructive of consciousness quality. The residents of PMR do not have a blank check to wreak havoc on themselves and the rest of NPMR – there are rules and limits – but they are granted a wider degree of latitude (a handicap of sorts) and additional protection under the law because of their limitations. For a rough analogy, consider laws that protect children or the mentally retarded from exploitation.

Our $NPMR_N$ experiment is about the dynamics of the evolution of consciousness. To oversimplify, the basic motivational dynamics (as opposed to structural dynamics) are: love, knowledge and wisdom vs. fear, ego and ignorance and the equally popular theme, good vs. evil. Could the dynamics of this fundamental struggle at the root of our consciousness be the source of our deepest self-expression? Our arts (literature, cinema, painting, theater, and music) are dedicated to expressing our interest and preoccupation with the motivational dynamics that are fundamental to our existence and the existence of our reality.

The same themes that universally stir emotion and captivate interest within every culture on our planet are those that describe what is crucial and important to the evolution of our consciousness. Because consciousness is common to humanity, tales of love, knowledge, wisdom, fear, ego, ignorance, and good vs. evil are also common to humanity as well as to all other highly aware conscious beings. The motivational dynamics of consciousness are our motivational dynamics as well because we are consciousness. Could anything be more simple or straightforward?

Within $NPMR_N$ there are some physical reality systems that are almost entirely evil and a few that are almost entirely good. You get the idea: There is lots of action and variety in NPMR and its subsets. There are many different and unique PMRs in NPMR. I have explored at least several dozen such realities, and several of these in great detail. Although they all follow the same basic reality mechanics described in Section 5, at the physical level (beings, culture, and environment), some are fundamentally similar to our reality (have the same basic structure) while others are not at all like OS.

From the viewpoint of digital mind-space, all realities, except the larger consciousness system we call AUM, could be described as virtual realities. The computer itself is a fundamental reality while the simulations running within it constitute virtual realities. From the viewpoint of the consciousness-evolution fractal ecosystem, the computer and its subsets and pieces form a vast interconnected interdependent system. From the first viewpoint, we are a product or result of the computer; in the second, we are an integral part of the computer. Because AUM represents All That Is, both viewpoints are compatible.

I do not want to explore these ideas more fully within this book because they are not pertinent to understanding *My Big TOE*. The various $NPMR_n$ are defined and discussed again in Section 5 (Chapter 4, Book 3). All of the above, as well as additional information and first hand experience is available on these subjects in NPMR. If you are interested, you should begin to develop the ability to access this information, and experience $NPMR_N$ yourself. It is not as difficult as you might think. ◀

Incorrectly applying familiar biological thought patterns may lead you to think that AUM the lean and mean evolution machine is incompatible with AUM the embodiment of love. AUM is not a shark. AUM is consciousness. The evolutionary result of highly evolved, low entropy consciousness is love-consciousness. As you evolve your consciousness, you decrease your entropy and increase your capacity to love. Love is produced, created, and brought into being by the action of a lean and mean evolution machine operating on consciousness. "Lean" implies optimized, efficient, minimum waste, and good economics and ecology – like our own efficient Mother Nature. "Mean" implies that dysfunctional, counterproductive or unprofitable evolutionary offshoots or experiments are ruthlessly terminated as soon as their unprofitabiliy is determined.

The connection between AUM and love is less about what AUM does and feels, or how AUM acts (AUM being unconditionally loving) than it is about AUM **being** unconditional love. Love, as an attribute of AUM's existence, is the source of (and hence more fundamental than) AUM's expression of love through feelings or actions. When we equate AUM consciousness with low entropy, and low entropy consciousness with love, we are talking about

AUM's fundamental nature, substance, and being, not simply its personality. Love is the animating dynamic of AUM; it is AUM's most salient property. AUM is an evolving digital-love-consciousness-being-thing whose actions and intents are animated and motivated by unconditional love – which is the natural mode and expression of a low entropy consciousness.

Are you beginning to wonder how the Fundamental Process could possible produce a creation this fantastic? Isn't this all a bit much? How could reality be this complex and exist on such a grand scale? I will tell you how – there's a trick to it.

Because evolution invests only in winners, it appears that the Fundamental Process consistently delivers the exact tools that are needed to facilitate successful evolution. This makes the Fundamental Process look exceptionally clever, but the fact is that only the cleverest moves persist while the others self-destruct. Think about it: If you can arrange for your failures to automatically disappear without a trace while your successes persist forever, you will eventually (if you live long enough) end up looking incredibly brilliant even if you are a random plodder. The products of evolution appear to be incredibly clever, but I'm not impressed. The Fundamental Process has been working a long, long, long time and I am hip to its slick trick of conveniently hiding its many mistakes.

AUM is interested in the science of the dynamics of consciousness evolution – the science of the creation of love-consciousness. Yes, there is evolutionary struggle, evolutionary winners and losers, but bear in mind that this is taking place in thought-space. The losers are not necessarily raped, pillaged, and sold into slavery. For example, let us say the Good Guys win the rat-maze struggle, then after all the rats make it, the anti-rats will slowly but surely be won over until **everybody** makes it because that is the nature of rats. On the other hand, if the anti-rats (Bad Guys) win, the rats will slowly and surely be exploited, subjugated, abused, and then exterminated because that is the nature of anti-rats. Oh well, that's honest evolution, impartial science, and love-consciousness at work.

We are not independent of AUM. Think of AUM as a loving, dispassionate, impartial, unbiased, independent scientist-engineer-philosopher: good and valid science is done dispassionately. AUM is an evolving brilliant consciousness with a high level of awareness that must figure things out as we do – good science is the only way.

Let go of the anthropomorphic image of AUM carrying a clipboard and wearing a white lab coat with pocket protectors – it is not like that. In an advanced consciousness system, good science, successful evolution, and exploring and populating the most profitable states all merge together as a single complex motivational pressure pushing the system toward self-improvement. Evolutionary pressure and intellectual process merge to become one in an aware, low-entropy, consciousness system. Think of AUM as an evolving "consciousness-system-being-thing" (with emphasis on the word "thing") instead of an "old-guy-with-a-long-white-beard-and-bushy-eyebrows-in-a-white-robe" (an all powerful version of us who promises to save us and defeat our enemies if we agree to worship him in return).

▶ Do you ever wonder why all the gods of men seem to have a strong want, need, expectation, or desire to be worshiped? An obsession with being worshipped and wanting or needing the little people to "believe in you" must be either an occupational hazard of godship or a prerequisite for the job. Haven't you always wondered what, exactly, gods get out of being worshiped and "believed in" and **why** – it certainly appears to be extraordinarily important to them.

The fact is, **unconditional** love, compassion, and humility can have **no** requirements, **no** ego, **no** needs, **no** desires, and **no** expectations. Consequently, don't confuse AUM or the Big Cheese with any god of the human tribe – their nature as egoless manifestations of unconditional love disqualifies them for the job.

It must be difficult to get people to join your organization and give you money and obedience if all you give them in return is permission to develop the quality of their consciousness in their own unique way and on their own time (which is the only way an individual can improve their consciousness quality). A spiritual organization can offer no more than casual nonspecific encouragement to its members without also becoming an inhibitor of their progress. ◀

▶▶ Hey, I just got a great idea! Listen, I hereby fully encourage you to develop your consciousness quality in your own way, on your own time, and at your own place so would you please send ten percent of your annual income to the address inside the front cover of this book?

And just for my dearly beloved favorite readers, a onetime special introductory bonus offer: After I get the entire ten percent, I'll throw in an autographed book and a set of twelve self-addressed tithing envelopes for next year – absolutely **free**!

Wait, there is more: a triple extra bonus! Wow! I hereby solemnly promise to 1) let you sleep in every Saturday and Sunday, 2) never lecture you or preach to you or make you wear a suit and tie, and 3) allow unlimited disobedience!

Jeez man, compare that package to what the competition offers! A fantastic deal at half the price! ◀◀

▶ Don't waste your time or money – there is no address inside the front cover of this book. I am just having some fun. Laughing at yourself is not only fun, but good medicine. Everybody enjoys an occasional dose of good medicine, right?

The point is: The process of encouraging spiritual growth does not lend itself to being organized. To the contrary, when a spiritually focused organization becomes successful (recruits a sustaining broad membership), it inevitably becomes part of the problem – it begins inhibiting spiritual growth instead of encouraging it. Although the raising of consciousness quality requires an individual process, the raising of good feelings within a secure ego requires a group process. Because the two processes are generally incompatible and destructive of each other, it is a good idea to be clear about which process best represents your personal investment in consciousness quality. ◀

The pursuit of truth through good science is one reason (only one of several) why human bio-scientists do not fall madly in love with their bacteria. An overly strong emotional-ego attachment to the bacteria in your petri dish might cause you to meddle unwisely and compromise the experiment. AUM is not fooling around in the lab; it is doing real science and real experiments that affect its evolution.

I am sure AUM wants the Good Guys to win, but it must let the chips fall where they may. This is not cruel or inconsistent with being the embodiment of love. AUM does not have a mean thought-bone in its thought-body (mind). Because AUM doesn't cuddle you and sing lullabies, (make you feel special, superior and valued – all syrup to the ego), doesn't mean it is an indifferent, heartless mind-shark that doesn't care what happens. AUM is giving you an opportunity to evolve your consciousness via the intentional dissolution of your ego; surely you understand that puffing up your ego by giving you special consideration would be terribly counter productive. A good scientist can care very deeply and profoundly about what happens – but still must conduct honest experiments. You cannot trick evolution. Profitability is assessed by **results**, not good intentions, brilliant theory, or preferred outcomes.

AUM is dim consciousness evolved into brilliant love-consciousness – which is how positive consciousness naturally evolves. The negative intent consciousness critters and beings (evil) can evolve only toward power-control-force. That is as far as evil can go – the establishment of power-control-force. Minimizing entropy by growing or evolving in the negative direction is extremely limited and relatively worthless compared to the advantages gained by a consciousness evolving positively toward the expression of itself as love. In PMR, power-control-force is a way of life – a primary motivator. That fact should tell you there is much low quality consciousness, negativity, and evil running loose in our local reality. The only way to help clean that mess up is to clean yourself up. You do not have the ability to improve anyone else. All you can do for others is to provide opportunity for them to do for themselves.

In the PMR elementary school of 3D space-time, power-control-force may seem to be a big deal. It may appear to many as a superior means for achieving material success and winning the latest round of "King of the Hill." However, in the bigger picture, in consciousness-space, power-control-force is, for the most part, a short-sighted, short-term ego booster which is a big deal only in the neighborhood of anti-rat town where it holds sway. Yet, the negative can eventually overwhelm the positive as a bacterial infection or a cancer might overwhelm and eventually kill a once productive, healthy and strong sentient human.

Disease has its function – it gives as well as takes. Free will choice must include the ability to choose badly. Though an individuated consciousness can lower its entropy through growth in the negative direction, negative growth, because of natural limitations, is a poor long-term investment. A fatal cancer, without meaning to, always ends up killing itself as it kills its host. The cancer is not aware its activity is self-destructive because it is trapped in a little picture with no vision into the larger system. The host on the other hand, living within and being a part of that bigger picture, must take care not to encourage the cancer or let the cancer get a foothold. An aware entity that chooses to lower its entropy by growing in the negative direction is, like a cancer – self-limiting and self-destructive in the long run. Evil contains the seeds of its own stagnation, if not destruction. A potential host's best defense is knowledge, truth, and Big Picture awareness.

If you are careful not to jump to conclusions, it will be profitable for us to consider interactive consciousness dynamics. How do kind and benevolent pacifists fare in a land without laws? What if you start with 90% pacifists, 8% everyday plain vanilla non-pacifists and 2% violence prone self-centered low-life scum bags that lie, cheat, steal, and worse? What are the natural survival and growth rates as well as conversion rates between these groups? The individuals within all groups are of equal size, strength and intelligence. How will the dynamics of this experiment play out under various amounts and types of law and law enforcement (remember, law enforcers must be able to be violent). I will let you come to your own sense of the dynamics and variables involved as well as what their outcomes are likely to be.

I do not expect you to derive the final answers to the preceding questions – at least not today. I simply wish to create some appreciation of the type and complexity of issues that a study of interactive consciousness dynamics must address. The above example barely scratches the surface of a discipline that growing consciousness systems would need to explore to ensure their continued profitability. Understanding how individuated units of consciousness and consciousness systems change relative to individual interactive intent is AUM's key to optimizing its own growth through the process defined earlier as the consciousness cycle.

Recall from our earlier discussion in Chapter 24, Book 1 that evolutionary pressure is derived from an entity's internal and external environment. The bottom line of that discussion was that the evolutionary goal of consciousness is to lower its entropy. Thus for consciousness, successfully evolving, increasing quality, self-improvement, spiritual growth, and increasing the capacity to interact with love, are all the same thing. These attributes, along with the increased functionality and capability that accrues with more energy available to do work (from our definition of entropy – near the middle of Chapter 24, Book 1), are artifacts of a low entropy consciousness.

From the limited PMR little picture view, the increased functionality and capability that naturally occur in low-entropy consciousness may be experienced as personal power, unconditional love, or paranormal ability.

Forget what you have been told: AUM is **not** in the role of your father or mother and you are not in the role of a child. AUM is not responsible for raising you – only for giving you the opportunity and responsibility to raise yourself. It is not AUM's job to take care of you – to force you to learn and grow, and keep you out of trouble or to make you feel comfy when things get tough. Nevertheless, AUM cares about, loves, and appreciates all because that is the fundamental property of low entropy consciousness – but don't take that too personally.

AUM has evolved individuated consciousness with free will as part of its own process of evolution. Free will gives you the responsibility for your growth and enables you to evolve. Without free will, there is no way for individuated consciousness to decrease its entropy. (If your hand is in the air, hang on, a discussion of free will, determinism, uncertainty, and randomness in digital systems is coming up in Chapter 11 of this Book) AUM sets up everything to help you succeed and provides an absolutely free top-of-the-line PMR learning lab with interactive feedback. Additionally, NPMR beings are assigned to help you in every way allowed under the law. These beings are focused directly on you – to plan, encourage, and guide your spiritual growth – the growth of the quality of your consciousness.

Teachers (typically Good Guys who have mastered the human-rat maze) sometimes return to PMR to help point the way. Nevertheless, we often manage to dilute, distort, and subvert their helpful instruction by burying the essential truth of their message under a blanket of dogma generated by an ego serving, fear manipulating, belief system.

The laws and rules that are instituted by AUM, and administered by the Big Cheese (the conditions of the experiment – the culture of $NPMR_N$) provide order and protection for you in $NPMR_N$. Our System (OS) is designed to give you maximum opportunity to succeed under the given conditions. You can sometimes, though it is rare because cross-pollination is discouraged, choose an alternate (not OS) reality system (one of the PMR_k within $NPMR_N$, or something from one of the other $NPMR_n$) within which to evolve your consciousness. Everything you need for success is laid at your feet, all the help you could profitably use is there for you, but **you** have to make the choices. You have to execute your intent. The AUM consciousness-love-being-scientist-thing demonstrates its compassion, love, and caring by giving you every opportunity to grow in the direction of your choice.

Balance, humility, compassion, joy, peace, sadness, love, and caring as well as a desire to evolve, learn, and grow are the natural attributes of a highly evolved and aware consciousness. We are an individuated part of the larger consciousness that has been constrained (matter bumps on the lumps in the AUM sheet) to go through the same evolutionary process as the whole. The value of knowing and understanding the origins and processes of your existence, as well as being aware of the available options and pitfalls that lie before you, is obvious. Knowing what you are doing and why you are doing it should contribute immensely to your ability to get the job done.

There is yet another reason for AUM to produce and work with individuated consciousness. As our individual consciousness evolves, we contribute to the quality of the entire consciousness system of which we are a part. Thus, we are an integral part of AUM's evolutionary process. AUM invests in honest science, but we good-guy rats pay an additional dividend. By lowering the entropy of our individuated consciousness, we also lower the entropy of the entire larger consciousness system. Our individual growth lowers AUM's entropy and helps push AUM along its evolutionary path.

We are profitable beyond our contribution to experimental results. That is why we get lots of help and encouragement. Although we Good-Guy rats may eventually be incorporated into the AUM organization as full partners, those entities evolving to the negative side eventually get recycled (new opportunity to grow in the positive direction) or are simply terminated. I told you their long-term benefits stunk.

Why would an entity take the negative route? Because they are short-sighted and do not understand the Big Picture; that is a common problem. Are the bacteria in the petri dish given briefings on the experiment in which they are taking part? Never! It might bias the results. Do we need to hide the experimental purpose and protocols from the bacteria? No, because the bacteria are not cognitive at the level of the experimenters, no one worries about it.

Going for the apparent short term gain is how most sentient entities, consciousness systems, or beings (in any reality or situation) function if they do not have the requisite quality and do not possess the perspective, capacity, or understanding to see the Big Picture. That is a simple fact of existence. Do you know anybody or any organizational entity that is fixated on the short-term view or lacks Big Picture vision? Wait a minute, I am afraid that I inadvertently put you in an endless loop – you will never finish that list. Let's ask it the other way. Do you know anybody (besides you and me) or any organizational entity that is **not** fixated on the short-term view and possesses a Big Picture vision? Now that is one short list!

If the experiment is about aware consciousness, the number of participants who have gained a clear view of the Big Picture may well be a metric that measures the progress of the experiment. We are allowed to know; becoming aware and operational within the Big Picture represents a natural part of our potential that we should make an effort to actualize through personal growth.

You should realize there is no alternative, in the biggest picture, to growing the quality of your consciousness except eventual termination. For those in the little picture, this piece of information will be discounted because it cannot be derived from the little picture. Get this: Little pictures must be derived from bigger pictures; it does not work the other way around. Do you see why it is not necessary for the experimenters to hide the experimental purpose and protocols from the bacteria or the humans? Living solely in the little picture is enough insulation to make sure that humans on the planet earth and bacteria in the petri dish are not confused or motivated by information that is beyond their understanding.

Complex, self-interactive consciousness can pull itself up by its bootstraps in the same way that bright awareness self-energizes and drives its own development. AUM's science is focused on understanding those evolutionary processes that affect consciousness and on making these processes as efficient and productive as possible.

What we do with the **opportunity** to evolve our consciousness is entirely up to us. It is our free will, our self-interaction, and our interaction with others that creates the possibility of learning, which in turn creates our potential for growth. Because of our relatively high entropy, we are slow learners; consequently, our cycles of learning and growth are designed to accumulate results over multiple experience packets.

Some of us become apathetic and cynical because we have to grow and learn on our own. AUM will not do it for us. We become annoyed because we are self-centered and because outgrowing a cherished and needed fantasy is often neither easy nor fun. It is just not fair! AUM will not cuddle us and sing sweet lullabies to sooth our ruffled minds and flustered egos. We think we want, need, and deserve that support – oh, how we miss it! Mama! ... Maamaa!! ... Maaaamaaaa!!!

Resembling spoiled children, we fuss and moan about our options, refuse to play the game, refuse to participate until the game is more fun and pleasant for us. As if our tantrum will force the powers that be to make it easier for us. Children who refuse to grow up always maintain the sense that a big fuss and good excuses will force life to be more accommodating. They sulk, get depressed and then get angry when their self-righteous protestations fall on deaf ears. Refusing to work on your spiritual growth because your life is not fun and full of joy is like spanking a baby in order to make it stop crying – counterproductive, and incredibly stupid.

Wouldn't it be nice if there were always a mommy and daddy to take care of you, to make things easier for you? This adult gig is a bad deal! Bummer! Adults need guidance, comfort, and reassurance more than kids do because the penalties and consequences of making mistakes and doing it wrong are more serious when you are an adult.

▶ Step right up ladies and gentlemen; come a little closer, boy, do I have a deal for you! There is no need to feel abandoned and suffer alone, there are lots of organizations and individuals that would like to play the mother or father role to your fear and neediness on various levels. Here is the deal: your ego gets to pretend that you are relieved of some of the adult responsibility for managing and directing your life as well as growing the quality of your consciousness. The parental stand-in gains some control and influence over you, your resources, and your decisions as you forfeit some part of your free will. Take your pick: friend, spouse, employer, religion, church, association, political party, club, support group, gang, charity, or welfare plan — I am sure you can find one or more of these to help you bear your burdens.

The weak, being easy prey, always can find someone willing to offer help for a price – someone or group that will take care of them and make them feel better. All the individual has to do is trade their money and a piece of their soul for the illusion of knowing the answers and the increased peace-of-mind that comes with an imagined offloading of personal responsibility. Listen to that ego purr – stroke, stroke, stroke. These illusions, properly marketed, are now and always have been best sellers. Many are mandatory according to the standards of each culture.

The bottom line is that predators and parasites can make an easy living (money, power and self-importance) by manipulating the fears of those who have no understanding of the Big Picture. That fact brings up another attribute of ignorance: The ignorant and fearful are always vulnerable and easily manipulated. Manipulating believers, regardless of what they believe, is as easy as appealing to wants, needs and fears. Ask any salesperson, politician, trial lawyer, or marketer – they will vouch for the truth of that statement. Having the courage, and taking the time, effort, and responsibility to capture and tame Big Truth is the only thing I know that can protect you from being had by the hustlers that are hawking the Big Delusion. Beware of Dr. Feelgood; his happy-pills and patented excuses will dissolve your personal power.

Don't misunderstand me: Finding and using help when you need it is a wonderful thing – good for everyone – but becoming dependent upon it, addicted to it, and unable to grow beyond it, is something altogether different. Dependence and interdependence can be helpful and rewarding as long as your free will is not held hostage and you are not trapped by your neediness, fear, wants, desires, ignorance, immaturity, and beliefs. In general, those who are trapped are not aware of being trapped – they are perpetual children predominately from the ranks of the personally powerless. Do not confuse the personally powerless (high entropy consciousness) with the materially powerless; they are not necessarily related. Assuming responsibility for your life is a good place to start anything.

If you do not have what it takes to find your own answers and take charge of the evolution of your consciousness, someone else will be happy to fill that void for a price that is actually much steeper than it appears. How do you calculate the price of being caught in a belief trap? In terms of opportunity lost, entropy gained, progress not made, misery prolonged, or time and energy (a life) wasted? However you figure it, it is too much to pay for a short-term feel-good illusion.

Does anyone wonder why recreational drugs are widely popular in our culture (and most cultures)? The feel-good mentality, pursuing its ego-soothing and fear-suppressing belief systems, forms the foundation upon which most cultures are built. Taking recreational drugs is simply acting out with our bodies what we do every day with our minds – escaping reality by making a belief-centered end run around ignorance and fear, and by avoiding personal responsibility for our growth toward love-consciousness.

We play hooky from the learning lab in order to hang out in a feel-good fantasy. Ego driven delusion is at the root and core of our existence – it defines our little picture reality. As always, the mind leads and the body follows. Taking recreational drugs is a direct consequence of an immature individuated consciousness feeling trapped by the anxiety, insecurity, and fear that is created by its own limitations. Low quality consciousness and drug use encourage each other.

A low quality consciousness uses belief, denial, and the obfuscation of ego in order to escape anxiety, insecurity, and fear. Individuals in PMR use recreational drugs to do the same thing. Is it any wonder that the drug-culture primarily attracts the young who have relatively high-entropy systems and adults who feel failed and inadequate? As a culture, and as individuals, we express the quality of our consciousness in many ways and forms but always with absolute accuracy. We are what we are. Belief, ego, and fantasy on the inside – recreational drugs on the outside – different escape methodologies but similar expressions of the same lack of consciousness quality.

To eliminate recreational drug abuse, a culture must raise its collective consciousness quality. This can only be accomplished at the individual level. Any improvement by individuals within the culture raises the quality level of the whole and begins to solve the problem. You personally must solve the problems of your culture. No one else can do more than you can. To believe it is someone else's problem to solve more than yours simply makes you a part of the problem. You can do nothing more than improve yourself. Fortunately, that single accomplishment constitutes your optimal contribution. ◀

Growing up is difficult to do. Sometimes we get so wrapped up in our fear, our ego's wants, desires, and needs that we do not try, or care, about anything but hiding from our own terrifying ignorance. "Quick, duck in here, you can hide out in this fantasy," says a helpful ego. Whew, just in time! Helpless little human, huddled, shivering, miserable and unhappy – trapped in a tiny corner of his mind by his ego-fear-belief-system fantasy. This is where the sadness part of love comes from.

To make things worse, as long as this needy human is in the PMR learning lab, the poor little fellow imagines that his existence and well-being is derived from, and supported by, a magnificent rubber chicken (see Chapter 21, Book 1). For this reason, he often refuses (only while he is in PMR) to use the help that is focused, coordinated and projected from the $NPMR_N$ part of OS to PMR to support his evolution within the loving and supportive reality in which he actually exists. A fear-driven life, lived from within the shell of a protective ego fantasy, is often demanding, tricky, painful, agonizingly shallow, and not much fun or full of joy, love, and peace. Poor guy – cuddling with his chicken in the un-illuminated darkness;

trying to make it through the difficult times that his needy ego has unknowingly created.

Growth requires a focused effort and this hapless human-rat does not have the required time or energy because he is preoccupied with maintaining his illusions. Unfortunately, the maximization of feeling good (mostly stroking the ego) and the minimization of pain (constructing and maintaining a good working fantasy), is **more** than a full time job. If this being does not escape this trap, he will in time (with age) end up in a never ending and self-perpetuating tail chase that either reaches an accommodating steady state or constantly loses ground. The hope is that one day he will wake up and realize there is more to his existence than just living and that the issue is quality, not comfort or power.

If you know anybody in a predicament like this, please be kind, empathetic, and helpful to them. They have been caught in a trap (many were born in captivity and know of nothing else) and deserve your patience and compassion. These maze rats are not dumb – they are merely confused and blinded by their belief systems. What should you do to help? Love them and let them be – they will eventually figure it out (explaining it to them often ends up confusing them more). Just love them and let them be – and evolve your consciousness to the greatest extent possible. That way, **if asked**, you can point out unseen opportunities and options from a more balanced and less ego driven perspective, serve as a good example, and provide encouragement through living proof that success is possible. That is about all you can do to help.

10

■■■

What is the Point?

■■■

We, the creations of AUM, are the source of its joy and sadness. We evolve our individuated piece of basic consciousness by lowering its entropy and increasing its quality. As we drop our ego delusions, we become more AUM-like – an embodiment of love and caring. This is our goal, our purpose. We began this trip as a chunk of individuated digital consciousness with enough complexity, memory, and processing capability to evolve ourselves from a high-entropy relatively dim awareness to a low-entropy brilliant embodiment of love. In the simplest terms, we are to follow in the evolutionary footsteps of AUO-AUM.

To accomplish this, we have been given two attributes. First, we are individuated into existence – a tiny snippet of the AUM hologram – an interactive subroutine or defined object running in its own piece of mind-space within TBC – a part of the Big Picture consciousness-evolution fractal that contains the pattern of the whole. Second, we are given free will so that evolution (growth) is possible. The evolution of our personal fragment of consciousness is directly and exclusively based on the individual choices we make. We exist, operate, interact, and individually evolve (modify ourselves to occupy lower entropy states) all within the immense digital mind that is consciousness. Fundamentally, we are consciousness. The evolution of our individuated unit of consciousness is the point of our existence. This is how the AUM-digital-mind-thing consciousness organism survives and grows. This is how the fundamental-consciousness-energy-ecosystem evolves, lowers its entropy, and avoids stagnation, regression (increasing entropy), and dissolution (death).

The Fundamental Process requires evolving systems to, in the long run, either grow or die. Trying to remain marginally viable, balanced in the astable state between the two is a poor strategy. The eventual price of not continually expending effort to reduce the average entropy within a consciousness system is to allow the average entropy of the system to increase, thus ensuring eventual disintegration. You are part of such a consciousness system. You are part of its strategy to survive through continuing growth and evolution. You are it. It is you. All That Is, is of the One. One consciousness organism. One energetic self-aware ecosystem. All live or die, succeed or fail, together.

Why one? Why not a herd of AUMosaurus thundering across the mental plains of almost infinite existence? Because one is enough to develop a fully complete (from our perspective) Big TOE; furthermore, as a scientist, I appreciate the connection between fundamental truth and elegant simplicity and thus avoid unnecessary complication that adds nothing. One apparently infinite, but finite, AUM is enough. What lies beyond a unitary finite AUM may be **indirectly** very important to our existence, but nonetheless remains beyond, and therefore irrelevant to, the grandest reality that we have the theoretical or practical capacity to comprehend.

Do you now understand why experiments in consciousness evolution are important to AUM? Do you now see why it is vitally important to you and to me and to every other chunk of individuated consciousness that **you** learn, grow, and improve the quality of **your** consciousness? We are all in this thing together; all are a part of the whole. The whole prospers through the contributions of its parts. Grow or self-destruct – that is the simple choice and a fundamental truth in both the little picture and the Big Picture. You, individually, right now, this minute, are either part of the solution or part of the problem: Your cumulative progress, or lack thereof, will eventually become a life force or a death force for yourself, for everyone else, and for the living consciousness organism that hosts your existence.

There is a point and a purpose to your existence. You have a mission. That your consciousness has the potential to evolve requires that you have free will. In order that you might succeed, AUM must allow you to fail. AUM has no choice. To survive, you must risk death – the Fundamental Process will not, cannot, function any other way. The initiative must be yours and yours alone. Your spiritual growth is not a group activity – it is a personal transformation achieved only in personal terms. No group or association can lower the entropy of (increase the quality of) your personal consciousness by even an infinitesimal amount.

Each individual contribution, however small, is vital to the health, welfare, and continuance of the whole. You are the contributor and the beneficiary of your contribution in both the little picture and in the Big

Picture. The ultimate reality is the living consciousness system, or consciousness organism of which you are a part. Seeing the Big Picture can be intellectually accomplished by understanding the philosophy and science of consciousness and how and why the consciousness system works. Contributing to the health of the Big Picture requires more than an intellectual effort.

> ▶ It has been brought to my attention that some of the technical types in the reading audience have about had it with all this philosophy, ontology, epistemology, and metaphysics. They want to know when we are going to get to the important stuff – the real hard-science that matters. Patience, dear brothers of the causal cloth: Philosophy must first develop the context before science can most effectively develop the content. Content without context eventually paints itself into a little picture corner. That is where traditional science is now and why its search for a unified theory has stalled. To escape the PMR petri dish, you must eventually come to understand that reality is more than a local rule-set, more than a mindless machine. ◀

You are on this growth-path whether you know it or not – a path first established by AUO-AUM – the path of consciousness evolution. PMR is nothing more than a virtual environment specially created to facilitate your (and others) evolutionary progress; consider it group therapy for dim awareness. I will explain how that works in detail in Sections 4 and 5.

Our goal? Our purpose? Why should we bother? If we are creations of AUM and AUM is (compared to us) the epitome of consciousness perfected, why are we wallowing around like a bunch of ego-bound self-centered pre-schoolers hopelessly lost in the middle of an advanced university of higher evolution? How are we significantly contributing to AUM's further evolution? Why does AUM need us – for amusement? Are we the carbon-based version of "Donkey Kong" or "King of the Hill" with 3D holographic virtual reality graphics? Does that concept amuse you as much as it does me?

Don't worry about it. These questions are the result of falling into another anthropomorphic trap. I am afraid I have set you up to fall into this one by referring to our consciousness relative to AUM's consciousness. This language cannot be helped because we must consider ourselves as individuals in order to conceive of and initiate self-improvement (evolve). Thus, we speak as if AUM and we were separate beings ("What does AUM need us for?"). This is not the case. We are AUM and AUM is us.

Keep in mind that AUM exists and evolves because of differentiating unique states within its oneness – creating dualities or changes relative to its uniform self – organizing its potentiality to squeeze entropy out of its system. Dualities became reality cells by the gazillions, from which TBC was created and from which we were individuated. We are part and parcel of AUM – a cellular digital consciousness that eventually defined a space-time subset which provides the causal framework for our physical experience, defines our physical universe, and our overall local reality system (OS). (Section 4 provides the logical background that leads to this conclusion and Section 5 explains how it works.

If you are partial to sound bites, try these: "We are one with AUM." "We are made in the image of AUM." "AUM is the One Source, the Creator of All That Is." "AUM is love." I am sure you could think up many more, but sound bites are often misleading in their brevity and usually created to deliver an emotional impact. Sound bites are best used to serve demagoguery and do not make for good communications. Resist turning knowledge into slogans.

▶ Likewise, resist the sloganeer's attempt to slip highly spun pseudo-knowledge into your mind. Without slogans, politicians would be forced to express real thoughts instead of just sniping at each other with test marketed sound bite bullets. Can you imagine a politician without emotion laden sound bites; can you imagine a politician with nothing to say?

Bear in mind that a politician, like any marketer, is interested in manipulating opinion and behavior, not communicating information. In general, do not look for truth in congress, court rooms, or in advertising, behind lecterns or pulpits, or on TV. Regardless of what the media might be, if the speaker (or writer) has a product or a point of view he is trying to sell, he is marketing to capture your opinion, not trying to give you information for **your** benefit. As always, open minded skepticism applied to **your own** data solves the problem but you must get out there and get the data before tentative conclusions can become actual ones. ◀

We are an integral part of a bigger consciousness system. Do not let your innate sense of self-importance allow you to disregard the fact that we are only a minor part of this larger consciousness system. Being a small part of the whole makes no statement about relative importance; without a doubt, the notion of relative importance within a consciousness system is a contrivance of needy ego.

We would never contemplate ripping out our colon and anus because they cannot, either singly or in combination, initiate and maintain polite dinner-table conversation. That is not their function. Some might consider them as undesirable parts, but that would be stupid. Their function is as important and critical as the function of other parts of our physical system. They are an integral part of us. We are an integral part of AUM. There is no justification for either feeling special or feeling not special because of the part you play.

Consider how important it is that all the cells, tissue, organs and other parts of the complex biological system that we call our body perform their individual missions and fulfill their purpose without worrying about what is in it for them. What if your liver, heart, or the bacteria in your intestine, in a fit of laziness and self-importance generated by not being aware of the bigger picture, concluded that their constant effort was too much trouble and decided to goof off? You get the point: If every part does not fulfill its purpose, the entire system suffers or perhaps dies. Your relationship to the whole of consciousness is like that. Although knowledge thrives on separateness, wisdom sees itself as part of a whole.

Let's look at some examples of entities that do not relate to the whole, that do not understand the larger system that sustains them – entities that live within a small picture. In the biological realm we have malignant cancers, parasites that destroy their hosts, and most people who, in a convincing imitation of the cancers and parasites, abuse their niche in the larger (ecological) system to whatever extent possible seeking only to maximize their personal short-term gain. In the consciousness realm, again it is people who seem to have a difficult time seeing the Big Picture. Do you notice a consistency in behavior here that tells us something about ourselves? If people understood the Big Picture within their consciousness system, the Big Picture within their physical system would be obvious and earn their utmost respect. They would naturally see themselves and all others (human and otherwise) as full partners in a shared experience of existence.

If the cancer, the parasites, or the people understood the relationship that they have with the whole, possessed a free will, and were intelligent enough to do something about it, they would first control, and then reverse, their self-destructive behavior. They would work to change the long-term lose-lose situation they are generating because of their lack of awareness and would develop a symbiotic win-win relationship with the larger system that sustains them.

We humans are part of several ecosystems that sustain us. We must be good citizens and develop and maintain a long-term win-win relationship with each. As aware, bright, sentient entities, either physical or nonphysical, consciousness is the largest and most fundamental sustaining system within the capacity of our awareness. Consciousness is the primary ecosystem to which we belong. $NPMR_N$ is our biome; OS is our community; PMR is our niche; and earth is our habitat.

At the next lower level of awareness, within PMR and on planet earth, the earth itself and its life-forms and element-forms comprises the largest sustaining system. Below that, there are species, cultures, nations, businesses, families and individuals. Most of us know that we must constantly expend effort to form win-win relationships with other individuals. That realization is a good start at locating the bottom rung of the greater ecological hierarchy and is the first step toward being a fully responsible individual making the most of your native capacity. You must become a responsible citizen (integrated contributing part) at all levels of interaction and relationship – from individuals, to organizations and groups, to the earth, to AUM consciousness. Growing up seems to be nothing more than achieving a series of ever widening perspectives. Don't quit prematurely, before you have fulfilled your full growth potential, outgrow your belief traps, and begin to enjoy the magnificence of your true heritage as a chip from the old AUM consciousness block.

Because of the efficiency of specialization, we and all other extremely complex products of evolution are not simply monolithic homogenized entities – we are made up of specific parts with specialized functions. Likewise, AUM is not one big homogenized uniform mind-thing with no parts. AUM is nothing other than consciousness and must design, build, and evolve its structures and subsystems with consciousness. AUM can structure and limit subsets of consciousness, information, memory, and digital processing power in a multitude of interesting and profitable ways. Every being, as it evolves on each level of its existence, must learn how to use and explore the possibilities within that level to improve its profitability. AUM is no different.

AUM needs us as part of its being for multiple purposes, just as you need your circulatory system for multiple purposes. As we are driven to explore ourselves, AUM is driven to explore and understand consciousness – its continued growth, evolution, and survival depends on it. We should find this particularly easy to understand: Our bodies, medicine, how we interact with each other, the environment, and the physical universe have always been the focal point and primary motivation of our science. We first want to, and need to, know about us. The AUM-thing wants to, and needs to, know about consciousness.

I am sure we could think up many interesting questions and issues about motivation, good, evil, delusion, creativity, ego, quality, love, fear, pain, profitability, productivity, new possibilities, competing ideologies, violence, pacifism, intelligence, evolutionary direction, initial conditions, rule-sets, and so on – all useful information about consciousness evolution that AUM might well be pursuing. I am also reasonably sure that AUM would be able to add a few we didn't think of.

Does that make us lab rats as well as partners and pieces of the larger system? Maybe; all depends on how you look at it. Do **you** consider the bacteria in your intestines or the ecosystem that provides your oxygen as your partner? Perhaps you should – your life depends on both of them. Fortunately, AUM is not likely to be as self-absorbed and disrespectful to its partners as humans are.

We may be the key active ingredients of a cyclical process that takes raw consciousness and transforms it into something more refined and valuable by mimicking or applying AUM's evolutionary process – like a consciousness transmutation machine or an entropy reduction factory that is an integral part of a larger consciousness cycle. We are part of the mechanism that eventually enables the conversion (evolution) of dim individuated units of consciousness into empowered love-beings. Could AUM be employing us similarly to how we employ bacteria to help clean up oil spills or use a compressor and fluid to cool a refrigerator?

Perhaps we are a work of art, created for its own sake, or a work of science undertaken to discover something new. We may be valuable because we express AUM's being in a way that is profitable, pleasing, aesthetic, or interesting to AUM.

AUM may be playing Jessica to our rendition of Roger Rabbit, and thus values us simply because we make him laugh. No doubt, there is great value in humor. Likewise, there is no doubt that we humans, as a species, (especially if one enjoys dark comedy and slapstick) often make Curly, Moe, and Larry look like serious college professors by comparison. Hmmm, perhaps that wasn't a good analogy – as I recall, Curly, Mo and Larry have always been indistinguishable from serious college professors. Oh well, you know what I mean: We humans do some really funny stuff; we are a wild and crazy bunch of animals. I can hardly wait to see what we come up with for the grand finale.

Perhaps our function from AUM's point of view represents some mixture of all of the above – along with a few others I haven't thought of. There are many ways to be an integral part of AUM's evolution.

I like the lab-rat and consciousness transmuting bacteria options best, but I will be the first to admit that I might not be totally aware of everything AUM does all day at the office. The point is: We can reasonably define an immediate purpose as well as a larger purpose and a larger, larger purpose, even if we are not absolutely sure about the details of the larger purpose of our larger purpose.

Picture consciousness pulling itself up by its bootstraps: Picture yourself as a bootstrap. AUM's science is focused on understanding the processes of consciousness evolution and making them as efficient and productive as possible. AUM does not exist for us. It does whatever it needs to do for its own reasons and according to its own profitability requirements; we are simply a part of that process.

The *Número Uno* Digital Dude **is** the larger reality – every other apparent reality is derived by applying various constraints and rule-sets to various interactive subsets of individuated awareness within a specific calculation-space called a dimension. Think simulation and virtual reality. (If I have gotten too far out ahead conceptually, be patient, Section 4 will develop much of the supporting logic for these ideas.)

We may, by the vagaries of evolution, be no more than the analogical equivalent of AUM's intestinal bacteria, or perhaps more colorfully, AUM's colon and anus, and as such we should expect to have no appreciation for the ultimate activities of the whole – such as polite dinner-table conversation. In that case, we keep on keeping on because that is what we do. Our perspective is too small to see the bigger picture that connects us to a whole that exists beyond our comprehension. Have a laugh or at least a chuckle, and let it go. Self-importance, the hallmark of the ego, is always self-destructive.

Why are people so poor at fulfilling their immediate purpose of becoming more, growing, improving their spiritual content, and evolving the quality of their consciousness? Given that this is our larger purpose – that this is what we are supposed to do – you would hope that we would be better at it. Most humans (and other residents of other PMRs) and most sentient nonphysical beings as well, are delusional (ego bound) because they live in a small-perspective reality with small-perspective knowledge and even less understanding. There is no privileged group. Everyone must start at the bottom and pull themselves up by their bootstraps. That is how consciousness reduces its entropy – by growing up, maturing, dropping limitations of vision and understanding, shedding ego and delusion – becoming all it can be.

Your ego, in its reaction to fear, insulates your delusion from reality with an array of self-protective and self-justifying rationalizations. The only way out of that trap is by making a serious effort to outgrow your limitations and overcome your fear by developing a Big Picture understanding of existence. A **personal** Big Picture understanding, improving the quality of your consciousness, and developing your capacity to love are all interrelated mutually reinforcing aspects of a successfully evolving consciousness being. There are no short cuts. You are an evolving chunk of individuated consciousness within the OS community; that by itself defines the nature of your being and determines the purpose of your existence.

Most sentient, conscious, self-aware beings (physical or nonphysical) experience the feelings described in Chapters 8 and 9 of this book as a mixture of joy, peace, pain, fear, and pleasure. The feeling of sadness follows the caring of love. Beings with higher intelligence are typically dominated by feelings of self-induced fear and pain. That is the price they pay for their advanced knowledge (a dangerous thing) and the greater opportunities that go with it. Eating that metaphorical apple from the tree of knowledge carried with it the potential for expanded evolutionary success or failure. Self-awareness and the knowledge that comes with it was the beginning of AUM's Great Experiment and our Great Struggle – the beginning of our employment as an entropy transfer media within the consciousness cycle, lab rats, high-entropy to low-entropy consciousness transmuting bacteria, expressions of art, participants in scientific enquiry, stand-up comedians, or all of the above.

11

■■■

Mind, Brain, and Body

■■■

Nonphysical conscious beings are not merely disembodied discrete chunks of information or knowledge, like a web page from another dimension. They are differentiated (bounded), individuated (singular unit) consciousness energy (self organizing) digital subsystem constrained to a specific form and functionality. They have unique bodies – defined boundaries that are composed of what is most descriptively called non-physical matter which may appear completely solid. They can be intellectual, knowledgeable, and feeling entities because they have the potential to be self-aware, self-modifiable, and have an evolutionary purpose.

We have established that AUM has feelings; however, without fear, ego, and delusion AUM's feelings are not at all like ours. On the other hand, if we can replace our fear and ego with love, humility, and compassion, we begin to look and act like distant relatives of AUM – chips from the old AUM block, sharing a single continuous awareness with the source of all consciousness.

How does all this feeling consciousness interact with what we experience as our bodies? In the physical world, in accordance with TBC's space-time rule-set, our limited senses collect the data that define our physical reality. Our nervous system sends certain types and patterns of signals (utilizing neurons, synapses, nerves, and the like) representing the collected sensory data to the brain, which interprets these patterns of signals (encoded sensory data) to create the perceived physical reality within the context of past experience. The nonphysical mind receives the PMR reality-experience from the brain's experience-limited interpretation of the signals. The mind then applies its unique knowledge and quality to produce a response that expresses its intent in terms of internal and external action.

Thus, it is a value-based nonphysical consciousness with knowledge, memory, fear, ego, understanding, intent, motivation, purpose, and individual quality that determines what the brain sends back down the communications links (nervous system) to guide the body in transforming the mind's intent into a new state of being that is in direct response to the original sensory data. In this simplified model, the brain serves as a transducer and a constraining filter between the physical and the nonphysical components of the being as well as a controller of autonomic body functions that must satisfy space-time biological requirements. Nonphysical consciousness energy animates the experience-body and gives it non-trivial uniqueness, originality and purpose. Fish, hedgehogs, foxes, and people all work this way. As a refresher, you may want to re-read the aside at the beginning of Chapter 29, Book 1 concerning the physical to nonphysical interface function of the Central Nervous System.

The mind-body process described above is grossly over-simplified and presented from the PMR perspective. Though it makes this discussion more abstract and thus more difficult to understand, it is more accurate if you think of your body as a virtual body. Consider that your body is a projection of your character into a multi-player digital simulation consciousness trainer (a virtual reality). Your projected character represents the total accumulated quality of your consciousness employing only a fragment of your individuated consciousness energy. Its allowable interactions (its experiences) are constrained by the space-time rule-set. This particular virtual reality has many trillions of interacting players – some sentient, some not. Additionally, there may be random components occasionally thrown into this complex mix to make sure that our free will always has a sufficiently rich array of possibilities to choose from in order to facilitate optimal evolution and learning.

One can think of these random interactions as the result of biological, psychological, and social Brownian motion – individuals bumping into, and exchanging energy with each other and with their environment in a process that ultimately defines their personal trajectories. These sequential interactions produce cumulative results and define new sets of possibilities with each bump. Unplanned interactions with others, and with our outside and inside environments, create novel opportunities to exercise our intent by making choices that reflect our inner quality. Clearly, personal growth requires us to use our limited awareness to improve our understanding of what is important and to use our free will to improve the quality of our choices. Growing up and decreasing the entropy of our consciousness obviously requires far more than simply acquiring, storing, and processing knowledge. Being conscious, we have the innate ability to modify ourselves – to pull ourselves up by our bootstraps.

Improving the quality and reducing the entropy of your consciousness (spiritual growth) is more than an intellectual exercise. The intellect (processing, memory and analytic function) can make no significant progress by itself. This is a particularly disturbing fact for those who live out of their heads by controlling and guiding their every thought and action directly with their intellect. Their need to **appear** rational in the little picture severely restricts their ability to **be** rational in the Big Picture, or even realize that a Big Picture exists. The belief in the infallibility and completeness of little picture rationality is another belief trap piled high with victims who are bright intellectuals from material-based cultures.

Enlarging the species database in order to improve future hardware (body and senses), software (attitudes and mental ability), and processing capabilities (brain and central nervous system) is not the only, or even the major, goal of implementing the Fundamental Process within the human race.

Fulfilling our individual purpose for existing, decreasing our overall individuated system entropy, improving spiritual content, or evolving the quality of our consciousness are more fundamental, crucial, and necessary components of our total evolution than biological evolution. Biological evolution merely provides the stage, props, and setting for facilitating consciousness evolution. Consciousness evolution is the main act, yet we spend lifetimes dedicated to nothing more than rearranging the stage props.

Perhaps we should call PMR "Theater of the Blind."

Ladies and gentlemen, tonight's feature presentation is: "Planet of the Idiots," – a comedy of missed opportunity. Starring Top Monkey the Magnificent, playing all significant roles by himself.

The evolution of our physical system (people, critters, plants, planet, solar system, and universe) plays out the choices and random events that are constrained to evolve within the limited possibilities of the space-time rule-set. The physical evolution drama moves forward as a **subset** of Big Picture consciousness evolution. It provides the setting for our virtual reality trainer and the context and rules for our interactions. Those interactions lead us to choices, and choices provide us with opportunities for self-improvement. Our physical reality, our perceptual experience, and the physical evolution of our species and our universe, is an extremely small part of a much bigger evolutionary drama.

▶ Uh oh, I feel some of the techies tugging on my sleeve again. They have been extremely patient with these high-level non-mathematical philosophical descriptions and I think we should take a short break and see what they want.

It appears that some of the more left-brained individuals traveling with us are having problems with randomness, digital systems, and free will. Actually, the issue they raise represents a well-known and important problem of both science and philosophy and deserves some attention.

Many individuals find the existence of free will to be so intuitively obvious that they do not understand what the fuss is all about. That these more right-brained individuals have somehow managed to intuit the correct answer without going through a rigorous intellectual exercise may be the result of fortuitous cultural belief, or, if they are more like you, the result of highly intelligent and accurate observation coupled with brilliant inductive reasoning. If the theoretical existence of free will is not an issue that challenges your understanding, you may want to skip to the end of this rather lengthy aside. Otherwise, please join us on this little excursion into the relationships that logically connect consciousness, evolution, psi effects, and free will. The choice is yours, right?

Randomness is not as trivial a concept as it first appears. Many mathematicians, digital physicists, and computer scientists get wound up over the distinction between truly random and pseudo-random. I have been using the word "random" to connote uncertainty in a process, input, or result. The randomness required to support the choice-making free will described above within a digital consciousness virtual reality like PMR is not dependent on the distinction between random and pseudo-random. Pseudo-randomness – the same randomness we use everyday in our computer simulations and models – is all that is necessary to grant us free will.

When multiple choices of nearly equal probability occur, the result is uncertain because it reflects the ever-changing minute details of the moment that are a function of our changing (growing) intent and quality. Significant choices are mostly made at or beyond the uncertain edge of our certain knowledge. Our choices, as expressions of our dynamic consciousness quality, are constantly groping at the vague periphery of our personal limitations. In more technical terms, making a choice and learning from it is analogous to sampling a noisy signal; individual measurements (executions of intent) are uncertain. That is why bootstrapping our consciousness quality is a slow tentative process that yields best to small steady pressures that are generally applied in the right direction. Personal growth often develops slowly and hesitantly from the seeds of our experience that are planted by our intuition at the ragged (noisy) outer edge of our understanding and awareness.

Given a dynamic consciousness system composed of interacting entities with free will, the final result (at the end of a DELTA-t) remains uncertain until it is achieved. During DELTA-t, while intent is directing, choices are being made, and actions are being taken (for individuals or groups), the uncertainty (degree of randomness) in the final results is primarily caused by the huge complexity and number of the potential interactions between large numbers of very complex self-modifying individuals applying their free will to make choices in a non-rational belief-space near the boundary between their known ignorance and their assumed knowledge. ◀

> ▶▶ Whew, what a mouthful! I deserve either a prize or a whipping for that last sentence. I am afraid I know which one you would give me if you had the chance. Listen folks, just slap the book a few times and go on – it's unhealthy to hold a grudge. No pain, no gain. ◀◀

▶ Uncertain results create additional opportunities for interaction and choice making. New choices, representing our applied intent, produce new actions that in turn create new results and thus, more new choices. We bump from one interaction to the next making choices as we go. Each choice generates new opportunities and additional choices. Feedback from previous choices encourages us to modify consciousness quality and refocus our intent thereby influencing subsequent choices. Thus we create, as well as participate in, an efficient interactive process designed to facilitate the evolution of individuated consciousness that can be described as Brownian opportunity with an underlying quality bias.

The assumption of the impossibility of true randomness within a digital calculation does not logically disallow the possibility of our free will translating our intent within PMR into a unique personal choice that affords an opportunity (through feedback) to subsequently modify our intent (personal growth). An AUM consciousness system can use randomness with a structure (algorithm) behind it to see how huge numbers of extremely complex, noisy, self-modifying subsystems interact under various dynamic conditions just as we can. Scientists and engineers engaged in systems simulation do this type of stochastic analysis every day.

In Section 5, we will discuss the mechanics of calculating probable future reality surfaces and explain the functional and operational relationship between your personal, shared, and local realities and the deterministic reality-simulation-database where everything that can happen does. Section 5 explains the mechanics or implementation-process of actualizing free will choices and contrasts that process with a similar process that produces deterministic, statistically based, un-actualized parallel realities. Here I address only the theoretical and practical necessity of free will to be an integral part of evolving consciousness systems. This aside will establish a theoretical and practical basis for free will, while Section 5 describes how our free will process is actually implemented within the bounds of a continually re-determined set of possibilities that describe everything that could possibly happen.

Some may think that the theoretical difficulty of generating true randomness in digital processes is problematical for free will. This erroneous conclusion typically results from wrongly considering consciousness to be a simple monolithic system that follows the rules of PMR causality. This problem melts away in the layered complexity of multiple levels of interacting local and personal realities that have their origins within an evolving consciousness system.

The bottom line is that true randomness, as it is understood by PMR theoreticians, is not required for free will to upstage predestination as the driver of consciousness evolution results in NPMR or PMR. AUM, the consciousness system, can (as can we) do honest science that it finds profitable to its evolution even if it is a rule-based logical system. A pseudo free will is logically free enough to do the job of defining and implementing purposeful individuated consciousness units like those constraining their perceptions to the PMR rule-set in order to lower their personal entropy.

Units of individuated consciousness have the ability to freely make choices from a finite array of possibilities. Individual choices are dependant upon how the entity applies its finite repertoire of motivations and intents that it has developed in reaction to the experience it has perceived through the PMR rule-set filter. Intent eventually expresses itself through action and reaction within an interactive virtual reality. The quality of your intentions or motivations reflects the quality of your consciousness. Simply put, an entity's profitability and top level goals must be pursued through a purposeful application of directed awareness and intent (sometimes called "will"). Units of consciousness exercise their intents in virtual reality simulators that provide results-oriented feedback from every experiential opportunity. Aware entities use this feedback to improve the quality of their intent and decrease their entropy. This is how consciousness learns and evolves within the PMR experiential virtual-reality learning lab.

Time enables experience, which is derived from a sequence of events. Experience is the memory of a sequence of perceptions. Perception is a sequence of datum exchanges. Creating specific experience as a learning tool can be implemented through an interactive sequence of perceptions that provide an opportunity for an entity to exercise intent by making choices based upon personal quality and by allowing the entity to assess the results of those choices. An assessment of the choice and the results of the choice (feedback) lead to self-modification in pursuit of fulfilling the purpose and goals of the entity.

We humans have employed interactive virtual-reality training devices (such as flight simulators for pilots) for many years. Experience is the key to learning; whether that experience is actual or virtual is irrelevant. Learning is the key to consciousness evolution. Experience (operational memory and interpretive processing), perception (data collection), free will (choice), and the ability to learn (information processing developing results and conclusions) and grow (self modification relative to profitability goals) are fundamental attributes of successfully evolving consciousness.

Compare that last sentence with the descriptions given in Chapters 24 through 28 of Book 1 and especially the beginning of Chapter 7 of this book, where memory, a rich array of challenging data exchanges (interactions) between the entity and its internal and external environments, self-aware information processing, and self-modification in pursuit of profitability were given as the fundamental attributes of consciousness. In Chapter 7 these fundamental characteristics of consciousness were used to define consciousness and to describe its evolutionary process in general terms. Now it becomes clear that an experiential virtual reality like PMR facilitates consciousness evolution by thoroughly and methodically exercising each of its four fundamental characteristics. PMR learning labs are well designed by evolution to accomplish their purpose – they deliver exactly what we need to optimize our opportunities for self-improvement.

Free will – the ability to make choices in order to effect self-modification in the pursuit of evolutionary profitability – is part of the definition of consciousness itself. Free will is not an outside condition that must be applied to consciousness, it is fundamental to the existence of consciousness. Free will is a necessary attribute of successfully evolving consciousness. Without free will, a profitable consciousness system is impossible. If you and your many sentient friends and acquaintances are conscious, consciousness must not only exist, but also support a complex interactive system of coherent experience. Given that consciousness exists, it must be enabled by memory, information processing capability (intelligence), the interactive sharing of data, and free will choice making in the service of profitable evolution. Thus, the question of free will reduces to the question of are you conscious, and, if so, is your consciousness part of a complex interactive system of consciousness? If these are answered in the affirmative then your consciousness, and the system of which it is a part, must be evolving against some measure of profitability because that is a requirement of all self-modifying interactive systems. Such a system cannot evolve toward greater profitability without free will to make the required choices.

Evolution requires choice between alternatives. For evolution to exist as a real process, the choices must be free. Pseudo-free is free enough within a sufficiently complex, interactive, feedback-driven subsystem for the Fundamental Process to be effective within that subsystem.

To illustrate my point, I am going to put you to work. Contemplate the consciousness of a clam or a bumblebee. Next, compare that consciousness with the consciousness of a future generation computer. Goodness gracious, great balls of fire! You accomplished that task in only a few seconds! I must say, I am mightily impressed, the depth and speed of your cogitation are truly remarkable – undoubtedly, a phenomenon worth studying all by itself. Did you list all of the **functional** similarities and differences? Did you notice how the list of functional differences becomes shorter and shorter the more you ponder the fundamentals of consciousness and its quality? In the areas of intent, process, and structure there are vast differences, but these have less to do with the basic properties of consciousness and free will than with the particular mechanisms and forms of consciousness implementation.

Next, examine the free will of that clam or bumblebee. Clams and bumblebees have many daily choices and decisions to make as well – and they live and die, grow or evolve, by the cumulative results of those choices as we do. How predictable are clams? I suspect their individual deliberate actions are spread over a statistical range that represents the decision-space of their species. Humans similarly exercise free will within their own decision-space. The size and complexity of that decision space (for a species or an individual) depends on the capacity and quality (entropy) of the consciousness that supports it. For a given fundamental capacity, lower entropy supports a larger, more complex decision space. Higher capacity also supports the potentiality of lower entropy.

In case you are wondering, the capacity of the human consciousness is immense, yet we exercise only an infinitesimal fraction of that capacity. Our potential ranges far beyond your wildest dreams. Unfortunately, the part of that potential we have intentionally actualized typically supports little more than the tedious soap opera we call "real life."

That's right: Beings with a higher quality of consciousness function in a larger decision space with a larger range of free will choices – they live in a larger, up-scale reality. The reality in which their awareness functions is a super-set of the reality experienced by a consciousness with higher entropy. That is an obvious conclusion when comparing yourself to a clam, and much less obvious when comparing yourself to a being of exceptionally high-quality consciousness, although the relative gaps are likely to be about the same.

Most of us have little appreciation for the depth and breadth of our ignorance. You are necessarily unaware of what you are unaware of. Some of us may even feel grateful for the merciful oblivion granted by that obvious fact of sentient existence. However, let me remind you that ignorance is bliss only in the service of maintaining a happily deluded ego. In all circumstances, ignorance (and the beliefs it generates) is a constraint upon vision, a limiter of awareness, a prison wall that prevents awareness from expanding beyond its present boundary, and is a great destroyer of potential.

I detect a look of worried consternation. Yes, the awareness gaps mentioned above actually are about the same, but hey, relax, unwrinkle that brow, there is no point worrying over what you don't know – the clams don't get it either. And, as everyone knows, clams are, well, happy as clams.

Big pictures are inherently difficult to see from the perspective of little pictures. Far out, unexpected, out-of-the-box paradigm shifts are **always** required. Oh no, don't look so disheartened – it is not impossible, just challenging. The fact that transcending belief and expanding your awareness is difficult to accomplish is not a bad thing. In fact, it is a necessary feature of all successful consciousness systems.

Undoubtedly, you see the virtue in restricting those dim-witted clams to experiences that they can deal with and learn from. Anything else would either go over their mushy little heads or greatly confuse them. How would you like to get mugged at the beach by a bed of Psychic Clams From Hell trying to exploit everything on the planet as well as each other? The non-negotiable requirements of consciousness evolution to earn your own way and pull yourself up by your own bootstraps are absolutely necessary to ensure that quality, power, and responsibility have the opportunity to develop together.

Do you feel immense relief at knowing there is a self-balancing merit system that keeps those brazen bivalves in their proper place? Jeez, the thought of a pack of wild clams watching sit-coms on TV, guzzling beer, and cruising the urban kelp beds in search of junk food sends cold chills up and down my spine.

Can clams and bumblebees learn (modify their actions and intents through experience)? Of course they can learn. Using memory, processing, and feedback to achieve self-modification (in reaction to internal and external environments) lies at the heart of our definition of consciousness. Consciousness has the natural, innate capacity to learn. Learning is purposeful self-modification created by the exercise of a free will that utilizes memory, processing, and feedback within a complex interactive environment. Learning, evolution, and growth – the steady decreasing of entropy – is impossible without the **functional** condition or attribute that we call free will. Are you beginning to see that free will, learning, and evolutionary growth opportunities are natural and necessary attributes of an evolving individuated consciousness?

Consciousness cannot exist without the ability to make self-determined, self-modifying choices. Without free will, there is no consciousness. Without consciousness, there is no free will. Consciousness and free will can not be separated – they are simply different aspects of the same thing. We shall see that it is our narrow, beginningless, PMR-centric concept of causality coupled with our misunderstanding of the properties of consciousness and reality that tricks scientists and philosophers into believing that free will is logically separable from consciousness.

The concept of evolving consciousness without free will is a mistaken and illogical theoretical construct that self-destructs in static, meaningless, determinism. The unintentional, but usually implicit, assumption of dead consciousness creates a conceptual sinkhole, a philosophical dead end. A deterministic reality model can logically only chase its own tail. Though self-consistent, it leads nowhere and produces no useful output because its implicit little picture assumptions are fundamentally flawed in the Big Picture where consciousness lives, grows, and evolves.

Let's look at free will from an evolutionary perspective. Consider that evolution can increase the capability of an individual or species only within the limits of the natural capacity of that individual or species. A free will needs only to be free enough to make choices within its own local logical system and decision space. Within its local reality system, a sentient entity must be free to make choices that directly affect future choices. Note that complex interactive environments, intent, memory, processing power, feedback, and self-modification are the enabling mechanisms of both free will and consciousness. Free will and consciousness co-evolve as mutually reinforcing aspects of the same AUM system-thing. Free will evolves as a natural and necessary attribute of living consciousness.

Only consciousness systems that evolve a **practical** implementation of free will can continue to progress toward some measure of greater personal profitability. Without a measure of cumulative profitability (self-improvement), there can be no evolution or progress. Dead consciousness would never evolve or progress; it could accomplish nothing, not even existence. Beginningless little picture logic (see Chapter 18, Book 1) may grant theoretical existence to a deterministic dead consciousness that comes from nowhere and goes nowhere, but a larger view that better understands the origins and properties of consciousness realizes that "dead" and "non-existent" are logically equivalent when applied to consciousness.

Consciousness integrated with a free will is how the AUM organism must evolve in order to evolve at all. Free will is inherent to our governing rule-set. It is the nature of evolving consciousness (or evolving anything) to make specific choices from the billions of available possibilities. Results reflect massive complex interaction, ever-changing self-modifying feedback loops, and are cumulative. Learning takes place relative to the choices made. Look around – that scheme represents the fundamental nature of individual and collective sentient entities. That all sentient entities seem to reflect the fundamental properties and processes of evolving consciousness is an important data point to consider.

A consciousness system containing many individuated units is similar to a body of cells, or an internet composed of billions of individual computers – no one in particular is in control. Choices are made, information packets go here or there, results are the aggregate of a billion independent and interdependent decisions. These results drive further decisions, which drive further results. No individual plans it, or controls it, or runs it. It changes and evolves on its own according to its capacity, its environment, and the constraints placed upon it. The individual decisions and choices of each cell, internet user, or consciousness-unit are made according to immediate self interest – however self interest is defined or perceived at that moment. Free will is inherent to each cell, internet user, or unit of individuated consciousness. The decision space may be relatively small at the cellular level, but if there is sentience, there is also a finite decision space to support the existence and functioning of that sentience.

Consciousness and free will go together like inhaling and exhaling, like mammals and sexuality, like chickens and eggs. Like birth, life, and death, consciousness and free will represent a **practical** combination of attributes necessary for the balanced functioning of a real (as opposed to theoretical) evolving system.

Our free will does not need to come from some theoretical consideration or independent process – it is simply part of the system, inherent to the existence and processes of evolving consciousness. The rule-set that defines our local reality must necessarily express free will because that is how choice-making evolving consciousness operates. If one conceives of free will as being theoretically derived from some independent random process, a circular logic trap is created. Recall Chapter 18, Book 1 where we discussed the PMR belief that everything must be caused by something else (no beginnings are allowed). This belief logically forces us to account for the independent existence of the egg before we can allow the possibility of the chicken – or visa versa. So, which came first, the chicken or the egg? The question itself carries the assumption of a causality that eliminates the possibility of a constructive logical answer. From a larger perspective, the answer is obvious: It is clear that neither came first – they evolved together – just like consciousness and free will.

The appearance of a logical problem is created by an illogical question. Don't get caught up unproductively in the chicken vs. egg logical tail chase. It may appear to be a great mystery, but is only a misguided question based upon a poor understanding of the logical requirements of beginnings and the inappropriate application of the little picture's objective causality (see Chapter 18, Book 1).

Scientists, philosophers, and theologians should resist looking for a process that creates free will, or equivalently, eliminates determinism. That bucket has a hole in it. Free will does not have to be constructed out of smaller parts, or derived through a controlled analytic process – that represents a typically PMR little picture misunderstanding based upon a belief in causal processes that cannot logically support beginnings. Chickens before eggs? Eggs before chickens? Do you see the flawed logic that makes these questions appear deep instead of dumb? It is a similarly flawed logic that supports the concept of determinism by evoking a little picture causality that is devoid of an appreciation of a larger reality which is based upon dynamically evolving consciousness.

So, which came first – consciousness or free will? Do we conclude from our little picture logic that neither can exist? That sums up the position of contemporary science and philosophy: Mind is nothing beyond physical brains and biochemistry, all reality is physical, and all information is theoretically knowable and eventually predictable. That these **beliefs** run counter to the carefully collected data of everyday experience, are inconsistent with each other, and do not make good scientific sense is conveniently overlooked to appease the demands of little picture causality in particular, and scientific dogma in general.

With an open mind and fresh vision, it is not difficult to see that most scientists, and philosophers too for that matter, have employed cultural belief and professional dogma to paint themselves into an intellectual corner. That free will and consciousness must evolve together as natural and necessary attributes of any successfully evolving sentient energy-form is a thesis that solves many outstanding problems of science and philosophy. Apply this concept to a sufficiently complex digital energy-form like AUO and you get AUM and **you** – along with a lifetime guarantee of free daycare and pre-school services within PMR.

You know what is said about cornered critters being particularly dangerous: Every word of it is true and I would be remiss if I did not also warn you. Be careful, your professional and personal credibility can be savagely attacked and badly bitten by a vicious and tenacious dogma. In fact, most organizations and academic institutions, with fine reputations to uphold, have guard dogmas patrolling their halls. These old, mean-tempered, intimidating, politically powerful creatures are entrusted with enforcing a conceptual correctness that everyone who is important can be proud of. In the high entropy real world of PMR where ego-politics powers almost every nuance of every activity, you need to learn to apply gentle soothing strokes, scratch them behind the ears, and always carry an extra hotdog in your pocket. Perhaps fighting fire with fire is a good idea in some circumstances, but combating ego with ego in a dogma fight is always a disaster for everyone involved.

Our conceptual limitations often generate logical contradictions. Mind-matter, wave-particle duality, and entangled pairs fall into this same causality-confused basket. The Big Picture expresses the true nature of reality, while the little picture expresses the shared delusion of a group of individuated consciousnesses enrolled in the PMR learning lab (this concept is developed more thoroughly in Sections 4 and 5). The conflicts and paradoxes you see are not real and do not exist in the Big Picture. Logical conflicts and paradoxes appear to exist within the little picture view because of the erroneous assumptions of little picture science.

An analog: The professional magician only appears to saw the lovely lady in half. Spending your nights worrying about the apparent impossibility of the lady paradox (how ladies can be sawed in half and then be put back together again) and concocting complex theories of tissue micro-fusion are generally non-productive and will never yield a satisfactory solution because the obviously correct (I saw it with my own eyes) assumptions the magician (your culture) has led you to believe are, in fact, wrong.

When our belief in PMR scientific causality dramatically fails before our eyes, we have a tendency to build up elaborate theoretical structures to maintain our belief and save the sacred dogma of traditional objective science. Resist the urge to make free will or psi more complicated than they are. It is not that you **have** consciousness, but that you **are** consciousness.

Determinism is a philosophically unproductive, unworkable theoretical possibility based upon omniscience or perfectly defined process for everything everywhere. It has no supporting real data and is generally based upon religious dogma (god knows everything) or erroneous little picture assumptions (scientific dogma – science knows, or can know, everything).

Without free will, consciousness is not consciousness – it is merely purposeless process. It is theoretically impossible to take the wetness out of liquid water or the coldness (relative to standard room temperature) out of ice. Consciousness without free will is like warm ice or dry liquid water. The concept of consciousness without free will creates a logical inconsistency. Because we of limited PMR vision do not appreciate the nature of consciousness, we separate the concept of free will from consciousness and try to give it a unique causality, an independent theoretical basis. The result is that we end up chasing our logical tail to conclusions that run directly counter to our everyday experience of individual consciousness.

Because of our little picture perspective, we project our PMR sense of finite knowledge into a theoretical assumption of omniscience, which eliminates free will and reduces consciousness to an analytical PMR physics or computer science problem. After that we are stuck with nowhere to go. No growth, no choice, no intent, no evolution, no personal consciousness, no purpose, no point. Determinism rules the land of limited dead knowledge. A complex consciousness ecosystem designed by evolution to be simultaneously out of control, in balance, and in a continual state of redefining itself leaves omniscience theoretically impossible.

The egg cannot logically exist without a prior chicken, and the chicken cannot logically exist without a prior egg — therefore, it is logically (given the implicit assumptions) impossible for either to exist. In terms of chickens and eggs, that conclusion is as dumb as it is logical. One might say that this conclusion is locally logical within the restricted solution space where the assumptions hold. In terms of consciousness, free will, and determinism, a similarly flawed process appears to provide an acceptable solution for many techies who have no logical way to derive a separate free will from the local causality of PMR.

Let's talk a moment about the implementation of free will within a local reality. Recall that a local reality is a unique dimension of existence and interaction — a computational subset — within the AUM system. That a **local** free will must be generated by a more fundamental **digital** consciousness system does not negate the effectiveness or functionality of that free will at the local level. A digital system can meet all of the requirements of a locally functioning free will operating within a restricted subset of the digital system. From the local perspective, the free will to express yourself (to exercise your consciousness quality) by choosing from the finite array of discrete possibilities that exist within your decision space is actual, effective, and real. That this self-modifying educational process is derived from a larger more complex **digital** algorithmic system is of no consequence to the efficacy of the local choice making process that enables unique evolution, growth, change, and learning within the local system.

Each conscious entity is exercising its free will to make choices within its own limited reality. Each knows little to nothing of what lies beyond. Think about each entity's free will in terms of practical operational requirements. Whether an entity is bright or dim, carbon-based, silicon-based, or reality-cell-based, it must make unique intent-guided choices within its operative finite decision space in order to find more profitable ways of existing and doing business. An operational free will is based upon each entity's specific memory, processing capability, and past and present input data (experience). Experience data are gleaned over time from the entity's perception of their internal and external environments. Think of free will as a practical evolutionary device of consciousness rather than a theoretical process of thwarting determinism with true randomness.

Functional free will, at whatever level of application, requires no more than the **practical** ability to make intent based choices where the intent is a function of the quality of the consciousness making the choice. If such a mechanism for making profitable choices at the local level (perhaps based on an evaluation of past choices) can be arranged, consciousness can provide the instrument for its own evolution.

At the local level where action is taken, an entity's decision space is defined by a finite set of discrete choices. Theoretical applications of randomness at the top level (consciousness evolving to be unable to look at the details of its own processes, or the invention of perfect or good enough random-number generators), are not relevant to the immensely complex, interactive, self-modifying, evolutionary processes taking place within local realities such as PMR. ◀

▶▶ Let's take a short break. I detect a few eyes beginning to glaze over and a head or two bobbing uncontrollably in the back row.

Everyone! Up! Up! Up! Yes, that means you too – get on up – and push that chair back! That's right, stand up! Stretch up straight and tall ....that's it. Now wait just a minute ... until everyone is up. Come on Jake, get up, you must join us.

Now, hop vigorously on one foot while practicing your best and loudest Tarzan yell. Go on, hop, hop, hop, hop, hop ... Louder! Louder! That's it, make Jane proud. Don't worry about what the people around you will think – you are about to give them a great learning-opportunity to practice compassion. As soon as you are done hopping and yelling, drop two ice cubes in your shirt, and if you are into extreme sports, drop one in your underwear as well. When they have melted, sit down.

Phew! Wow! Didn't that feel great?!

That is Uncle Tom's patented wake-up technique – guaranteed to work every time. If you actually bought this book with your own money, you have my full unrestricted permission to use this technique any time you want to – one of the many benefits of Big TOE ownership that accrue to you because of your wise choice of reading material. We are almost done so hang in there a while longer and you might learn something useful. Don't look at me like that ... you never can tell, it could happen. ◀◀

▶ Perfect knowledge (the omniscience needed to support determinism) does not, will not, evolve because it is not a practical possibility within real, interactive, self-modifying systems that are large and complex. From the perspective of evolution, a stagnant determinism is not profitable to the system. Self-improvement, learning, and meaningful goal-directed growth are profitable to the system – and these, by definition, cannot exist within a deterministic system. The meaningless random results of meaningless random processes can produce no increase in cumulative profitability. Such a system cannot support the properties and quality of consciousness as we experience it. An evolving consciousness system like ours cannot be supported by either a wholly random or a wholly deterministic system because there can be no cumulative profitability in either.

Are you beginning to see the connection between free will and our two basic assumptions (consciousness and evolution – see Chapter 24, Book 1)? Given the dynamic duo of consciousness and evolution as we have described them, free will falls out as a necessary logical result of their interaction. It is not an added ingredient that somehow must be accounted for. Free will is simply the result of consciousness energy and evolutionary process slipping into bed together for a joyous moment of creation that has not yet ended. From that union, all reality and existence flows. Our two basic assumptions not only allow and account for free will, but logically demand it and then create it out of a successful synergistic interaction.

Theoretical omniscience is meaningless within a real evolving consciousness system. Because real systems come into existence through **profitable** evolution, those that do not have the design, rule-base, or structural processes to evolve toward being more and more useful and profitable to themselves go nowhere; they do not grow or become more. Instead, they become stuck in an unfocused, meaningless, unguided, unprofitable, process (whether random or deterministic) that can never actually form into a real system. They do not become. They remain high entropy nothingness or represent inert meaningless process. Evolution cannot progress them forward toward greater profitability. As rejects of evolution, they go away, die, and disappear unable to maintain a coherent existence.

Incoherent existence can not persist or converge to a working system. By definition it must dissolve as easily and readily as it forms. A consciousness system evolves (increases its profitability) by decreasing its entropy. By definition, randomness and determinism can have no long term goal, point, purpose, or profitability – no successful, real, working (dynamic) system can be generated under these conditions.

All of reality, as far as we can know it from the data gathered thus far, fits the form of an evolving consciousness system that has obvious rules, focus, and purpose. Growth toward greater profitability permeates all existence. There is no indication that existence is either random or without dynamic purposeful profitability, however, there is a preponderance of circumstantial evidence to the contrary. If you have no experience of PMR's purposefulness or of the attributes of consciousness – even if you are totally without knowledge of your greater purpose and completely distrustful of your intuition and subjective knowledge – still, you can find no indicator pointing to a random, static, or deterministic reality.

Construing ignorance of purpose as purposelessness is a logical error. Existentialism made this error because, although it clearly saw the crippling limitations of many little picture belief systems, it was unable to transcend its own little picture belief in a universal causality. With no beginning (understanding of consciousness and our connection to it) and no end (evolutionary purpose of consciousness), existentialists are left drifting and rudderless.

Consciousness and free will are of the same evolutionary root. Like the trunk and branches of a single tree, they must grow together – inseparably joined and success- fully evolving as one entity. The system of free will and consciousness evolution works because it was designed (has evolved) to work. The rules of the game of evolutionary success define it into existence and maintain its integrity.

With respect to big PMR-based digital simulations (war games or meteorological modeling, for example), the people who build and use these simulations do not know how the results are going to turn out; if they did, there would be no need to develop or run the computer models. Should AUM be any different? The complexity of these sim- ulations, as well as the modeled randomness, is what makes the results (output) unpre- dictable (for a given set of input values) and useful.

Let's have some fun and strain our brains a little. Imagine that some simulation uses billions of billions of neural nets and fuzzy logic and lots of other non-linear self-modi- fying imprecise functions we haven't invented yet. Let it be a billion, billion, billion times larger and more interactive among its objects than whatever it is you can possibly imag- ine. Let each object be allocated its own unique memory, processing capability, and set of multi-layered (system goals and personal goals) profitability algorithms, some of which are self-modifiable. Perhaps every object interacts in very complex and condi- tional ways (with some uncertainty or ambiguity tossed in) with every other object. Also, let billions of billions of intermediate outputs of the simulation automatically modify the simulations inputs toward some larger purpose (winning the war or predicting the weather), and you will have the tiniest sliver of a shadow of one small calculation space (reality dimension) within TBC.

Next, change the random number seed and vary all input values that are expected to have some intrinsic variation or ambiguity. You might also want to modify some of the distributions that define the operational properties of specific statistical activity as the simulation runs in order to create specific situations or conditions of interest. Implementing these changes on-the-fly may dramatically alter both final and interme- diary results. Implement all such changes in a systematic and clever way over many iterations (like parametric analysis) and perhaps the collective results will form an exceptionally meaningful statistical ensemble.

Perhaps the simulation will run for such a long time that it will seem like forever to the individual objects who keep time by counting their own processing cycles. Consider that many of the objects could exhibit the four attributes of consciousness and have limited access to each other's data. They may pass data back and forth interacting (making free will choices) with each other according to their goals, self-modified defining algorithms, and within the bounds of their shared-reality defining rule-set. One higher level goal may be, for example, to lower the entropy of their individual assigned calculation space. Contemplate the advantages to AUM of an entire set of independently seeded PMRs.

This is only a start; this game can go on and on. I am sure your imagination can raise this hypothetical simulation to higher levels of complex and meaningful interaction. I simply wanted to get you started and to help you imagine a dim glimmer of the origin of the free will needed to support profitable choice making within a limited local reality.

Free will is part of the consciousness evolution game in the PMR learning lab. The free will consciousness evolution interaction is only required to be a practical process – a functional way to derive profitable, convergent evolution from local experience. Free will does not need a separate theoretical basis; for us, it is a practical methodology for growing consciousness quality (lowering consciousness entropy) in local realities. For a local consciousness system such as PMR, a locally derived pseudo free will that supports intent guided choice and feedback within the available decision space of each individual is necessary and sufficient.

In our big simulations, we use similar processes to gain insight and knowledge by employing pseudo-random numbers to add a greater sense of reality to our simulations. This randomness actually adds accuracy to our calculations because within our reality choice making and ambiguity are natural attributes of both sentient and non-sentient entities. We believe that we use randomness in our simulations to make up for our ignorance, to fill in for the details we cannot easily express analytically. What we do not realize is that our ignorance runs much deeper and is more fundamental than we suspect. We think, because of our little picture perspective and belief in a beginningless causality, that "perfect knowledge" is theoretically obtainable and that it would necessarily produce determinism. A better understanding of the bigger picture points out the theoretical and the practical impossibility of perfect or complete knowledge within an evolving consciousness system. The highest fidelity model must contain randomness.

Quantum mechanics bothered many scientists (including Albert Einstein) because it seemed to posit a statistical basis for our reality. It seemed obvious that sentient beings and their reality were fundamentally more real, solid, and dependable than could be attributed to a statistical representation. However, when you understand the digital nature of consciousness, realize that PMR exists within a calculational subspace (dimension of reality) of TBC, know that we physically interact according to a shared rule-set that defines the perceptions of our individuated digital consciousness, and appreciate the interactive nature of intent, free will, and choice-making that leads to entropy reduction in complex systems, it is not at all surprising that our fundamentally digital-mathematical rule-based perception of existence should display statistics at its root. The surprise would be if anything other than digital, quantized, statistical, entities were found at the most fundamental level of our reality.

We have just learned that individual free will is also an expression of a necessary condition for the evolution of consciousness. The PMR learning lab is defined into useful existence by its rule-set which determines perception, awareness, and causality. (Causality defines the logical relationships and allowable interactions between various objects within a local reality or given dimension.) The PMR space-time rule-set constrains the consciousness of those particular individuated units participating in PMR to experience only what the rule-set determines to be appropriate for the efficient functioning of that particular reality. Thus the PMR rule-set appears to define and bound a **limited** knowledge within PMR.

The illusion of determinism is the illusion that this rule-set represents all reality and not merely the local calculation space, reality, or dimension of existence we call PMR. From the PMR perspective, our limitations and the local space-time rule-set that defines our causality team up to produce the illusion of determinism in order to provide us with an optimal environment for learning through experience. Efficient learning requires definite structure. A system without structure has no potential for profitable growth. Everyone knows that a lack of structure is antithetical to the successful development of children. Structure, by its nature, sets limits or provides constraints. Optimizing our evolutionary opportunities requires the constraints of the PMR rule-set. The appearance of a deterministic casualty is the result of a limited understanding extrapolating the restrictions of an imposed local structure upon all of existence.

By design, little picture knowledge appears (from the view of PMR) to be deterministic – an erroneous conclusion based upon the success of science in discovering more and more of the space-time rule-set that defines our local PMR causality. However, there is more to the experience of PMR than the rule-set that defines the possible interactions within PMR. We need to account for the experiencer as well as the logical constraints of the experience. PMR is a virtual reality that is designed to produce a certain type of constrained experience for the benefit of interactive units of individuated consciousness. Consciousness awareness is the active element that experiences the opportunity to exercise its intent as it interacts with virtual mass, energy, time, and other consciousness units that also possess free will.

Only when mind and consciousness are **assumed** to be nothing other than PMR physical brain phenomena does PMR begin to appear totally deterministic to some philosophers and scientists. These folks believe that their conscious awareness is derived completely from a complex physical bio-computer (brain) which interacts with its physical environment. Not a bad guess, given the viewpoint from which it arises. I support the notion that computers can develop consciousness but that is not the rationale behind this particular assumption. The assumption of a physically-based consciousness is a logical requirement of the little picture – it is made to maintain the belief that reality cannot be other than physical – that our causality is universal.

Consciousness that is experienced within the PMR training simulator may appear to be brain centered, but that connection is only a shadow on the wall of the PMR cave. Consciousness is the invisible media upon which your individuated awareness floats – much like the fish that cannot perceive the unchanging water it swims in (see Chapter 23, Book 1). The evolution of consciousness follows a greater purpose, logic, and causality that provide the key to a better more productive understanding of both the little picture and the bigger picture. A nonphysical consciousness-based Big Picture reality enables the full range of our accumulated human experience to make good sense within a single integrated and coherent theoretical structure.

The **traditional** little physical picture model of reality creates as many Big Picture paradoxes and problems as it offers little picture solutions. By comparison, a **deterministic** little physical picture model of reality creates additional Big Picture paradoxes and problems while offering few, if any, new solutions. These paradoxes and problems are traditionally dealt with by stretching old belief systems and establishing new ones. As always, beliefs are used to ease the anxiety of ignorance and make our knowledge seem more complete than it is. The little physical picture model of reality has been unable to produce a **little** TOE that unifies our understanding of the space-time rule-set that defines PMR causality, much less produce a satisfactory **Big** TOE that not only fully explains little picture space-time causality, but also explains the greater human experience as well.

Given the algorithmic digital nature of the space-time rule-set, a little TOE may or may not exist, however, a Big TOE that solves profound contemporary problems of philosophy, metaphysics, and physics all at the same time and within one overarching theory must exist because we are here and are as we are. Our existence and human nature exhibit clear universal patterns that contain much more consistency and direction than randomness – a fact that must have a holistic, comprehensible explanation at its core. Because our existence is about us, about who, what, and why we are, surely the explanation lies accessible within us. However, until it becomes clear that a non-mathematical logical analysis of the origins of free will, consciousness, spirituality, or paranormal events **could potentially** represent accurate and honest **science**, that explanation will forever remain beyond your grasp.

Some may feel that philosophy and metaphysics do not pose real or legitimate problems because their solutions lie outside science and are therefore impossible to solve analytically. Bullpucky! These problems yield to accurate knowledge the same as any other. The difficulty is not that logical scientific solutions are impossible. The difficulty is that a self-limiting belief-based science inadvertently makes it impossible to comprehend the correct answer.

Science has the mission to pursue **all** knowledge leading to a better, more profitable understanding of the natural world – not merely the slice that falls within the confines of its traditional belief systems. Discovering fundamental truth and developing useful solutions are what science is all about. To find truth you must go wherever it leads. Belief-blinded closed-minded individuals who travel the path of least resistance and derive their respectability from supporting the beliefs held in common by their peers choose the safety of the herd over the ability to discover Big Truth. To maintain that respectability and the ego and material rewards that come with it, these individuals give up the ability to understand what is critically important to them and to their professions. A sad story of self-inflicted wounds which is so common that it defines normalcy and sets the standard for professional success.

Consciousness exists in many forms and at many levels, capacities, and scales – each built upon and extended from the others through the repetition of a simple process itcrating its way toward an improved profitability. The result is a cascade of evolutionary creativity that aggressively explores all of the forms, configurations, and embodiments that consciousness systems can employ to improve their profitability. This energetic living complex pattern of evolving consciousness is what we have metaphorically referred to as the consciousness-evolution fractal. It is the nature of a fractal processes to generate monstrously big pictures by recursively applying a few basic rules and assumptions.

It is a mistake for an entity within this vast reality fractal to believe its own tiny local reality subset of the greater consciousness ecosystem is The One, The Only, The Center, the pinnacle of creative expression. Individuals with little picture views can see nothing other than themselves emerging from the possibilities of existence. Such a limited vision produces not only a misplaced determinism, but robs its owner of the knowledge he or she needs to actualize their personal potential.

Only a failed and desperate theory (cultural, social, theological, or scientific) will feel the necessity to deny the existence of the facts it cannot explain. The facts of science, consciousness, free will, paranormal events, and the human sprit are left lying about everywhere; open your eyes, explore them for yourself; they are not secrets, nor are they difficult to find once your mind is opened to the possibilities.

Let's make a quick connection between free will and psi phenomena. Both are part of our reality because they are natural attributes of consciousness. Free will must be part of our little picture experience because we are consciousness with the mission to evolve and we cannot do that without the ability to make free choices. The free will inherent to consciousness must be fully operable in PMR or the learning lab would be unable to support learning. Likewise, psi effects must be largely constrained in PMR or the effectiveness of the learning lab would quickly degenerate. The psi uncertainty principle is the mechanism for maintaining that particular growth-optimizing balance.

Everything has its purpose. A local deterministic causality reflecting the PMR rule-set is required to provide the overall structure within which our experience can be profitably defined and coherently generated. An effective educational opportunity that encourages consciousness to evolve must engage free will, limit serious-psi to those who are likely to use it in pursuit of consciousness quality, and provide the structure of an apparently objective rule-based causality to rationalize experience.

We will more carefully define psi effects and their relationship to consciousness and consciousness quality, as well as introduce the psi uncertainty principle in Chapters 13 and 14 of this book. At the experiential level, imagine psi phenomena as a brightly colored flower enticing those who have some potential to profitably understand it, and as a prickly, scary, or ridiculous weed to most others. Anyone can experience psi phenomena or psi effects. Many can wield a shadow of its power but only those who understand it deeply can effectively use it as a springboard to significantly reduce their personal entropy and the entropy of the system of which they are a part.

Let's get more specific by defining "psi effect" as an acausal (outside PMR causality) phenomenon that is attributable to the operations of consciousness. From this more technical definition, let's explore a few semantic twists and turns. One could argue that free will is a psi effect because free will and psi effects are fundamental, interdependent attributes of consciousness. Similarly, describing or defining consciousness simply as "psi" can be supported from a general conceptual perspective. A free will effect is a psi effect is a consciousness effect.

Consciousness is the energy system from which our reality is created. For us, consciousness is the root of all reality. What we call psi effects and free will are direct expressions of the fundamental attributes of that consciousness system and of how that system operates and evolves.

If you want to know whether or not you have free will, simply ask yourself whether or not you are conscious. If the answer is "yes," you have free will; if the answer is "no," you are probably a lawyer and have simply confused the word "conscious" with "conscience." If after consulting a dictionary, the answer is still "no," you must be either a lawyer who has been elected to an important government position or an impressive professor (perhaps the dean of faculty) at a major university. In either case, put the book down verrrrry slowly – be careful not hurt yourself – and call your mother to come get you. She is probably very worried.

All is consciousness. Consciousness is all. Do not think of NPMR and PMR as **separate** places with fixed mental pathways between them: That is a sometimes convenient, but misleading concept. The psi uncertainty principle, as a part of the PMR rule-set, provides necessary structure to PMR by imposing limits. You cannot build a physical or nonphysical bridge between PMR and NPMR. The physical bridge can not be solidly connected to NPMR, and the nonphysical bridge cannot be solidly connected to PMR.

You are the bridge, which is why you cannot build one exterior to yourself. Consciousness is personal.

You are an individuated unit of consciousness hallucinating a physical reality (perceiving a virtual physical reality). As such, you can, within the limits of your quality and ability, experience and apply free will and psi effects because you **are** consciousness. However, you cannot make your hallucination (virtual physical reality) exceed the limits and function of its defining rule-set.

Is this not as simple, elegant, and straight forward as a bowl of plum pudding? Oh, I see, you have never experienced a bowl of plum pudding. You are in luck. The next two sections will develop the recipe and cook up a yummy batch from scratch.

We have once again jumped ahead of our story and taken an unsubstantiated peek into what lies ahead. However, you will find the logical development leading up to these unusual statements resides primarily in Section 4, which is around the next corner. Furthermore, in Sections 4 and 5, we will discuss the nature and the mechanics of experience, multiple PMRs, and local realities.

To summarize, free will is a natural and necessary part of our consciousness. Without it there is no profitability, learning or growth – consciousness itself dissolves. Look around – outside and inside yourself – the data are clear. There is purpose and direction to everything. All existence is in a state of continual profit-based evolution. Our reality is large, complex, and interactive. Perfect knowledge leading to determinism is like the concept of dry liquid water: a practical impossibility born of an incomplete understanding. From the view of a little picture causality, determinism may seem scientifically logical as well as theoretically unavoidable as one approaches the limit of perfect knowledge within PMR. However, from a bigger picture we see only a local structure required to support the coherency of experience within a small subset of reality called PMR. Determinism is a local rule-based virtual-reality illusion, engineered within TBC for the purpose of optimizing consciousness evolution within the PMR learning lab.

Determinism believes that you are a rule-based body hallucinating a consciousness with free will, when in fact, you are a consciousness with free will hallucinating a rule-based body. Once you see the Big Picture (by the end of Section 5), you will understand that determinists, by definition, must be unconscious – an apparent paradox that is easily verified by logical analysis.

If you, like me, have never lain awake at night worrying about the impossibility of true randomness in digital systems and what, if anything, that has to do with predestination and free will within a digital consciousness system, you didn't need to read this aside. However, if you read it anyway, be sure to ask your mother for an additional gold star – of course, that's assuming she didn't see you applying Uncle Tom's patented wake-up technique.

If all you learned from this rather esoteric discussion is that a digital consciousness system can generate the free will we require to decrease the entropy of our personal consciousness, you got it all. Enough said: this particular point, though vitally important to many philosophers and scientists, is off the critical path to Big Picture understanding for most of us.

I feel freer already. ◀

Now that the left half of our techie-friend's brains are fully occupied with the interconnectedness of free will, psi effects, and consciousness – and with the unexpected lack of determinism in the big digital picture – I think it would be beneficial for us to step up to a bigger picture of the bigger picture. Because most of us have been immersed in a detailed theoretical exposition of free will for the last half hour, now is a great time to take a broader view of where we are, and of the role our individual consciousness plays in the larger evolutionary drama. The next chapter does exactly that, furthermore, you will be pleased to know it is also brief and contains no asides.

In the preceding free will aside, we have been risking brain-strain in order to lay out some of the infrastructure of the science of consciousness. Having accomplished that, we can now relax. Whenever possible, I avoid dragging *My Big TOE* through the conceptual weeds, but sometimes logical thoroughness and the details of process are necessary to support a general understanding. Though sharing some of the more technical theoretical details of *My Big TOE* is important and necessary, this trilogy is primarily focused on a big picture look at the Big Picture.

In fact, any major new branch of science must begin its unfolding as a top-down big picture analysis of the pertinent data. New scientific paradigms generally begin at a broad conceptual level and then eventually move, over time, toward more specific applications. Such a top-down process often begins with the discovery of a more general relationship between common objects or events. Typically, the old paradigms become special cases of the new – applicable only under certain conditions.

The basic conceptual foundation must be clearly laid-out and thoroughly assimilated before the more traditional bottoms-up scientific approach can be constructed upon it. Only after scientists achieve a certain minimum level of basic understanding can they begin to profitably calculate and experiment their way toward a deeper and more productive knowledge.

Approaching a new understanding of reality by a bottoms-up application of the known tools of physics is like trying to chop down a mighty oak tree with an ice pick. A rather dull ice pick at that, because the assumptions of physics are thoroughly rooted in little picture causality. The broad sharp blade of an unfettered mind logically focused on the bigger picture of cause and effect is a much better tool for whacking stout ontological trees. As always, the proper approach implemented with the proper tools most readily finds success.

The point is: The **public message** of *My Big TOE* is focused at developing the conceptual foundation upon which a more traditional future science will one day be based. You see, I have not written *My Big TOE* to frustrate and torture left brained techies with incalculable generalities; the time for calculation has simply not yet arrived. At this point in the conceptual revolution presented by *My Big TOE*, everyone can come along on the journey. Scientists have no particular advantage over nonscientists as long as I am careful not to couch my descriptions in techno-jargon or be too techno-boring. In fact, at the front-end of discovery, right brainers, and better yet, whole brainers have the decided edge in leaping new paradigms in a single bound.

Some patience is required. By the end of Section 6, *My Big TOE* will have provided a rational, logically consistent Theory Of Everything, developed the required new paradigms to support that theory, constructed a solid scientific foundation for future explorations to be built upon, and explained the interfaces and connections between newly derived knowledge and the existing database of scientific and personal experience. It will have subsumed physics, redeemed philosophy, and explained many public as well as private phenomena. A broad conceptual top-down exposition of the fundamentals of Big Picture Reality is where this train must start. If and when the Big TOE conceptual brain-train begins to move and pick up speed, it may well initiate the beginning of an independent outpouring of Big TOE science, social science, and philosophy that will begin to take root immediately, and slowly produce fruit over time at ever greater levels of specificity. That is how science moves from concept to application – very slowly, and with casts of thousands. Increment by increment, discovery by discovery – the more people who get involved and apply their brain power, the more quickly the train picks up speed.

Once the ground is broken and the foundation laid, history tells us that many bright, open, and curious minds will begin to build upon it. Thus, as always, the ball eventually bounces back into your court. Perhaps your career or personal growth path, ability, or intuition will urge you to apply these new understandings and paradigms to whatever commands your professional and personal attention. If a significant number of readers are so moved, the time for public and private calculation and experimentation (developing and applying the detailed logical implications of this Big TOE) will arrive more quickly than anyone expects. Nevertheless, by evolutionary design, movement toward profound shifts in widely held paradigms usually progresses slowly and with deliberate caution. Patience will always be a necessary virtue.

Because the experience of consciousness is essentially a personal one, the **private message** of *My Big TOE* is for you, dearest reader – yes, just for **you**. The real power to effect significant positive change lies not with governments or professions, nor with science and the technology it spawns. The real power behind meaningful progress and growth, at any level of aggregation or organization, is the quality of the individual consciousnesses driving the action. Raising that quality can be accomplished only by the **self-directed** personal evolution of each individual. Clearly, the private message of *My Big TOE* is offered up for **your** personal use and benefit. Its potential value lies not in the words, nor in the ideas, presented. The potential of its value is the possibility of positively influencing the potential of your value – a potential that is profound and beyond estimation.

12

∎∎∎

The Chairman of the Board, and
Our Probable Relative Importance

∎∎∎

It will be helpful to our overall Big Picture understanding if we can frame a more accurate and humble perspective about the nature of our reality and our place in it. Some, who for their own reasons, have not found a satisfying bigger picture within a traditional philosophy or religion, often posit an unknowable something such as "The Mind of God" (MOG), as Stephen Hawking refers to the term at the end of his book, *A Brief History of Time*. Even something that is as expansive, open, and mystical as the Mind of God usually represents only a little picture view of AUM because it is derived from the diminutive little picture perspective of god the creator and animator of our physical universe.

Let's review how our universe relates to the larger reality. In Chapter 33, Book 1, we pointed out that our universe occupies only a minuscule sliver of the available physical reality-space within our own space-time dimension. Likewise, we will see in Chapters 3, 9, and 10 of Book 3, that our local reality represents just one branch of many divergent probable realities. Recall there are many independent PMR-like realities that exist within $NPMR_N$, which is itself only one of several more or less independent reality systems (one of the $NPMR_n$). The point is: Our favorite PMR universe is not exactly at the core of the larger reality. In fact, its overall relative significance would appear to be almost infinitesimal when compared to the sheer bulk of All That Is.

AUM is thus chairman of the board and Chief Executive Officer of MOG Corp., as well as the entire evolutionary experiment itself (substance, results, conclusions, and open ended possibilities – all combined, and all at the same time). Continuing with this decidedly funky but business-like metaphor, the Big Cheese is the division manager of "N" division, dedicated to a specific subset of evolutionary development models containing many PMRs. Progressing on down the chain of command, one eventually gets to a few assistants and their helpers who are concerned with our beloved OS and its inhabitants. Our physical universe is a subset of OS.

Given that one or more of these low-level assistants directly concerned with the administration of OS applies for the job of "God of PMR," then AUM would be the Mind of the God of god's god. Yes, I am just having some fun, but you get the point.

If the Big Cheese's division is especially profitable, perhaps he will be promoted to junior vice president one day and be awarded a private space in which to park his mind, stock options, omniscience without looking, and a grand vacation where he can get away, you know, go out of his mind for a few weeks. What are you in this goofy analogy? You, my friends, are the rank and file peons who appear (from your point of view) to do all the work and receive none of the credit, just as in real life. Perhaps getting the credit is not as important as it first appears.

In a light metaphoric moment, you could refer to AUM as the Mind of the God of god's god, but AUM is also much bigger than that. MOG is only one hat that, from our viewpoint, AUM **appears** to wear because of our minute perspective of the concepts of reality and god. That tiny perspective comes naturally, because we (us, our reality and history) are merely an itsy, bitsy, teeny, weenie yellowish polka-dot on a much bigger picture that is itself wrapped around something more grand and sublime than we can imagine. Sorry, but we are not likely to be at the center of this bigger picture; the odds are clearly against it. We are not likely to be at the center of our PMR universe, much less the center of **our** larger reality, much, much less the center of the Big Cheese's reality, and much, much, much less the center of AUM's reality.

Be realistic. We (Our System) are important, but so are many other history threads running through other universes, in many other reality systems spread over many PMRs, which reside in the many NPMRs that exist within each of the many evolutionary manifestations of AUM. Itsy, bitsy, teeny, weenie is probably an outrageous overstatement of our likely importance relative to the whole. We are, by the odds (statistically), likely to be much smaller than that.

Even if we are more important than the statistics indicate, there is no advantage in knowing that fact and there may be considerable disadvantage (not to you and me in particular, of course, but surely to others).

Such knowledge would constitute a serious disadvantage if it encouraged egos to invent grand theories of our special importance (as a species or as individuals), which could, in turn, lead us to see everything else (beside ourselves) as relatively unimportant and insignificant. Self-importance might breed arrogance and lead us to ignore opportunities to improve ourselves. Convinced of our special value, we might end up with a haughty disregard for the significance of others as well as a disrespectful attitude toward the ecosystems that sustain us. Do you think that could happen? Are humans capable of that type of blind arrogance? To be on the safe side, I think we should be careful not to encourage these particularly dysfunctional attitudes even if they do represent traditional values.

Do you think I have been unnecessarily harsh in laying out some of the conceptual foundation for the description of reality that will follow in the next two sections? Have I been ruthless in deflating egos, bursting cherished bubbles, and pushing difficult and discomforting concepts at you from every direction? I hope you don't feel that way. To me, the logical premises and conclusions found within *My Big TOE* are emancipating, empowering, and fun. I hope you are finding them interesting and potentially useful as well, and that you are encouraged to pursue and self-direct the evolution of your consciousness.

I hope you are having fun stretching your mind around these ideas, whether you are finding solid agreement with your personal data or carefully formulating a debunker's rebuttal. Lighthearted fun is an important component of learning.

13

■ ■ ■

Uncertainty and Manipulating the Future With Intent
The Nature of Psi Phenomena – Measurement and Validation
Taking the Path of Knowledge

■ ■ ■

We have discussed how AUM and we are related – how our nature and purpose derives from the nature and purpose of the evolving digital consciousness system we call AUM. We have seen that we are a part of a larger consciousness organism that is dependent (as all growing and evolving complex systems are) upon all of it parts pulling together to ensure its continued growth and existence.

In this chapter, we shift gears and explore the larger reality from a more human perspective. We'll take a look at how uncertainty, constraints on consciousness, psi phenomena, and spiritual growth are related to our existence in PMR and in the Big Picture. This chapter will tie together many of the ideas we have been talking about from a more personal perspective.

From the title of this chapter, it would seem that a random inelastic collision in topic space has glommed together three loosely related, but separate topics. In fact, these three topics are so thoroughly intertwined that considering them together, within a shared context, will enhance the understanding of each.

To create an entity or bounded system, one must impose constraints upon some energy-form such as physical mass or nonphysical consciousness. These constraints define and maintain the entity. If the constraints are removed, the entity will disintegrate, dissipate, or dematerialize. Nonconscious, non-growing, inanimate objects (from the PMR point of view) tend to stay in the state in which they are left unless there is some applied energy, or some background energy available to remove internal or external constraints (causing motion, state changes, degeneration, decomposition, dematerialization, or sublimation). The entropy of inanimate objects, if left alone, tends to increase – this fact is expressed by the second law of thermodynamics (see the entropy aside near the middle of Chapter 24, Book 1). The second law of thermodynamics results from the fact that natural physical processes are irreversible and seek the lowest available energy state – it is a natural artifact of the functionality of space-time.

The creation of a conscious entity follows the same rules as the creation of any entity except conscious entities have the ability to modify themselves with free will intent. External constraints are imposed on a subset of conscious potential energy to form an individuated consciousness that is an individual sentient entity. Additional external constraints are imposed on the interactions and perceptions of that individuated consciousness (such as through the PMR space-time rule-set) in order to create an environment that facilitates evolutionary progress. However, with the attributes of conscious, a sentient entity can create its own internal constraints. The internal constraints that a sentient entity typically imposes upon itself will inevitably limit the evolutionary potential of that entity. Some self-imposed constraints may appear to serve a temporary purpose and some are obviously more dysfunctional (unprofitable) than others, but all must eventually be removed by the entity if it is to actualize its full potential.

Adding uncertainty and minimizing constraints within a given virtual reality will always generate wider evolutionary potential for the entities within that reality because greater freedom and additional choices support a more diverse set of potential outcomes. When you are caught in a belief trap (have a belief), you create an additional **internal** constraint that further limits the capacity and function of your consciousness. Creating or maintaining unprofitable internal constraints that limit your personal consciousness requires energy (dysfunctional organization) and increases the entropy of your consciousness.

Though constraints may configure a system for some specific purpose, they generally limit the potential energy of the system. Internal constraints within a consciousness system that limit growth and profitability represent suboptimal or profit inhibiting digital organization. Organizational energy is expended but the results are counterproductive (are dysfunctional and unprofitable to the system or block future profitability). Think of self-imposed internal constraints in terms of a negative digital potential energy or a negative potential synergy.

Adding unprofitable internal constraints (belief, fear, and ego) to your consciousness is analogous to scattering bricks and concrete blocks on a highway. The highway was built by employing **profitable external** constraints (all traffic confined to a convenient and efficient roadway of a specific type and location), while littering it with obstacles represents the addition of **dysfunctional internal** constraints that reduce the roadway's functionality and efficiency.

The energy of consciousness has the potential to organize itself more effectively – to develop more complete and brighter awareness, generate and creatively utilize understanding, feeling, caring, love, and directed mental effort in a way that is useful and helpful to itself and to other consciousness struggling to evolve. Each individuated consciousness generates its own unique path toward increasing or decreasing profitability, yet all are expressions that reflect the process and purpose of the whole. Better quality within the larger consciousness system is actualized through the synergistic self-improvements of its individuated parts. Entropy reduction is the name of the game at all levels and within all dimensions of the consciousness-evolution fractal wherever evolution is succeeding. Wherever evolution is not succeeding, that portion of the consciousness-evolution fractal is stagnant, deteriorating, or dying.

The entropy within a consciousness system (including an individuated subsystem) represents the unavailability of consciousness energy to do work. The primary work of consciousness is to more effectively organize itself, to take charge of its own evolution, and to increase its overall profitability through self-modification (growth). Higher entropy states within consciousness represent unprofitable organization: disorganization, fears, beliefs, dimness, diminished potential, self-centeredness, and an inability to understand complex interrelationships or see big pictures. Higher entropy results in consciousness systems having less power that can be applied to overcome the inertia of ignorance and ego dysfunctionality. Not decreasing the entropy of consciousness results in a squandering of potential.

The fewer internal dysfunctional constraints (such as fear, ego, needs, or beliefs) that limit a particular consciousness, the lower its associated entropy and the more effectively it can populate the most profitable states available to it. The drive or urge to be helpful to, and care about others (love) is an innate property of low entropy consciousness. A low entropy consciousness is an effective and powerful consciousness. Consequently, a low entropy individuated consciousness represents an effective individual with considerable personal power.

The self-removal of internal self-imposed constraints from sentient entities provide opportunities for reducing entropy and increasing synergy, while internal constraints removed from inanimate objects provide opportunities for increasing entropy.

Constraints come in many forms. For example, if someone who has the ability to manipulate nonphysical energy is asked to remove (dissipate or dematerialize) a tumor (noticeable lump) from someone's PMR body, the energy required is dependent upon, among other things, the degree to which this tumor is connected to PMR reality – its force of being in PMR. (This hokey sounding "force of being" is actually well defined in chapter 11, Book 3). Quantitatively it is the expectation value of the future event on the associated probable reality surface – a discussion that we will have in detail in Chapter 7, Book 3. If the body's owner and a few others are mildly distressed about the **possibility** of a malignant tumor, the removal energy may be relatively low (easy to accomplish). In this situation, much uncertainty exists within PMR – but not necessarily for the one viewing and manipulating the body's nonphysical energy from within NPMR – to that person, the nature of the lump may be perfectly clear.

If, on the other hand, four doctors and half the residents at the local hospital have looked at the CAT scan or felt the lump and are relatively certain the tumor is malignant, the removal energy is somewhat higher. When all of the above get the biopsy report confirming a fast growing, incurable, always-deadly malignancy, the required energy increases. The more firmly the malignant tumor's existence and likely outcome (degree of causal certainty) is held and shared in the minds and expectations of credible sentient beings, the taller and denser its probability function becomes. The uncertainty of the outcome dissipates and the probable event of dying in PMR from this cancer becomes much more difficult to change by manipulating energy in $NPMR_N$. Fortunately, the intent and attitude (mental focus) of the body's owner has the greatest potential impact. Unfortunately, this attitude is often driven by its fear and the opinions and fears of others.

Now, by definition, it takes a miracle, where before no miracle was required. The confident knowledge of the doctors, which is based on test results and historical precedent (mortality statistics), actually affects (decreases) the probability of actualization of **other alternative possibilities** such as the cancer spontaneously going into remission, or the tumor turns out to be benign. As in quantum mechanics, performing the measurement forces the result to pick a state compatible with PMR causality (compatible with the PMR space-time rule-set). Typically, the most likely state at the time of the measurement is picked unless there are several states of equal probability, then one outcome is picked randomly from among the set of outcomes (future states) that are all most likely. The individual with the tumor, along with his or her friends and loved ones, can inadvertently help drive the final outcome to an unhappy ending by causing the probability of a fatal outcome to grow, and the probability of a non-fatal outcome to shrink. Beware: you can be easily drawn into a fatal dance of expectation with those connected to you, or to your condition. The best time for intervention, whether from PMR or NPMR, is long before "fatal" becomes a near inevitability.

The future is not a done deal. PMR is an interactive reality – we have free will and the potential ability to manipulate or at least strongly influence the probability of any particular event manifesting into the physical. There are rules and wisdom that must be applied to the use of nonphysical energy – there are things that one should and should not do as well as things that one can and cannot do. For example, one needs to know when help becomes interference. Helping out in the more immediate small picture can sometimes be counterproductive within a larger perspective because difficult challenges often represent great opportunities. When one removes the challenge, one removes the opportunity as well.

Most of us would be surprised at how effective a knowledgeable and experienced individual can be working from NPMR. The point is: Reversing the causal laws of space-time (a miracle) requires much more energy than directly modifying the outcome of an uncertain event. Later I will formalize this concept in what I call the psi uncertainty principle.

I am **not** speaking about what is often referred to as the power of positive thinking or the power of belief and faith to manifest physical effects. These effects are real, but are typically weak, inconsistent and unreliable. I am talking about **directly** and precisely altering the probable future with the intentional power of a focused, clear, and coherent mind. Positive thinking and putting energy into wishes or prayer **can be** useful and effective, but their effects are often not very potent or predictable because the energy of conscious intent supporting them is typically not well focused, coherent, or aware of the larger issues.

There are exceptional people – sometimes in exceptional circumstances – who have used these typically impotent forms forcefully. Hoping for or trying to project belief or faith into a measurable result **typically** produces (if it produces anything at all) a mild, diffuse, unpredictable, and unfocused effect driven by fuzzy emotions and feelings instead of precise knowledge and experience. It is the difference between feeling the gentle warmth of the sun through a window, and using a large and powerful magnifying glass to enable that same sunlight to burn holes through whatever blocks its path. It is exactly the same sunlight radiating heat through a piece of glass in both cases, but differing methodologies of interacting with the sun's energy produce very different results. Similarly, without an enforced coherency, a laser is just an ordinary red light. The methodology that intentionally employs a sophisticated energy manipulation technique (optical lens, laser, or NPMR awareness) to focus ambient energy is the one that has the power to produce dramatic effects and dependable results. Such techniques (large diameter accurate error-free lenses, laser coherency, or an ability to manipulate NPMR energy) embody the accumulated knowledge and experience of many generations and typically require skill and practice to produce and apply.

This discussion will, unfortunately, lead many to one of two intellectual extremes. The first and most common concludes that if a cancer whose existence is unverified (greater uncertainty) is the only cancer that can be cured by the proper focusing of consciousness, then such activity is fake or based upon self-delusion. That is not a logical conclusion. It may be a reasonable conclusion under some conditions, but not necessarily all conditions. In no case does "is fake" follow logically from "unverified." We tend to jump to that illogical conclusion because of our dogmatic cultural and scientific beliefs. Logic does require a physically unverified problem to have a physically unverified solution. However, we will see below that the psi uncertainty principle requires that problems that are physically verified (known malignant tumor) must have either a physically verifiable physical solution or a physically unverifiable nonphysical solution.

The second extreme, more illogical than the first, concludes that until the cancer is verified by measurement (in PMR exclusively), the cancer does not actually exist. Clearly, fundamental existence is not logically dependent upon performing physical measurements. It is true that until the cancer is verified by measurement in PMR, the cancer cannot be proved to exist in PMR. That fact, though logical, carries little practical significance in either the Big Picture or the little picture because existence and the proof of that existence are two very different things. Likewise, actually dissolving a tumor by manipulating nonphysical energy and proving that a tumor has been dissolved through the manipulation of nonphysical energy are two very different things. The first is not logically dependent on the second, although the second is logically dependent on the first.

That nothing can be considered real or significant until it has been **objectively** proven is an illogical position based on the assumption that PMR constitutes all reality and that you (your consciousness) are a derivative of physical matter. This mystical belief requires existence to be proven or validated by little picture causality: The existence of the Big Picture requires validation from the little picture. Same old story. This belief is not only illogical and irrational, but limiting as well. Objective PMR-based proof is valuable in some circumstances (exploring the space-time rule-set), and totally irrelevant in others (exploring consciousness and the larger reality). Making PMR objectivity a universal requirement banishes logical beginnings and forces PMR to be a universal reality. When you view PMR as a universal reality, everything beyond PMR vanishes before your eyes as your vision contracts to perceive the little picture exclusively.

Hard (but not necessarily only material) evidence and a careful scientific process is absolutely required. Keep in mind that knowledge constrained solely to PMR defines only a limited **perception** of reality and not necessarily reality itself.

The fact is, your existence extends beyond its physical manifestation in PMR. Most people resemble Flatlanders criticizing the concept of a sphere because it doesn't follow (isn't derivable or conceivable) from their two-dimensional science, philosophy, or reality. Without an open and capable mind you are stuck, ignorant forever, in Flatland. [A reference to the book *Flatland*, and how to find it online, appears in Chapter 20, Book 1.]

You may be wondering how you could learn to be sentient and operative in NPMR. It may seem nearly impossible from your perspective to achieve consistency and clarity but it is not. Steady effort and due diligence eventually will produce clear and consistent results for anyone. The limiting constraints, which are within your power to remove, are not constraints placed on your consciousness by fate, biology, or from the outside. They are internal constraints of your own making that you have created with your belief, ego, and fear. Your natural mind does not limit or constrain your NPMR experiences: The unnatural mind that you and your culture have created is the problem.

Learning how to be sentient in NPMR does not represent a new skill that must be mastered, it simply occurs spontaneously after self-imposed constraints are removed: It is an unlearning that is required. That sounds easy, but if you have ever tried to break deeply ingrained thought patterns (hard-core habits) you know it is not easy. Nevertheless, unlearning always yields to steady serious effort.

Viewing a clear picture of the larger reality will, for most of us, require stepping outside normal habituated thought patterns and cultural beliefs – unlearning or escaping old patterns must precede learning new ones. It is not easy to overcome limiting habits of mind, but it is well worth the effort. For those few who have broad and deep experience with the larger reality, *My Big TOE* will read as if it were a story about Dick, Jane, and Spot – familiar, simple, and obvious. For a few others, it will be as impenetrable as a wall of granite.

I am strongly encouraging you to think out of the box, non-conform, transcend your culture, and expand your notion of the possible beyond what is **commonly** held to be acceptable. As you are well aware, thinking big thoughts in small places can be socially and personally risky. This challenge is not for everyone, but if you have read this far, more than likely, it is a challenge that you can successfully meet.

▶ I expect that I have by now exceeded the credibility threshold of many readers. In techno-jargon that means that I have pegged their BS meters. I can smell the smoke! Before I completely burn out your super sensitive, culturally calibrated BS detector, let me digress a moment because it is important for you to understand how the quality, content, and intensity of your thoughts affect (typically limit) the options and opportunities of your being. The open minded skeptic is free to explore anything, anywhere, with demanding standards for converting experience into knowledge (truth). The closed-minded skeptic is trapped by the limits he places on his thoughts and abilities. He is caught in the following dilemma. Fearful of exceeding the safe and acceptable limits of cherished religious, personal, cultural, or scientific dogma, he believes it is fundamentally impossible to find truth in a wild and crazy **subjective** world which is obviously populated by plenty of fools and liars.

Religious creed (his in particular) and scientific objectivity (his in particular) appear to provide safe havens free from the ubiquitous fools and liars who would gladly induce everyone else to join their delusional and manipulative ranks.

As long as his boundaries are rigidly defined by (can't be expanded beyond) his limiting beliefs, he is not able to learn, grow, experience or evolve his being along the Path of Knowledge. This path, which often wanders through the lands of the paranormal, **requires** a fundamental (experientially based) **understanding** of reality and **knowledge** of truth. One must be both careful and courageous.

Such a limited individual usually feels he is maximizing his human potential by dedicating his energies to the optimal manipulation of intellectual objects, beings, and relationships in PMR. He has never had an objectively **verifiable** (proven) experience that would **necessarily** (scientifically) indicate a bigger picture exists because this type of experience is emphatically defined within his belief system to be absolutely impossible (the self-referential Catch 22 of the closed mind).

Individuals trapped in the little picture selectively restrict, view, and interpret their and other people's experiences to make sure that what is believed to be impossible does not appear to happen. Additionally, they negate the validity of anyone else's data or experience (of a larger reality) by assuming it to be contrived, ignorant, manipulative, or delusional (by definition). This façade of a scientific and logical evaluation, steeped in tradition and in support of the status-quo, is used to wrap the entire sleight-of-hand in a mantel of professional respectability. This particularly shallow circular logic (it can't be true because it can't be true) is subsequently offered by conventional scientists as proof that their beliefs are actually facts.

This is an emotional ego-driven position rather than an objective one. A rational argument rarely has any affect on an irrational belief. Ironically, the closed-minded skeptics interpret internally derived knowledge as mere **belief**, because they do not **believe** that objective knowledge (truth) can come from subjective experience.

The PMR-only view of reality, along with its tiny picture of the potential of your being and its associated relatively tiny subset of truth, is usually culturally based (particularly in the West), intellectually justified, and socially supported by the collective mind. The collective mind, unfortunately, always represents the lowest common denominator in concepts and understanding. It is relatively safe, easy, low risk, non-threatening, and not subjected to ridicule by your peers. It is, therefore, particularly attractive to fearful, under-developed, insecure, under-powered, and materially focused minds.

If you feel uneasy after assessing how that string of adjectives in the previous sentence applies to you, relax. Many good people of outstanding quality exhibit some of those characteristics. The point here is to recognize the arbitrary, unnecessary, and debilitating conceptual limitations we place on our reality, on our significance, and on ourselves.

If you have attained high status within your profession and among your peers, or are rich, powerful, and famous, these trappings of success say absolutely nothing about the quality of your consciousness or the evolution of your being as viewed from the bigger picture. The biggest fish (have the most power, notoriety, and make the biggest splash) in the PMR farm pond may be among the smallest fish in the gigantic NPMR$_N$ ocean. Conversely, some of the smallest, most humble fish in the PMR pond may be some of the biggest fish in the NPMR$_N$ ocean. ◀

By growing the quality of whatever state of being we presently find ourselves in, we evolve the quality of our consciousness. You can start from any point, but the optimal place to start is from wherever you happen to be today.

If you or anyone you know has an interest in personal growth, even if they require the comfort and safety of a relatively closed mind, there are two viable alternatives to the Path of Knowledge: Doing good deeds (Path of Service), and devotion to the highest expression of spirituality they can comprehend (Path of Surrender). Unfortunately, both of these paths are especially difficult to follow in Western cultures where material progress and success are dominate social values.

▶ Let's take a break before some of you burn out your analytical clutch – it keeps slipping like that because of a lack of personal high quality data. You should immediately scrape the sticky belief residue and corrosive pseudo-knowledge off your main brain-drive mechanism. That will get you by for now, but remember to get that condition (lack of high quality data) repaired as soon as possible. If you keep your speed down and avoid jumping over challenging new concepts in order to more quickly reach comfortable old conclusions, it should be safe for you to continue on after this short aside.

A brief description of the common paths leading toward self-realization, conscious-ness evolution, or spiritual growth will provide a helpful perspective on the entangle-ment of psi phenomena, spirituality, knowledge, and truth – and give all our brains a short cool-down rest from analytic activity.

We can divide the approaches to spiritual evolution into three **equal** but distinct paths that suit or accommodate three distinctive personality types. Eventually all three paths converge, with each path containing the essential truths of the other two. Each individual seeker's growth path can contain any proportion of each of the above men-tioned three ways (paths of knowledge, service, and surrender) of approaching spiritu-ality in order to obtain a best fit to their individual personality.

If the concept of seeking a **spiritual** growth path falls to the uncomfortable or neg-ative side of your learned sensibilities, let me point out that the concept of a growth path toward improving the quality (decreasing the entropy) of your consciousness means exactly the same thing.

Because the three paths to consciousness quality appeal to diverse personality types, typically one process will dominate an individual's approach. Individuals choose the path that suits them best and afterward add in the other two as complements. An equal balance of all three might be theoretically advantageous but it would not neces-sarily be better for any specific individual. The main thing is to optimize progress (spir-itual growth) by matching the process to the personality.

The Path of Knowledge is often called the "warrior's path" because of the courage, determination, and constant struggle required to gain spiritual knowledge and defeat the ego for control of the process of consciousness evolution. This path requires con-siderable intellectual capacity and is more suited to the linear thinking of the Western mind than the alternatives. It is on the Path of Knowledge that you learn, first hand, about the larger reality and how to manipulate energy to put the so-called paranormal or psi phenomena to work in the service of spiritual growth (yours and others).

These paranormal abilities are the natural result of a lower entropy consciousness having more energy available to do work. You can accomplish more and you have more power with a lower entropy consciousness. This additional available energy can (but does not have to) be utilized to manifest paranormal or psi effects. We can now answer the question: What do love and psi phenomena have to do with each other, reality, spiritual growth, and digital consciousness? The answer: The ultimate reality is cellular (digital) consciousness. Consciousness naturally evolves to lower entropy states; psi effects and love are both artifacts of low entropy consciousness.

In the Big Picture, the paranormal is perfectly normal and **available** to (not thrust upon) anyone who sufficiently lowers the entropy of their consciousness. Love describes how a low entropy consciousness interacts with other entities. Both accrue to a high quality of consciousness – which, for an individuated consciousness, is equivalent to a highly spiritual individual. For sentient entities, psi-power is love-power is quality consciousness power. All are the result of consciousness systems and subsystems evolving to lower entropy states of being.

The Path of Service involves doing good deeds, being helpful, serving others and must come sincerely from the heart, not the intellect (Mother Teresa comes to mind as a well known example). On this path, the ego is transcended through focusing on others' needs.

The Path of Surrender requires that you give yourself up to a higher (supreme) spiritual concept or being, or to the expression of more perfect spiritual values. This is the traditional religious path that transcends the ego by dedication and devotion to higher ideals and values, and through emulation of the beloved master, teacher, guru, or god. (Look near the end of Chapter 21, Book 1 for additional discussion on this topic.) ◀

Let's get back to the main issue. The entanglement (interaction) of uncertainty with the measurement of psi effects leads to what I descriptively call the psi uncertainty principle – where the uncertainty surrounding an event allows the event a larger selection of probable outcomes that may be more easily altered by the application of a focused (low noise - small ego) mind with a clear intent. Here, psi (as defined earlier in Chapter 19, Book 1) refers to psychic, paranormal, or acausal phenomena.

The psi uncertainty principle makes the scientific objective measurement of psi performance problematical, but only from the PMR perspective. As soon as there are outside observers to report and measure the miracles (reduce the uncertainty about reported violations of traditional PMR physics), the miracles diminish – and insiders cannot be trusted to be objective and therefore cannot be believed.

Let's explore how the randomness of certain natural events is related to the psi uncertainty principle. A focused and directed consciousness (physically embodied or not) may take advantage of the uncertainty or randomness in physical interactions, situations, or phenomena by subtly applying psycho-kinetics (PK) or telepathic suggestion to manipulate events toward a particular outcome. The results of these manipulations would simply appear within PMR to be good or bad luck, an intuitive bolt out of the blue, or a random skewing of the expected statistical distribution. Such manipulations are typically helpful and relatively common. They create no contradictions and pose no causality problems within PMR as long as there is enough uncertainty (lack of **objective** proof) to hide the paranormal outside influence and satisfy the psi uncertainty principle.

If we would learn to make better use of the guidance and breaks that we are given, growing up wouldn't be so difficult. Most parents would probably say the same thing about their teenagers. Teenagers, just like their parents, ignore as much of this outside guidance and beneficent manipulation as possible. Do you see how the same patterns of individual growth are repeated at every level? Repetitive pattern is the nature of a fractal system. The pattern of consciousness evolving toward higher levels of organization (better quality and lower entropy) is applied at many levels and scales simultaneously. What you see your children doing is a reflection of what you are doing, is what computers will be doing when our hardware and software allow it, is what the Big Cheese is doing, and what AUM is doing. Consciousness does not evolve in a thousand different independent ways; it evolves in the same way in a thousand different forms at various level of interdependence.

I hear someone asking: "Are you implying the paranormal is purposely being hidden from us by some uncertainty principle?" Absolutely not! It may appear that way from PMR but in fact it is just the opposite. The paranormal is not hidden by anything other than ignorance and limitations. It is you who are hiding from the paranormal by allowing your beliefs and fears to create an impenetrable smokescreen of objective obfuscation.

The psi uncertainty principle's job is to maintain the integrity of the PMR learning lab, not to hide psi phenomena from you. If you have defined the paranormal out of your reality, that is because there is no logical place for it within your little picture.

Why do the residents of PMR need the psi uncertainty principle? How does the psi uncertainty principle help lower the entropy of individuated consciousness within space-time? Breaking the rules of PMR objective causality would, at this time, interfere with what the beings enrolled there must accomplish (improving the quality of their consciousness). A rule-set is specifically designed for each virtual PMR learning lab to optimize the learning potential of the typical inhabitance of that PMR. More advanced players can access a wider set of rules.

You may be wondering how the psi uncertainty principle constrains your personal experience and how high quality consciousness can and cannot be used to your advantage in day-to-day interactions within PMR. Rarely is acausal or paranormal information obtained from NPMR and then directly applied to develop or invent physical devices because the psi uncertainty principle would generally forbid that sort of overt information transfer. It is not likely that a novel solution (like instructions describing how to build a Buck Rogers antigravity belt) could be **effectively** transmitted to an individual within PMR from a higher-dimensional source. It would be impossible for such an individual to be technically or conceptually prepared unless the transferred technology represented only a very small step beyond the receiver's current understanding. Imagine trying to describe color television or microprocessor chip technology to Alexander the Great or Alexander Graham Bell.

The near impossibility of being technically prepared is only half the problem. The receiver would need a very high quality of consciousness to receive a clear technical transmission and such people are not particularly interested in inconsequential physical gismos and technology no matter how useful it might be in PMR because better gizmos are not relevant to the purpose of consciousness evolution. Additionally, there is the problem of needing all sorts of unavailable parts and materials – building a color TV or microprocessor chip with the materials and tools available to either Alexander would have been impossible even if they had a clear signal and were good at following directions.

You cannot cheat evolution or circumvent evolutionary process. Evolutionary process defines the rational structure of your system; undermining it would destroy the system's integrity. Psi uncertainty is required to maintain the integrity of your causal system – it is applied at all levels of the consciousness-evolution ecosystem to maintain local causality within each dimension.

On the other hand, a more limited but very similar transfer process working through individual intuition continually feeds inventors and creators of all types the answers and inspiration they require to take the next step. An adequately prepared person in touch with their intuition will often receive some key point or understanding that resolves an issue upon which they are stuck or that somehow lubricates the creative process. Again, the step must be small and the receiver must come to the intuitive process prepared to understand and implement the solution.

The psi uncertainty principle makes it exceeding unlikely that paranormal information will provide a useful giant-step solution to an **objective** PMR problem. Think of the requirement for psi uncertainty as a constraint that limits the size of the leap that insight is allowed to take in any given circumstance within PMR – or, for that matter, within any reality dimension, either physical or nonphysical.

The usual highly filtered, low bandwidth connection between NPMR and individual intuition is designed to preserve psi uncertainty. Both a prepared intellect and an evolved consciousness are necessary for you to purposefully and effectively use your intuition as a source of insight.

Ask any innovative problem solver about the source of their creative solutions and you will hear about their non-logical connection to resources within NPMR expressed in a way that makes sense to them.

A lower entropy consciousness improves our ability to clearly see relationships among the data we normally gather and assess from PMR. Understanding these relationships provides a bigger picture that delivers an enormous practical advantage to low entropy individuals within PMR without violating the psi uncertainty principle. Individual intuition, insight, artistic, personal, and scientific epiphanies that result in physical creations within PMR must be integrated with the ideas that presently reside in that individual's current PMR experience packet (temporarily stored in the physical brain). It is the quality and capacity of our consciousness that allows us to see PMR relationships in a creative new way. Because no discrete acausal or paranormal information transfer from NPMR to PMR is required for consciousness to develop and improve its natural attributes, lower its entropy, or be creative, the psi uncertainty principle is preserved.

Quality consciousness not only gives us the ability to see relationships clearly, but also to find meaning, significance, value, and direction from the data and experience that we normally gather in PMR. A lower entropy consciousness interacts with reality at a higher and more complete level of integration, and, if enrolled in the PMR learning lab, is able to apply what it learns from that interaction to future interactions. Humans, as well as other units of individuated consciousness, learn to develop their consciousness quality through the interactions and feedback provided by virtual PMR learning labs.

Electrical engineers study systems with two kinds of feedback. Systems with **positive** feedback are like big snowballs rolling **down** a smooth steep snowy mountainside. Systems with **negative** feedback are like big snowballs rolling **up** a smooth steep snowy mountainside. The characteristics and response of the system is represented by the size of the snowball and the depth of the snow, while the affect of the feedback and its impact on the system is analogous to the steepness of the slope. Relative to the manipulation of psi energy (intentionally reorganizing bits within the larger reality) or the transferring of paranormal information, individuated units of consciousness are in a positive developmental feedback loop (bootstrapping process) to expand and grow those abilities and processes that are important to improving consciousness quality. In contrast, physical activity and interactions that are not important to improving consciousness quality (though they may seem extremely important from PMR's little picture point of view) are kept in check by a negative feedback loop that uses the constraint of psi uncertainty to dampen counterproductive intentions. Pumping up the physical with information transfers from the nonphysical is forbidden unless the transfers are sufficiently vague (negative feedback) to ensure a sufficiently dampened system response.

The uncertainty principle is required to maintain and optimize the purpose of the larger reality – to increase quality and lower entropy. The constraint of psi uncertainty keeps PMR focused and functioning toward its goal, which is **not** to generate physical improvements within PMR, but to help individuated consciousness pull itself up by its bootstraps. The generation of a more comfortable, physically productive (including better science) PMR is clearly the main issue within the local little picture and therefore appears to be very important from the PMR view. Although physical progress plays a part in the bigger picture by locally impacting consciousness evolution, it is only a minor player on the periphery of the greater consciousness ecosystem. Consciousness does not exist to promote physical evolution within PMR; physical evolution within PMR exists to promote consciousness.

The constraint of psi uncertainty allows the energy of organization to be pumped into (equivalent to sucking entropy out of) what is important (spiritual progress through exercising the ability to see relationships clearly and to find meaning, significance, value, and direction from PMR experience) while **avoiding** pumping energy into what is not important (power, control, domination, and physical progress). Psi uncertainty is simply a rule, a natural constraint that has evolved to improve the profitability of the consciousness cycle. Think of the psi uncertainty constraint as a negative feedback mechanism that is required to optimize the productivity of PMR virtual reality trainers.

The apparent subterfuge of hiding psi phenomena under a cloak of uncertainty is an illusion created by the rudimentary nature of human consciousness. No one would leave knives, guns, axes, hammers, saws, expensive cell-phones, or laptop computers lying about on the playground at a daycare facility. The kids might love it and have great fun, but the adults know that children must grow up first before they can productively (and non-self-destructively) use such tools. It is not required that the tools be hidden from the children, but the children must be unaware of how to access these tools until they are capable of using them productively. As the kids grow up, various tools naturally become available to them. Believe it or not, most consciousness kids, after they reach adulthood, have little overt use for, or interest in, the tools of psi. Wielding power within the virtual world of the learning lab becomes irrelevant unless it is the power of setting a good example and offering helpful guidance.

The disappearance of psi effects when objective science shines its spotlight on the paranormal scene does not necessarily indicate fraud. The requirement to work only within a narrowly defined subset of physical reality and to exhibit perfect repeatability for everyone to see is a good methodology for the development of some science because, within a limited realm, those requirements do separate a limited truth from an unlimited fiction. However, it is a totally **inappropriate** measure of significance when applied to **some aspects** of the science of consciousness, the science of being, the science of mind, or the science of NPMR.

Instead of viewing the requirement for uncertainty as a cover-up for fraud or delusion, consider it to be a requirement of the space-time rule-set to maintain the integrity of the physical reality we need to experience in order to stimulate our growth. Mixing physical apples with nonphysical oranges only muddies the waters of our experience and decrease the effectiveness of space-time as a learning lab. Having our experience directly related to our responsibility for that experience and keeping our interactions with others straightforward and an integral part of an obvious feedback loop are the major design goals of our PMR space-time reality. A widespread intentional use of psi would seriously undermine those goals.

If you are not sure where I am coming from with these statements, reread the beginning of the "AUM: scientist at work" aside located in Chapter 9 and at least the last half of the free will aside in Chapter 11 – both are in this book. You will see that PMR was specifically designed to constrain psi effects in order to produce a better learning environment. Psi effects within PMR are relegated to the subjective fringe where they can be easily obscured by uncertainty. This arrangement is a requirement of our reality as long as the average level of consciousness quality is so low.

Individuals may experience and use the paranormal as they lower the entropy of their consciousness enough to gain that ability, but it cannot become generally accessible through objective science without wrecking the primary value and usefulness of PMR as a training simulator for low-quality consciousness. Don't worry, the system is designed to prevent that from happening and the psi uncertainty principle is only part of that prevention strategy. If you have no access to paranormal power and think that psi effects are a bunch of bullpucky ... well, that is probably as it should be. Such a view does not constitute a failure, an error, or a problem; it simply represents a particular state of developmental understanding – like being twelve years old.

There is nothing wrong with being twelve years old: In fact, it is an absolutely necessary and desirable state to be in if you ever expect to be a teenager. You cannot be a teen until you have been twelve, and you cannot be an adult until you have been a teenager. No one jumps ahead; everyone must start from wherever they happen to be. Truly, anywhere you are is a terrific place to start – there are no bad seats in the house. Everyone must progress under their own power and at their own rate. That is simply how the game must be played – there is no other choice and no other game.

If from time to time it appears to you that *My Big TOE* has cleverly or unfairly backed you into a logical corner, consider the principle that all systems of law and justice are based upon: The only thing that can logically corner you consistently is the truth.

The truth can sometimes be unpleasant, particularly if it leads us to an unsettling conclusion. "Feels good" or "Feels right" is not a reliable way of discerning truth. To be accurate and trustworthy, your intuition needs to be free of fear, wants, needs, desires, expectations, and ego.

Psi effects and paranormal powers are sometimes dangled as a carrot in front of those newly on the Path of Knowledge to provide incentive, but successful travelers of that path soon realize that paranormal abilities can also be a growth limiting trap if their ego becomes enamored of them.

Using or requiring inappropriate methodology in any area of endeavor typically leads to dead ends, no progress, and false conclusions. Some of the knowledge, facts, laws, rules, structure, and science (obeying NPMR causality) that define paranormal activity cannot be seen, experienced, or understood until the observer grows to be capable of it, and will consequently never exhibit perfect repeatability for **everyone** to see.

Quality of consciousness and the directed applications of consciousness energy are personal in nature because consciousness is personal. Because psi effects are not of PMR, one cannot force them to abide by PMR causality, nor can one explain them with PMR causality.

The awareness and personal growth that enables an individual to exhibit controlled paranormal applications of consciousness must be developed from that individual's subjective experience. Researchers studying psi effects can not produce them, reproduce them, nor control them from the outside; nor can they **force** psi effects upon themselves or others from the inside. On the other hand, they can easily retard it and make it more difficult and problematical for their subjects to demonstrate psi effects. For a physically focused mainstream science, this lack of **physical** control makes the serious study of psi almost impossible. The traditional scientific requirement for tight **physical** control over a **completely nonphysical** entity such as consciousness (including its attributes and artifacts) in order to prove its **physical** existence (the only type of existence there is, of course) produces an amusing example of circular belief-trap non-logic. The absurdity of this reasoning would be funnier if it weren't the position most scholars and scientists support quite seriously. Or maybe that is why it is so funny!

▶ While we are on the subject of cultural insanity and funny scientists, let's practice a little remote viewing. I see three typical looking university scientists dressed in white lab coats, standing in a small room with a metal table. On the table is a child's microscope.

Shhhhh, listen, and you can clearly hear Curly talking to Larry:

"I've got the answer! I've got it! I figured it out! Listen, nobody can **prove** the nonphysical is physical, so it must not exist!"

"You imbecile!" says Larry with obvious contempt as his two out-stretched fingers jab menacingly at Curly's eyes, "of course the nonphysical isn't physical. It's not supposed to be!"

"Yuck-Yuck-Yuck-Yuck!" answers Curly as he cleverly blocks the eye-jab with the side of his hand. "If the nonphysical isn't physical, then how am I going to examine it with this microscope?"

"Good point," says Moe thoughtfully. "What we need is a nonphysical microscope."

Curly and Larry glance at each other quizzically and begin to look in their pockets and under the table.

Moe watches them search in vain for the nonphysical microscope for a few moments before he says, "You two numbskulls couldn't find a nonphysical microscope if you tripped over it!" Curly and Larry immediately begin using their hands to search the empty floor around their feet for the invisible microscope.

Moe moves quickly. He grabs Curly and Larry by the ears and proceeds to bang their heads together. All three begin to quarrel.

"I just had a nonphysical myself and the doctor said that both of you were verrrrry, very sick!" interjects Moe, trying to recapture the attention of the other two.

Larry and Curly suddenly stop squabbling and look at Moe with seriously worried expressions. "How bad is it?" they ask in unison.

The ensuing pregnant pause suddenly aborts. "I had a physic too!" Larry interjects to break the worried silence, "but everything came out all right."

"So, **that's** what happened to your brains," Moe quips, as if suddenly receiving great insight.

"Now, you two get back to work. We aren't going to leave this lab until we can prove that we can read each others' minds."

"But, I can't read at all," protests Curly.

"No problem – you're a mad scientist, not an angry English teacher," says Moe matter of factly.

Curly and Larry pause for a reflective moment as they absorb the apparently profound and obvious truth of Moe's statement. Soon everyone is nodding in agreement.

Larry suddenly leaps on the table, assumes a "swami position" and scrunches up his face in a display of great concentration while Curly and Moe look on.

In a few seconds Larry jumps up, stands in the middle of the table, and says dejectedly, "I am trying and trying, but all I get is a blank, … actually…," he continues after a short reflective pause, "… I get two blanks."

"Great!" says Moe, "that's all the proof we need, let's get out of here!"

"I want to do it! I want to do it too! It's my turn! My turn! My turn! My tur…."

Whap!

A strong slap from Moe stops Curly in mid sentence. "Go ahead and give it a try, you nincompoop," says Moe indulgently.

Curly scrunches up his face, turns his head to one side and begins to squeal as he quickly pumps his feet.

Whap! Whap! Whap!

Moe gives Curly a quick triad of hard forehand-backhand slaps.

"All right swami, what did you get?" asks Moe with obvious skepticism.

Curly grins and puffs up his chest with pride. "I got lots of blanks! Lots and lots of blanks!"

Curly turns and looks at Larry. "I got more nothing than you did!" taunts Curly contemptuously.

"Oh yea," says Larry, as he grabs Curly's nose and begins to twist it.

Whap! Whap!

Moe reaches out and delivers a hard ricocheting double slap to the two squabbling scientists. "Cut that out!" he demands. "We are only supposed to read each others' minds, not tune in to the entire faculty! If we do too good of a job, nobody will believe us. Too much success will get us fired."

They look at each other with somber expressions as each ponders the steep and obvious downside to unbridled professional success in their chosen field.

"That much truth is dangerous!" Moe states emphatically.

"Yeah," agrees Larry as they exit the room, "If the dean finds out he is just as smart as we are, he may want our jobs for himself." ◀

Because of its subjective and personal nature, it is difficult for researchers to encourage, define, or systematically and objectively study paranormal phenomena at a deep level. The most they can hope to do is observe and document its existence – a relatively simple thing that has been done thousands of times by hundreds of fully credentialed scientific researchers.

Good objective scientific protocol requires the experimenters to remove all possible uncertainty, thus interfering with, and limiting, the psi effect being studied. Where some uncertainty is allowed, better results (from an insider's viewpoint) are produced. From an outsider's point of view, only less credible results are produced. There are always many more outsiders than insiders. (Here, insiders are the experimenters and their subjects; everyone else is an outsider.)

Remote viewers, for example, cannot produce perfect high-resolution photographs for their experimenters – there is always some uncertainty, and usually (over an in-depth set of experiments) at least some inconsistency. Additional uncertainty grows quickly in the minds of individuals who are not **personally** in **total** control of the experimental protocols; it grows more quickly in the minds of those who are not physically witnessing the paranormal event (they read about it, hear about it, or see it on TV). How much uncertainty is necessary? Only enough to ensure that the vast majority of PMR citizens will not have their cherished delusions **forcibly** perturbed to a significant degree.

If a paranormal event (precognitive dream or vision, for example) is without uncertainty, the number of people who can objectively verify this perfect demonstration of psi will always be small enough to produce no major or lasting impact on the larger society. Those individuals who are not yet ready to perceive and understand the larger truth represented by paranormal events must not be forced to experience what they can not productively deal with. In the bigger picture, there must always be enough uncertainty to ensure that the perceived causal integrity of PMR (the delusion that the only reality that can possibly exist must be objective and physical) can adequately be maintained by all who are not yet developmentally ready to move beyond that most basic worldview. From the opposite direction and within a smaller picture, the natural uncertainty surrounding a given event, or sequence of events, enables and simplifies the application of focused consciousness to paranormally influence that event without violating the psi uncertainty principle.

On the other hand, objective physical experience is designed to be shared and held in common. Our physical experience forms an interactive virtual reality exhibiting a uniform common causality defined by the space-time rule-set. PMR physics is simply a subset of the space-time rule-set (this idea will be developed thoroughly in Section 4). Everybody can experience the same measurable effects in PMR; however, the necessary (by the psi uncertainty principle) uncertainty that must reside at the root cause of psi effects (from a scientific PMR objective perspective) is not appreciated by the PMR scientist whose methodology requires him to eliminate uncertainty. The inability to eliminate uncertainty will frustrate the scientist's desire to understand the deeper causal mechanics of psi phenomena.

PMR scientists are culturally driven to **interpret** what they experience in a way that is in consonance with their belief that PMR causality must contain all possible phenomena. At best, if they are patient and careful, they can demonstrate that psi phenomena merely exist, but the causal mechanics and certain repeatability of it will elude them. Their attempt to describe a phenomenon belonging to a **more general** and **less constrained** causality in terms of a **less general** and **more constrained** causality is futile. The Big Picture and Big Reality cannot be fully contained within the little picture – quite the contrary, the little picture and little reality must be a subset of the larger reality. This is **not** rocket science. The little limited one must be a subset of the big unlimited one – it cannot be the other way around.

Requiring the Big Picture reality to be described exclusively in terms of a local little picture reality is an incredibly dumb idea – Moe, Larry, and Curly understood that much. However, it is an amusing fact that many of the world's scientists are totally stumped by this trivial concept. If they can not **physically** define and control consciousness and psi effects, then neither can be verified to exist as an independent entity or real phenomenon. Consciousness is seen as a hallucination of physical biochemical processes while psi effects are seen as a hallucination of psychological processes. By believing that what is real is delusional, and that what is delusional is real, scientists have boxed themselves into a small corner of reality that does not contain the answers they are looking for. Worse yet, their standard definition of an unscientific fool is anyone who does not share their mystical belief in the sacred One Physical Reality. Some things never change. Hey, look on the bright side; at least physicians are no longer bleeding us with leaches.

PMR science will always fail to explain **nonphysical** phenomena as **physical** phenomena. Psi phenomena, from the PMR-only viewpoint, will never be sufficiently well behaved nor deeply understood, thus generating much uncertainty in the minds of the masses. The mystery of how or why psi works (or even the existence of psi effects for that matter) appears to remain unsolved and unsolvable regardless of how many times it is thoroughly solved and demonstrated by knowledgeable individuals. If you are not one of those individuals, or involved with one, or do not know one well enough to fully trust their intelligence and integrity, you probably do not get it at the personal level of Big Truth. Without personal study and careful evaluated first-hand experience, those who are unable to maintain open minded skepticism are forced by their ego-needs to either believe in the actuality of paranormal events or to disbelieve in the actuality of paranormal events – both of which are illogical positions that produce a plethora of worthless unscientific blather.

The realness of psi effects must be personally experienced to be accepted or understood. Thus, sharing a piece of Big Picture knowledge or Big Truth (gained through the first hand experience of psi effects by psi researchers or anyone else) by publishing research papers, books, or using the mass media is totally useless and ineffective. The results of psi research that confirm the existence of psi effects will never be widely accepted or **believed**, irrespective of how carefully and professionally the experiment was conducted, because **believing** such results directly conflicts with other **beliefs** more deeply held. On the other hand, when scientifically evaluated psi effects are part of your **personal** experience (especially where you are the actor, not the observer), then a larger reality is no longer a matter of belief and you know the truth even if you do not understand the mechanism behind the truth.

Those who are ready to progress to the next level of being will somehow discover the truth, while those who are not ready will remain clueless until some growth experience opens their mind to the possibilities. One cannot develop a deep personal understanding from somebody else's research or from somebody else's experience. This particular learning process is **not** primarily intellectual, like learning calculus; it is more experiential, like a one year old child learning to walk.

Much of the uncertainty clouding psi effects is the result of belief traps retarding the evolution of consciousness within OS. As long as conscious awareness and quality remain dim and low respectively, psi effects will remain shrouded in uncertainty, mysterious, and without credibility. As the quality of consciousness grows and awareness brightens across our culture, the purposeful application of psi effects will step out of the shadows and take their rightful place alongside contemplation, complex verbal and symbolic communications, and tool-making as innate human capabilities.

If a PMR scientist is looking at the result of someone else's positive measured experimental psi results, and has not done the work himself, he can **imagine** all sorts of uncertainties into the experiment and easily dismiss the results as sloppy science. Thus it is relatively easy for him to maintain the belief that his little picture (PMR-only) remains intact (the no-growth, no-stress, no-thought option). He is not burdened by the facts, nor does he have to be, because the impossibility of the stated results is a given while the potential uncertainty surrounding the results looms large in his own assumption-driven scientific mind.

A large uncertainty matched to an untenable result immediately leads to a strong conviction in favor of sustaining the little picture belief and ridiculing the apparently sloppy pseudo-science and ineptitude that produced the positive measured psi result in the first place. Although one scientist has adequately and scientifically proved, within reasonable certainty, the existence of some psi effect, there will be no impact on the scientific community. The existence of a broader reality will only become apparent to the few directly associated with the experiment.

Merely proving, beyond the shadow of a doubt, the existence of some singular, difficult to repeat, uncertain, and mysterious psi phenomena out on the fringe of respectability is not enough to impact the opinion of anyone in the rational center. Even if a psi researcher started his career from the center of accepted science, he would soon be relegated to the fringe, with perhaps no way to get back into the respectable center. Who needs those kinds of career killing associations? Is it any wonder that scientists shun psi research like the plague? Do you see why those who have the courage and gumption to undertake psi research are not taken very seriously by anyone outside their own fraternity unless they pretend to know much **less** than they actually know?

All problems of science and knowledge (philosophy, ontology, epistemology, cosmology, and physics) do not necessarily have technical or hard solutions – some can be comprehended only by an experienced mind with a larger perspective. That is another fact of existence that you simply have to live with. Cheer-up, particularly you hard-science types: The situation is not as hopeless as it appears. Soft solutions, though inaccessible to a random simultaneous hard-science group-proof, can be real, scientific, productive, repeatable solutions with objective and measurable **results**. Yes they can – you just don't know how yet.

You do not need to do an about-face relative to what your mother told you about life and what you learned in school. Simply open up the blinders a little to allow in a larger set of possibilities, and continue in more or less the same direction. *My Big TOE* and I want to expand your world, not blow it up – we are showing you a bigger picture that contains your familiar little picture as a sub-set. Relax, take a deep breath: You are not sinking into quicksand. That sucking sound coming from around your ankles is your fear trying to maintain its grip and hold you back. It takes courage to step out of the box by yourself, dear reader, it takes courage!

A device or technology solution (such devices do exist) that threw someone's sentient consciousness into NPMR would simply leave that person a temporary stranger in a strange land. Their ego or mind or rational-self immediately upon return would most likely deny the reality and validity of the experience. Without an open mind, and concomitant spiritual growth (elimination of fear, ego, and material attachments, as well as the mastery of mental energy), the technical solution is totally useless.

Likewise, a demonstrations of genuine psi phenomena to the average person (be they scientists or not) would be of little value beyond the theatrical and gee-whiz effect (unless this average person were the advantaged subject of the demonstration – it dissolved **his** tumor, solved **his** problem). He might change his beliefs if he were a witness or were personally involved (if he were teleported to China and left to come home on his own, for example). But so what: His **beliefs** are **not** important! It is his usable knowledge, his state (quality) of being, his spiritual evolution that **is** important – and none of these important things would be affected.

The larger world will not believe him (that he had been teleported to China) and he will be considered an unreliable insider with an overactive (delusional) imagination unless he denies his experience. Absolutely nothing important or productive would be accomplished by affording this person such an experience. If loss of credibility, denial, confusion, paranoia, or assumed mental dysfunction were the outcome, he may have been done significant harm.

Wisdom says, do not demonstrate psi effects – they can achieve no significant result within the Big Picture, may actually do some harm, and have only entertainment value. On the other hand, if one wishes to be an entertainer, psi is a cool tool until ego diminishes its power.

The function of the psi uncertainty principle is not to deny the existence of psi – the reality of psi effects is absolutely certain to anyone who cares enough to discover them for himself. Those who do not know that psi effects are real are merely ignorant (or in denial) of information which is widely available and of personal experience which is relatively easy to obtain (see Chapter 21, Book 1 for several references). Some serious effort and a little research can solve that problem. As long as belief-blinded individuals and a belief-blinded culture demand that **nonphysical** phenomenon be described in terms of **physical** causality, psi effects will remain cloaked in uncertainty, difficult to study, without credibility, and relegated to the fringe of human activity.

The psi uncertainty principle – a **natural** artifact of the interface between the nonphysical and physical – primarily masks the causal mechanics and denies the efficacy and perfect repeatability of psi effects. While psi effects break, escape, frustrate, and void the PMR sacred causal chain, the psi uncertainty principle clouds that breakage enough to allow the center of thought within the PMR learning lab to maintain the illusion of the exclusiveness of little picture causality, an illusion that is necessary to optimize individual growth potential within PMR. Providing an individual with access to too much interactive power and capability before he is able to handle it wisely is always counterproductive if not dangerous. Power of mind is gained naturally and usefully as the entropy of an individual consciousness is reduced.

If you need a reality check concerning the overall quality of consciousness among humans, watch the evening news or read a newspaper: There will be absolutely no doubt about the general level of unconditional love, awareness, mental entropy, consciousness quality, fear, ego, wants, desires, expectations, and needs that are loose in the land. From month to month and year to year, the news stories (from a bigger picture view) are all basically the same. Only the names of the victims and perpetrators are changed from day to day to protect the innocent from noticing the utter repetitive consistency that clearly points an accusing finger at the quality of the individuals who make up our culture. Whether we are in the news or not, we are all fine examples of, and proud participants in, our culture – a good case, if there ever was one, for finding the innocent guilty by association.

Living in your culture and not being of it is exceptionally difficult. We are it, it is us – all are integrally connected. Like it or not, we are undeniably part of the problem. Fortunately, we also have the **potential** to be part of the solution. The good news is that by developing the quality of our consciousness, we can become a much smaller part of the problem and a much larger part of the solution.

Given the elementary level at which the PMR learning lab is designed to function, the psi uncertainty principle is, by itself, enough to ensure that the PMR learning lab experience is uniformly direct, straight forward, simplistic, safe, and user friendly for beginners in the consciousness evolution process. In general, though there are some exceptions, serious paranormal ability must be gained through a significant decrease in the entropy of your consciousness.

To move beyond superficial paranormal energy manipulations, you must actively and purposely improve the quality of your consciousness. It is not a matter of technique, magical incantation, or allying yourself with powerful entities: Understanding, wisdom, and paranormal ability must be earned through your personal spiritual growth.

For the most part, consciousness evolution takes place within a self-balancing, self-policing system. Pre-schoolers are never given power tools or guns to work and play with. Access is normally available only to those who have earned it and can profitably use it. In Section 5, we will see how the psi uncertainty principle interacts with future possible and probable reality surfaces to enable you to affect the probability that a given future possibility will or will not actualize into our physical reality.

The source and scientific nature of the law of psi uncertainty is no different from the source and scientific nature of the law of gravitation; both are simply the natural results of the space-time rule-set. Both are reflections of the constraints placed upon a consciousness in order to define a virtual-reality learning-lab (PMR) for the purpose of evolving that consciousness. Psi effects and the psi uncertainty principle are no more mystical or arbitrary than gravitation. Their application, mechanics and interactions are as understandable, regular, and predictable as the orbits of the planets about the sun.

The ability to effect and control a broad spectrum of paranormal events is available to everyone who is willing to grow the quality of their consciousness sufficiently. However, psi ability should never be your end goal – if it is, your capability to manipulate the physical through the nonphysical will be severely self-limited and perhaps even self-destructive. Psi power should be seen as nothing more than a collateral benefit of an effective path well traveled – it becomes naturally available as your Big Picture understanding deepens. As your capability increases, your interest in wielding it decreases because you discover that you have everything you need without it. Additionally, you learn that the desire to acquire and use paranormal power often brings out the worst in those who would like to be powerful but have not earned it. It sensationalizes and trivializes the pursuit of quality in consciousness. It can be a great educational tool, a valuable device for helping others in special circumstances, as well as an ego tickler that quickly becomes an enormous distracter of spiritual value and focus. Forget about using someone else's paranormal power to obtain some information or effect that you want – it won't work, that shortcut will turn out to be a dead end. You have everything you need inside of you.

14

■■■

A Closer Look at Psi Phenomena, NPMR, and You

■■■

There is no "now you see it, and now you don't" hocus-pocus here – it only appears that way from the limited vision of a PMR-only perspective. At a higher level of awareness, psi and psi-uncertainty are straightforward scientific concepts subservient to a higher level of causality.

We no longer believe that the sun and moon are pulled through the heavens by angels (a one time very serious and popular theory strongly supported by the best and brightest of the Western scientific, philosophical, and theological establishments). Similarly, we must not jump to the conclusion that the psi-uncertainty principle is enforced by nonphysical entities pulling strings from the NPMR background. Such simplistic, anthropomorphically driven concepts serve only to compound the original ignorance.

It seems that whenever we humans are confronted by our ignorance in a grand manner that cannot be denied, we tend to extrapolate a super-stretched version of our old paradigms into an obvious solution that is supportive of the status quo. For a less obvious, but still troubling, ignorance, we often turn to spooky science or faith-based solutions or simply deny that the data, which demonstrate our ignorance, are real. Such circular belief-based logic creates its own intellectual whirlpool.

Today, we are greatly amused by the idea of angels moving the heavenly bodies around – I mean, really, how could those people be soooo stupid!? Actually, they were not stupid at all; they had about the same mental capacity that we have. They merely covered over their ignorance with theories that were in consonance with their personal, scientific, religious, and cultural beliefs – exactly as we do. Before feeling too smug about the silliness of planet-toting angels, you should know that modern science and philosophy use the exact same devices, with the exact same zeal, to deal with today's challenges to the core belief systems of our culture.

Many years from now **our** present belief-limited science, philosophy, and theology will provide future generations with good cause to shake their heads and snicker with astonished amusement, "I mean, really, how could those people be soooo stupid!?" Inevitably, our present notions of science and significance are one day going to look incredibly silly – perhaps within this century. It is one of our greatest conceits to **believe** that we could not possibly be **that** ignorant and **that** out of touch with reality – we are, after all, exceptionally smart and advanced, you know.

▶ "Ignorance? No way! Not us! Our Western science has clearly demonstrated brilliance and unparalleled achievement during the previous century. We finally understand how the natural world works. You must be referring to those belief-based touchy-feely folks in the third world. They remain largely ignorant, but eventually we will either need to bring them up to our level of understanding or take care of them. Subduing, educating, maintaining, or eliminating entire cultures of perpetual children may seem to be a thankless task, but it is our evolutionary responsibility – our inevitable burden to bear."

"I believe that self-imposed belief-based limitations do not exist, much less that they will eventually make us look unbelievably stupid to future generations. Impossible! Utterly impossible! As a species, we have become incredibly smart and scientifically advanced – everyone knows that. You must be stupid if you don't know that."

"I am sure that you are fully aware that we, of Western culture, now know, or almost know, everything that is significant. There are only a few fundamental details still missing – and our brilliant scientists are working on those, even as slackers like yourself waste their time reading books such as this one. It won't be long, a few generations at most, and we will have all the important information under our control. Jeez, won't life be great then – you know, after science has eliminated all our problems. Wow! I can hardly wait! We are so close....so close ...yet ... today, as I listen to the nightly news, scientific progress somehow seems almost irrelevant...and so far away."

The general attitudes and beliefs expressed above are both current and ancient. People have felt like this since history has been recorded. And they will, most likely, continue to feel this way for a very long time to come. Does one or more of the preceding three paragraphs roughly represent your core beliefs? Dig deep and be honest.

Have you ever noticed how insecurity, ignorance, arrogance, and ego often team up to play a particularly ugly joke? And that the joke always turns out to be at your expense? ◀

Most of us can think of at least a dozen or more instances (personal and historical) where we humans have created acceptable (at the time) explanations by over-stretching old paradigms until gaping holes appear that must be ignored. We have ascribed mysterious effects to angels, devils, other spooks, spooky science, and employed many other nonspecific metaphors for action-at-a-distance and invisible meddlers. The easiest and most effective explanation of all is to simply deny that conflicting data exist. These are a few of the standard devices that we humans have used to deal with our ignorance and reduce our fear of the unknown. We use them no less today in our private and public lives – they make us feel more in control and provide us with the means of controlling others. Concocting comfortable solutions that maintain the integrity of our belief systems is always more acceptable to most of us than admitting ignorance and then open mindedly and skeptically **living with that ignorance** until either new paradigms or new data show up.

Living gracefully with the unknown is a simple and natural process in the absence of fear. However, given a widespread fear of the unknown and of new paradigms, it is no wonder that many have found, and continue to find, it easy and convenient to manipulate these deep seated bone-level fears (more subconscious than conscious in Freudian terminology) in order to control the energy, actions, and resources of others. Our fear and ego provide ready handles that others can use to position us to their own liking.

There are many devices you can use to deny your experience. The most obvious is to simply ignore it, to claim (believe) that you were tricked (blame others – conspiracies are always in fashion), or that you are suffering from temporary insanity or some other mental dysfunction. If religious, you may blame your experience on witchcraft or the devil, or perhaps if there is a little paranoia lurking in your makeup, you may explain your experience as the result of some diabolically clever hypnotic manipulation, or believe that drugs must have been surreptitiously dropped into your morning coffee. When it comes to justifying what you want (or need) to **believe** (pro or con), your creativity and induced myopia can rise to meet any challenge. That is the nature of the ego. It is also the origins of most, if not all, belief.

There is no point in demonstrating psi effects – the gee-whiz effect exhibited by those in direct participation (who do not invent a way to discount or deny the experience) is useless. The same is more or less true of natural psi experiences such as the precognitive dreams or telepathic communications that hundreds of millions of people have experienced. Generally these experiences lead nowhere and are not particularly important in PMR. However, they often serve as a catalyst to pry open a mind far enough for it to glimpse a larger reality or light a fire of inquisitiveness and can be immensely valuable to an individual ready to take the next step.

An individual not ready to take the next step does not usually have these experiences. Where is the value in causing people to have experiences that they are not ready to profit from? Doing so generally causes more stress and confusion than enlightenment and in the end, usually reduces the credibility of Big Truth rather than enhancing it. Real evolutionary progress, real improvement in your quality of consciousness, must come from the inside out.

Following our discussion about the relationship between psi phenomena and uncertainty, it would seem far **easier** to teleport someone to China and back again (rather than leave them there) because of the larger uncertainty involved in proving the teleportation. It would be easier yet if they returned with nothing but their memory of the trip, their experience. Even if they returned with a handful of souvenirs for evidence, others would think it very easy for them to have bought the souvenirs at the local import shop or rigged the evidence by some other means. They would be generally seen as liars or delusional – that much would be obvious.

The evidence would only be valid evidence to them – and perhaps a few others who **trust** them totally and implicitly. They would have a choice. They could be a delusional nut in the eyes of almost everyone, though secure in their knowledge of the truth or believe themselves to be a delusional nut by denying that their experience was actually real experience (plead insanity). The Path of Knowledge is not for the easily influenced and impressionable, the intellectually timid, the fearful, or the insecure. People with these traits will tend to remain uncertain and confused and are easy prey for New-Age charlatans, as well as the well intentioned but unknowingly ignorant. A warrior's strong mind, focused intent, and fearless attitude combined with a scientist's patient probing, high analytical standards, and fundamental inquisitiveness is required for optimal results.

How is your progress and sanity to be judged if you follow the warrior's Path of Knowledge? Pragmatically and objectively – by looking at the results. Check to see if your knowledge and psi experiences (teleporting, healing, traveling, remote viewing, or communicating telepathically with either physical or nonphysical beings) are meaningful and significant (in the Big Picture) to yourself and to others. Determine if your understanding of the Big Picture produces consistent measurable results in terms of the quality of your consciousness and the depth of your perception of the larger reality (including the physical). Your spiritual growth, and your ability to help others grow spiritually, should be obvious to, and **measurable** by, you and others. If not, what you are experiencing is delusional.

You will unquestionably and unambiguously know if you are truly knowledgeable, kind, humble, compassionate, helpful, balanced, and focused on what you can contribute to others. If you are wise, understanding, considerate, insightful, thoughtful, and loving, you and everybody else will know that you are not insane. A highly evolved individual sticks out from the crowd like an elephant in a pea patch. These individuals are beloved and held in highest esteem by all who meet them – they have a gentle and highly effective power which is fearless.

Others who are not wise will know only if another individual **appears** to be wise, knowledgeable, kind, balanced, helpful, and not insane. You will know that you are not delusional if your capacity to love, to give, to exhibit humility and compassion in daily interactions is significantly increasing as your ego, fear and material attachments are significantly decreasing. The artifacts of spiritual growth are not esoteric or subtle.

If, on the other hand, your spiritual state is stagnating or non-existent (of low quality – ego driven) and you interact with people by manipulating or impressing them for material or ego ends, you are failing in your efforts to improve your quality even if you have convinced others of your success or have gained some limited control of psi effects.

The effects of reducing entropy in your consciousness will eventually become as obvious as being hit by a truck – you will have no difficulty telling the difference (growth or delusions of growth) about yourself **if** (a big if) you actually want to know the truth. Evaluating others can be more difficult than evaluating yourself, but the truth eventually yields to the same analysis – it is simply more difficult (sometimes) to gather the necessary data about someone else because of your limited understanding of their motivations.

If you have never experienced significant progress in lowering the entropy of your consciousness, you may have no idea what I mean or that what I am saying makes sense. I am trying to communicate the results of my experience clearly, but I know it is extremely difficult for anyone to understand in a deep, profound, or personal way without similar experience of his or her own.

If a spiritual teacher's interactions with others are more accurately described as "marketing" than actually helping people significantly change their life by enhancing their opportunities for spiritual growth, then the description "delusional nut with delusional or naive insiders" may be an accurate description of that teacher and his or her followers regardless of how real their paranormal experiences are.

How do you evaluate others? When looking in from the outside, one without wisdom can typically not tell the difference between the wise and those who are merely marketing themselves cleverly. You need to get involved and you need to participate. How do you separate the true from the false? You must personally experience the larger reality. You must build your knowledge of your dynamic (changing and growing) spiritual being and trust your ability to figure out what is valuable to you and profitable for you.

You must grow your own wisdom. Only then can you judge what holds great value, truth, and knowledge for you (progresses you toward your spiritual goals) and what is a waste of your time, or worse, a step backwards. Thus, the proof of the pudding is in the tasting. Personal truth flows only from personal experience. All Big Truth and wisdom is personal truth. Those who judge (the metaphorical pudding) from the outside, **without** tasting, **without** personal experience, (typically emotionally driven – by fear, ignorance, and discomfort – at worst vitriolic scoffers and virulent closed-minded skeptics) are the most obviously delusional of all, like the emperor in his very respectable, socially acceptable new clothes. The difference being, in this particular situation, that the emperor and his most loyal subjects all use the same highly recommended tailor.

There is a requirement for uncertainty to surround nonphysical to physical manifestations. **Because of the psi uncertainty principle, you are required to gain real knowledge of NPMR through only your personal experience and growth.** Thus the psi uncertainty principle is a fundamental requirement of all virtual PMR space-time learning labs. The constraint of psi uncertainty is not a punitive restriction imposed upon you because you flunked the last quality test, but rather a designed-in feature of your local reality that provides you with an optimal opportunity to lower your entropy. Do not struggle against psi uncertainty, try to get around it, or wish it were otherwise – you need it to accomplish your mission efficiently. If you did not, it would melt away.

Big Truth is not something that someone else can make you understand, even if they show you paranormal events all day long. You can learn facts about it from others and choose to **believe** it or not. However, to have real knowledge, to use that knowledge as a catalyst for the evolution of your being, to improve the quality and decrease the entropy of your consciousness, requires **you** to get involved and gain your knowledge through your experience, experimentation, and spiritual growth. **There is no easier way**.

You have to do it; no one can do it for you. You cannot escape, or circumvent universal truth or fundamental principles – you can ignore them, but only at the cost of personal progress and opportunities lost.

The requirements for spiritual growth on the Path of Knowledge and the requirements for awareness and functionality in NPMR are similar and related. It is the dropping of ego and material attachment that produces the high signal to noise ratios required for being sentient in NPMR – see Chapter 4, Book 3). Spiritual knowledge and paranormal ability do not have to occur together (making that connection depends on your interest, focus, and intent) but on the Path of Knowledge, they often are intertwined. On the Paths of Service and Surrender, paranormal abilities may or may not be encountered. Spiritual knowledge and paranormal ability are not opposite sides of the same coin, but rather mutually supportive and strongly related activities. Paranormal ability is an **available** byproduct of the Path of Knowledge that you can choose to ignore.

> ▶ Though quality consciousness and paranormal abilities often occur together like families and children, they are not logically dependent on each other and though normally related, each can exist separately. For the sake of completeness, it should be mentioned there are other less consistent and less controllable ways to gain a specific (as opposed to general access to all) paranormal ability but these are not directly on the path to Big TOE understanding and consequently will not be discussed. ◀

Focusing on, or being attached to, paranormal abilities will halt, retard, or degenerate spiritual progress as well as degrade the abilities themselves. Thus, the potential for great misuse is self-correcting as is an interest in doing paranormal demonstrations or tricks for science or curious individuals. It is not only a waste of time (as described previously), but is also self-limiting – a drag on your energy and personal progress. A good performer (accurate and consistent) may perform only on his own terms (which may or may not require uncertainty) and may not stay a good performer (or remain interested) for long. A marginally interested subject makes it difficult for the experimenter to produce the precision, consistency, and repeatability required by objective science. Exceptions exist to this rule of diminishing returns in parapsychological experiments, but they are rare.

A difficult to manage psi-performer is not necessarily covering up a lack of ability with demanding crankiness. Experimenters create a difficult situation for everyone by requiring nonphysical phenomena to be (behave as) physical phenomena. Trying to trap nonphysical phenomena in a physical bottle is problematical at best. Remember Curly and Larry trying to find and study the nonphysical with a physical microscope? That doesn't work.

Another related problem that makes our traditional scientific analysis of psi phenomena difficult to achieve is that demands of performance (repeatable and measurable as required by scientific methodology) tend to involve (tug at) the ego of the subject who wants (is willing) to demonstrate his or her ability. A desire or need to perform will usually increase the noise, which lowers signal-to-noise, which produces a failure to perform – psychological psi-impotence. Thus, the best performers (perhaps the only great performers) are those not particularly interested in performing, or those unwilling to perform. Again, exceptions to this rule of uncooperative competency may exist from time to time, but they are rare.

You might become an advanced scientist by reading and studying books, but do not expect to develop an advanced consciousness (become spiritually adept) by studying books or hanging out with a spiritual master: You have to be it, live it, experience it, and subjectively interact with it. There is no easy process, short cut, or technical solution. PMR actions alone (studying psi phenomena, following meditation techniques, reading books, believing anything) will not open NPMR to you unless you experience spiritual growth and decrease the entropy of your consciousness. And if you try in your mind (like a Flatlander) to force NPMR to conform to the form, function, and properties of PMR (science, or philosophy, or 3D space-time reality), you will, like traditional contemporary scientists, be haplessly and hopelessly trying to force the proverbial NPMR camel through the eye of a PMR needle.

The experiences you need to grow the quality of your consciousness happen to you every day. What you need to learn to evolve your nonphysical being is not a secret that is hidden from your view. It is your effort, direction, and intention that determine how you utilize, embrace, or shun the available opportunities, experience, and information. Being open minded and willing to **personally** experiment as well as expend considerable effort is the **only** way to make serious progress along the Path of Knowledge. Because personal experimentation is often subjective (not the stuff group-science is **traditionally** made of), it requires a commitment to continue working and learning until you have developed enough knowledge and understanding to produce objective results that can be validated. Substantial progress requires a substantial commitment – like the commitment it takes to get through college and graduate school along with the commitment required to become an accomplished musician. Everybody **can** do it, but not everybody **will** do it.

▶ I think at this point it might be useful for you to develop a more concrete sense of NPMR. This short aside will offer a description of $NPMR_N$ and its inhabitants that may help you see NPMR within a broader more solid perspective.

Life forms in $NPMR_N$ seem to be much more varied and abundant than they are in PMR. Not all entities inhabiting $NPMR_N$ are sentient – some are elemental. The good, the bad, and the ugly – and the beautiful – all exist there. There is violence and peace, rip-offs and gifts. You can get hurt (self-inflicted or by the actions of others) or even killed, though it is very unlikely – there are strict rules regulating violence. Death is by disassociation or the loss of your internal organization. Your identity is dissolved if your energy is reduced to a maximum entropy state approximating the final state predicted by the second law of thermodynamics. Think of degaussing a floppy disk.

Death of an entity is exceedingly rare. If it should happen to you, you would cease to exist in that particular dimensioned reality as well as in other related realities – your defining code and memory, once hopelessly scrambled, is deleted from the simulation. Your current individuated consciousness is held as part of a historical record (last saved file), but you are no longer part of an active actualizing interactive reality; you no longer evolve within that reality, you are gone. You could theoretically be reconstituted from the historical record, but I have never seen that happen and suspect that it is rarer than rare. It would be the Big Cheese's call and entirely dependent upon the circumstances of your demise. There are only a few circumstances where rats and anti-rats are allowed (by the rules) to destroy each other permanently.

Unfortunately, sometimes NPMR rules are broken just as the laws of your state and nation are sometimes broken in PMR. Rule-breakers are sometimes caught and must pay the price, and sometimes they get away with it. As far as I know, only the Big Cheese can execute a capitol punishment for specific offenses. There are no lawyers, you plead your own case – all your actions and motivations are transparent. Every action and event (information or energy transfer) is stored in memory and consequently, exactly **what** happened and **why** it happened is always available for post-event analysis. The truth cannot be effectively hidden; lies are always counterproductive.

Other NPMRs are generally not as structured, peaceable, friendly, productive, or safe as $NPMR_N$. In $NPMR_N$ there are lots of parasites, males, females, neuters, bullies, and social workers – there is unnatural death and employment, but no natural death or taxes. No one grows old – only more or less knowledgeable, powerful, loving, caring, balanced, compassionate, humble, wise, fearful, needy, greedy, violent, vicious, egotistical, controlling, or manipulative.

Among sentient beings, there is a much greater range in quality than there is in PMR. Beings and other objects in $NPMR_N$ are individuated consciousness energy and have associated bodies or forms of various shapes, and sizes. The experiential perception of these nonphysical bodies is defined by the rule-set that lays down the laws of being and interaction within NPMR (NPMR physics). For example, within one sensory view (one specific query of a subset of the NPMR database within TBC) of the non-physical parts of physical beings and objects, there are variations in **apparent** densities of forms. Denser is associated with dimmer awareness, higher entropy, and higher ego and fear content.

From a different sensory view (different query filter applied to the same subset of the NPMR database), denser indicates a higher probability of being manifested or maintaining manifestation within the physical. Within this view (primarily working with the subset of data that describes and specifies the transition region between the nonphysical and physical), the denser the energy **appears**, the more solid the object seems to be. More nonphysical "m" requires, or stores, more potential nonphysical "E" (as in $E = mc^2$) and requires more Force (focused mental energy with intent) to modify its present state relative to its extant dimensional container (as in $F = ma$).

In other words, sharply focused mental energy applied by intent (F) can modify the inertia, density, coherence or persistence (m) of a thought-form by constraining the dimension in which it can be extant as a function of time. In PMR, our dimensional container is space-time as defined by the space-time rule-set, thus "F" modifies the existence of "m" by constraining (defining) its 3D position as a function of time to a particular set of values. The two equations in the previous paragraph represent two rules within our PMR's space-time rule-set that provide a rough idea of the more general rules that apply within NPMR. In both realities, inducing change is a force meets inertia (resistance to change) type of phenomenon.

The visual appearances of nonphysical mass, delineated bodies, and various energy densities and probability densities within NPMR are the results and consequences of the NPMR rule-set which defines causality in NPMR and the particular way the viewer interprets the information received. As in PMR, it takes effort and training to ensure that one's personal interpretation of the data (experience) is not biased, is independent of collection methodology, is not an artifact of limited awareness, and does not modify the content of the data. The form of the data (how the data are internalized into personal experience) is subject to individual interpretation and therefore not particularly important. The content, message, or meaning of the data, however, is the same for everyone with a clear unbiased mental connection. Big Truth is universal; one's experience of it is always personal.

Uh oh, why is everybody yawning and getting up to go get a snack at the same time? All right, I promise, no more technoid blather about forces and inertia – let's get back to basics. You are out cruising NPMR and see a visual representation of a subset of non-physical matter that is attached to, or a part of, a particular physical PMR entity. If this nonphysical matter-energy-data-thing has the **appearance** within NPMR of greater density it would mean it has a higher expectation value (less uncertainty) of manifesting as part of that PMR physical entity.

A specific example might help. If the nonphysical aspects of a brain tumor appear to be very dense, that tumor either has, or is in the process of, manifesting physically. The greater the apparent energy density of a nonphysical entity (incipient tumor), the more energy per unit time that is required to significantly affect or modify the expectation of that object manifesting into physical reality. Again, tumors that appear very dense when viewed from a nonphysical perspective have a higher probability of being actualized in PMR and are much more difficult (require more energy) to dissipate.

Why would anyone want to dissipate the nonphysical part of a physical or pre-physical tumor? In Section 4 we will discover that physical reality is a secondary manifestation wholly dependent upon its primary nonphysical source. The implication is that tumors dissipated within the nonphysical will automatically dissipate within the physical as well. Having said that let me also say that meddling with the natural results of the PMR learning lab (purposely modifying expectation values) is not always a good thing. The application of great power must be tempered with great wisdom.

Think of the apparent density of nonphysical energy as having the combined qualitative properties of persistence and inertia – staying power, resistance to change, heaviness, and the ability to survive and persist under the duress of external forces.

Within realities where energy appears most dense (the PMR_k) is where change is relatively slow, steady, and smooth; existence is relatively simple, basic, and stable; and interactions between sentient beings are relatively inelastic, viscous and sticky.

This description of the nonphysical matter or nonphysical mass that visually appears to define the boundaries and make up the bodies of all entities (sentient and non-sentient) in terms of energy density, persistence, and inertia is greatly simplified. I am describing only a minute piece of the perception mechanisms available within NPMR – the set of queries and filters that can be applied to the data within TBC and EBC. What we are talking about is a rule-set that defines the properties, quality, and limitations of our perception of the interactions of beings and objects with other beings and objects within NPMR. These are rules that define how we perceive the possible record-sets that are the result of our query, as well as rules that define the properties, form, and content limitations of transferable information and that define the allowable energy transfers (interactions) between players.

The "different views" that I spoke of above are like looking at the same body or body part with the unaided eyes, an X-ray, a CAT scan, a thermogram, or a sonogram. Each view requires its own skilled interpretation before data can be converted to useful information. It is even more like looking at the same database through several different query filters.

Trying to view or understand a more general system from the perspective of a highly constrained less general subset of that system is always as difficult as it is easy to do the opposite. Fully gaining the broader perspective of a low-entropy consciousness within NPMR makes understanding and optimizing the experience of PMR almost trivial. To such a consciousness, life in PMR becomes transparent and simple, rewarding and fun, productive and meaningful. The amazing maze becomes a wonderfully exciting and fun challenge that becomes easier and easier as it delivers an endless supply of exquisite cheese.

I know that much of what I have described is next to impossible for many to understand because it is not possible to have a sense of the specifics of what I am talking about without direct first-hand experience in NPMR. Nevertheless, even if you have no direct experience of NPMR, I am hopeful that you will capture a flavor, an idea, an intuitive sense of what interactions within NPMR are like. They are similar to interactions in PMR, but with a wider, less limited access to information and a different set of social and physical rules (international law, local law, and physics). That's all. ◀

In order to build new concepts, there is no other construction methodology except stretching existing concepts and metaphors beyond their current use – beyond their common applicability. That is why transcending paradigms is exceptionally difficult. You must, by definition, start with inadequate conceptual tools for the job and somehow develop the necessary perspective that necessarily lies beyond simple linear extrapolation. You must combine a creative synthesis of old ideas with inspired intuition to find a new paradigm, which is nothing less than a new, more complete, more functional, bigger picture of reality – a more profitable organization of the available data.

To get a glimmer of understanding of NPMR science, you need a more general concept of mass than most of us are used to. I realize that nonphysical mass sounds both oxymoronic and just plain moronic, but it conveys the qualitative sense of what I am trying to explain better than any other words I can think of. For example, this concept implies that physical bodies exhibit a greater inertia or resistance to energetic (mental energy directed by conscious intent) change than nonphysical bodies. It also implies that this fact is the result of how the various rule-sets define and constrain the interactions of consciousness within and between each reality subset or dimension. Think of rule-sets as data filters that define your energetic interaction with the data. You may have read privileges only, or be allowed to read, write, and modify.

For those with no first hand experience in NPMR, no experience with database queries, and have long forgotten basic physics, what I explained above will no doubt seem vague, arcane, and hopelessly opaque. I also know that most readers are drifting along in a similar lack-of-NPMR-experience boat. Not to worry, you are not hopelessly lost: All I want you to take away from this discussion is a sense that NPMR, like PMR, is a structured, rule-based, objective, causal reality and that its physics is a superset of PMR physics.

I want you to get at least a vague sense that the rules, and the beings, objects, and energy that must obey those rules in NPMR are similar to those in PMR but more general (more things are allowed, the evolutionary process has more degrees of freedom, and the possibilities of existence in the form of individuated consciousness are less constrained). In Section 4, rule-sets, and how they define the experience we perceive as reality (both physical and nonphysical), are discussed in detail.

I think you get the picture: We apparently physical beings are very dense – without a doubt, we are among the densest beings within $NPMR_N$! That sense of the word "dense" fits like a glove doesn't it?

Let's take a short break. I need to speak with the technical types for a moment; the rest can skip this aside and wait for us at its end – we will catch up with you there.

All right, the left-brainers in the reading audience need to come on over here – we need to talk.

▶ I understand from my undercover sources that some of the techies feel as though they have been left holding a bag full of unanswered questions. I am aware that my discussion has been quick and shallow. This is because I have purposely omitted much of the breadth as well as the detail that you detail-types love to get your teeth into. This trilogy is not the place for that level of detail – it is already very long, places a considerable strain on a reasonable attention span, and is seriously challenged to keep you focused on the logical unfolding of core concepts. Too much detail too soon is almost always counterproductive.

Recall that physical science books (basic physics for non-techies) that discuss ballistic trajectory dynamics will purposely neglect to mention atmospheric interactions (air friction or temperature and density variations), non-uniform gravitation, Coriolis effects, and ballistic dispersion because only a few people at the introductory level want to know that much about it or have the background to understand what the issues are. How and why these more precise considerations more accurately describe reality is not of interest. Most would much rather get the basic low fidelity concepts so that they can approximately understand the major concepts without being subjected to the boring particulars that are left to the boring specialists. Nothing personal; that is simply how the majority of right-brained non-technical people feel about it.

Scientifically and carefully exploring (experiencing) the larger reality of consciousness within the metaphysical disciplines of cosmology, ontology and epistemology is something that most readers are prepared to deal with (have the tools or experience to understand) only at the beginning or introductory level of explanation. Feeling that you could take a giant leap forward if you had a more detailed technical (mathematical) description of the physics of NPMR and the NPMR-PMR boundary is an error of misplaced emphasis and understanding. That is not where it's at.

Mathematical physics represents the logic (in symbolic form) of the little picture. We have shown repetitively that little picture understanding, logic, and causality cannot lead to Big Picture understanding, logic, and causality. Little picture logic can lead to a better understanding of only the little picture. You cannot pull an elephant out of an acorn, and you cannot logically derive the Big Picture from the little picture.

Remember Curly and Larry searching for the invisible nonphysical microscope? Metaphorically, the nonphysical microscope is your mind and equations cannot help you find it or evolve it. They may help you understand and manipulate NPMR, but putting that cart in front of your consciousness-quality horse will not get you anywhere. All would be better served if you focus on and achieved personal solutions before focusing on, and trying to achieve, technical ones.

First things first! Crawl… then walk… then run! I know that you want to run in the worst way because running is obviously superior to crawling or walking, but if you try to run before you are ready, you will simply fall flat on your face and probably come to the erroneous conclusion that running is impossible. That is a worse outcome than being frustrated because you are not able to run right now. Why? Because getting the horse far out in front of the cart by trying to run prematurely may permanently damage your ability to ever be ready to run.

"Hey, I tried it myself – running doesn't work! It's all a pile of horsepucky! It is not only impossible, but dangerous as well! People who say they can run are delusional, nuts, or egotists trying to impress everyone else! Beware! Don't listen to a word of it – trust me on this one, I have first hand experience – look at that black eye and bruised nose. I will never try to run again! Anybody who tries to run is either an idiot or a fool."

Eight-month-old humans sometimes feel like that but they keep trying because the success of others within their physical reality is eventually undeniable. On the other hand, intellectuals who are committed to justifying their cultural beliefs occasionally become champions of denial in order to convince themselves that their ignorance, rather than their belief, is the delusion.

Jeez, those belief traps are amazing – they can transmute simple ignorance and incompetence into blind stupidity in a flash. Now that we have spotted that trap and settled the bag of questions problem leading to it, let's join up with the others and get on with our exploration.

That is it for the heart to heart, techie-to-techie talk – take a deep breath and let it go. We are intentionally skimming across the top here; this is a survey course at the 101 level, not a post-doc dissertation. ◀

$NPMR_N$ is not a different place, separate from PMR. It is continuous, integrated, and one with PMR. PMR is a dependent subset of $NPMR_N$, and it exists in, with, and by $NPMR_N$. All beings in $NPMR_N$ are not space and time constrained – space and time are local constructs within PMR and are direct artifacts of the space-time rule-set. Every being in our PMR is extant in $NPMR_N$; the converse is not true. Though you live, operate and function in $NPMR_N$ as well as PMR, you may be unaware of it because of the constraints you place on the awareness of your consciousness.

The ramifications of a continuous interrelated reality structure between PMR and NPMR will be explored in Chapter 12, Book 3 where we discuss communications, time travel, teleportation, multiple bodies, getting along without your body, and a few other interesting subjects. These topics need to be deferred until later because we have not yet developed the conceptual base required for understanding them. Be patient: Many interesting things lie ahead of us in subsequent chapters. To get there too quickly is equivalent to not getting there at all.

15

■ ■ ■

Section 3 Postlude
Hail! Hearty Readers
Thou Art a Stout (Figuratively Only)
and Sturdy Bunch

■ ■ ■

By now you may be convinced that I enjoy torturing you, but that's not true. The nature of reality is an extremely complex subject which is difficult to grasp because it can be seen and understood only from a Big Picture perspective that must necessarily appear wild and crazy when compared to your familiar little picture. Big steps or leaps forward in understanding always have and always will seem wild and crazy when first encountered from the viewpoint of the old perspective which is, by definition, built upon a less expansive knowledge.

The revelations of modern Relativity and Quantum mechanics, the fact that solid physical matter is composed of atoms that are mostly empty space, and that our beloved earth is not at the center of the universe were all seen as ridiculous absurdities existing on the delusional fringe before they were accepted by the mainstream. **Successful** explorations of consciousness, mind, and the larger reality must by necessity seem similarly absurd because they will conflict with the traditional ways of thinking about and defining reality.

We humans, in general, know much less of what there is to know than we think we do. Given the depth and pervasiveness of the belief blindness that reflects the quality of our species at the dawn of the twenty-first century, if this Big TOE did not seem wild and was not difficult to understand, it could not possibly be correct.

Many people feel that Western culture is slowly growing up, opening its collective mind, becoming more able and willing to take the longer and broader view. Optimism and seeing ourselves through rose colored glasses are two of our most pervasive cultural traits. It is true that explorations of consciousness, mind, and the larger reality that remain strongly connected to our little picture belief systems have become somewhat more acceptable during the last thirty years. Unfortunately, the failure of such efforts to deliver profound insights has encouraged the commonly held belief that no solution exists and that a scientific **Big** TOE is impossible.

Significant theoretical progress seems unattainable, inaccessible, and forever beyond our reach because our thinking must be based upon traditional ways of defining reality in order to maintain at least marginal respectability and support from the center of power that dispenses research funds and credibility. Failure is assured by the requirement to use a proper, rational, and scientific exploration and analysis process which is, at its root, based upon the dogmatic belief that all reality must be physical. Under this handicap, researchers may easily prove that something truly strange is going on, but they will never figure out what or why. This recipe for failure resembles a resolute decision to look for your misplaced car keys or sun glasses only in places that you have never been.

Belief traps, dressed up as obvious truth, **always** make new Big Picture concepts struggle for credibility against the prevailing social, scientific, or religious currents of assumed rationality. That is simply how it is, and how it will continue to be, for a very long time.

When one is only a little fellow starting near the bottom of a long evolutionary ladder, as are most humans, Big Picture perspectives are difficult to come by. It is a designed-in feature of our larger reality that makes Big Truth appear to be an impenetrable mystery to the limited perspective of the average person, yet it is also a designed-in feature that a grand panoramic view of the whole is available to anyone who makes the effort to climb the mountain. Indeed, climbing the mountain is one gateway to the successful evolution and advancement of our individual being. For those wondering why opacity should be a designed-in feature, consider what your neighbors, coworkers, spouse, children, boss, mother, and mother-in-law might do to you if they knew how to manipulate you with their minds: It is better that they grow up first.

I salute your curiosity, intellectual determination, and toughness. I am thankful that you are tolerant and hardy enough to have made it this far. To get to this point you have suffered the ravages of rat-maze vertigo, ego deflation, belief trap withdrawal, and an annoying heart-to-heart talk from your Dutch uncle. You undoubtedly deserve to paste four more brightly glistening gold stars next to your name inside the front cover of this book.

Because my Big TOE is based upon a lifetime of personal experience and because it is very unusual, effectively communicating the perspective wherein that Big Picture makes sense to a broad range of individuals who may lack first hand experience of the larger reality is an immensely difficult job. I hope that I have successfully met at least some significant part of that challenge. Unfortunately, whatever I fail to meet inevitably becomes a challenge to you – something you must figure out for yourself.

Thanks for coming along on this trek; I hope you will continue on the journey with me through at least the next two Sections where the mechanics of NPMR and PMR are more fully explained. In Section 4 we will explain how we can have the cute and cuddly physical bodies that we love to indulge and at the same time be nothing other than consciousness. We will solve the mind-matter dichotomy and delve deeper into the nature of experience and the phenomenon of digital consciousness.

Along the way, we will demonstrate that PMR physics (our hard-headed little picture science) can be derived from the same two assumptions that we have used to construct this Big TOE. Showing that PMR physics is contained within, and can be derived from, *My Big TOE* is (from the PMR point of view) the one and only test a candidate TOE must pass to lay claim to the title of a true TOE. That is a fair and necessary test. A successful TOE must explain and contain PMR physics as well as paranormal phenomena, intuition, mind, time, and more. We will accomplish all of that before you reach the end of *My Big TOE*. The deriving of PMR physics is accomplished in Section 4 with a little help from our friends. Come on along for the tour through Section 4, and see how the individual concepts we have discussed thus far begin to pull together into a more rational and understandable whole.

Section 4

■ ■ ■

Solving the Mystery:
Mind, Matter, Energy,
and Experience

■ ■ ■

16

■ ■ ■

Introduction to Section 4

■ ■ ■

In this section we are going to examine the origins and circumstances of physical existence. I will explain how PMR, at its most fundamental level, is a product of consciousness and provide a clear understanding of the connection between mind and matter. By the time you reach Book 3, it will seem more logical and less strange that matter is an experience of mind and that physical existence is a virtual interactive experience designed to facilitate consciousness evolution.

A TOE, by definition, must explain all the facts that are known to exist as well as new facts that belong to a bigger, more complete picture. *My Big TOE* is no different. It must subsume all present knowledge including PMR science. As we all know, traditional science is nowhere close to producing a credible Big TOE that explains intuition, mind, consciousness, and the paranormal, as well as the normal physics of PMR. PMR scientists and their egos deal with their inability to see a bigger picture by denying the existence of what they cannot explain. Facts to the contrary are either ignored or attacked as an unacceptable heresy that offends the obviously correct **beliefs** of the current scientific establishment. There always seems to be a plentiful supply of self-righteous scientists who spare no venom in defense of the sacred dogmas of contemporary science. From their limited view, PMR science and truth are synonymous and define each other.

▶ Do you see the parallels here? The last four sentences in the preceding paragraph apply equally well to religion and culture as they do to science. That should not be so surprising: At the bottom level of their belief-based foundations, traditional science, culture, and religion share the same genetic material. That is why their members and their institutions exhibit many of the same individual and organizational traits. In the West, science and culture have made an alliance of mutual support, while in the Middle East and East, religion and culture have allied themselves. Together they provide a throne from which the human ego reigns supreme.

Discovering a more profitable bigger picture, as well as raising the average quality of the human spirit, is a job that necessarily is left entirely up to you. We the people remain **objectively** clueless because our awareness is far removed from an integrated holistic view of reality. We the people remain **subjectively** clueless because our belief systems forbid the truth. Having been artificially separated, our objective and subjective cluelessness feed and maintain each other. ◀

There are two conditions that a successful Big TOE must meet. First, a successful Big TOE cannot be logically inconsistent or conflict with known facts. It must explain and contain (be a super-set of) what is presently known. Second, a successful Big TOE must appear to be logically **inconsistent** and conflict with traditionally accepted **beliefs** and the opinions based upon those beliefs (pseudo-facts). It could not possibly be a correct Big TOE, or even a major step toward a new Big TOE, if it did not dramatically conflict with our limited little picture belief-based culture, science, and knowledge.

Because our traditional science believes that the little picture is all there is, it restricts its investigation of the Big Picture (epistemology, ontology, cosmology, quantum physics, evolution, metaphysics, physics, consciousness, mind, psi effects, and intuition) to little picture phenomena. Traditional science is placed in the hopeless role of expecting the Big Picture to be contained within, and be derivable from, the little picture. Looking to extract the Big Picture from the little picture is a totally illogical approach and will produce nothing but frustration and the **apparent** conformation that either the Big Picture does not exist or it is beyond objective knowing. This approach to reality is analogous to trying to ascertain the properties of the larger forest by interrogating the moss growing on a tree, or perhaps expecting to understand modern microprocessor design and manufacture by studying a chunk of raw silicon ore.

The door of your mind must be opened at least a crack before you are likely to notice the passageway to a more complete conscious awareness and step through it to investigate what lies on the other side. If you have the courage to seek the truth, the *My Big TOE* trilogy is meant to facilitate the opening of such a crack in the belief barrier constructed by the ego-mind. A primary goal of *My Big TOE* is to help you get your Big TOE, or perhaps your entire foot, wedged in your mind's door to prevent it from slamming closed before you are able to explore the true

nature of your consciousness. This is more difficult than it first appears because you are easily seduced by your cultural, scientific, religious, and personal beliefs to seek the habitual comfort and refuge in the safe bliss that ignorance creates. Delusion, like a drug addiction, is a habit that is difficult to break.

▶ You might think that separating fact from opinion is not difficult. We all think we know how to perform that operation reasonably well. Nevertheless, it is obvious that many people are not especially good at it – but we, you and I, truly know how to separate BS from truth. It is not that difficult because… well… we just know. We have been around the block a few times and are experienced and perceptive enough to know what is genuine and what isn't. Separating fact from fancy is intuitively obvious – our BS detectors are sensitive and finely tuned – we know how people think, what they want, and the games they play. It is difficult for anyone to pull anything over on us; we are not naïve or easy targets for New Age hustlers or status-quo promoting traditionalists.

Everybody feels like that, including teenagers. It is a pile of belief-trap-crap that you should be careful not to fall into. The reason that discriminating truth from falsity is extraordinarily difficult is: 1) you are unaware of what you don't know and 2) it is your ego's solemn job (remember, your intellect is a servant of the ego) to convince you that your belief-based pseudo-knowledge is actually real knowledge. Because of invisible ignorance, the needs, wants, and desires of a slick ego, and a self-justifying intellect, your apparently solid grasp of either Big Truth or little truth is likely to be delusional. There are exceptional people who see things clearly, but except for you and me, I don't know any of them. ◀

In a culture like ours where scientific, religious, and cultural beliefs forcefully constrain and dominate most intellectual effort and essentially define the boundaries of each individual's local reality, it is more difficult to think out of the box and to separate the facts from the beliefs and opinions that masquerade as facts than you might imagine.

Of the two conditions mentioned above that a successful Big TOE must meet, I have the second one (high strangeness) well in hand. In this Section, the remaining gaps in the first condition (containing PMR physics as a subset) will be addressed.

Ladies, gentlemen, and others, do not panic: I promise not to drag you through a physics class. I know that physics first overwhelms and then perhaps amazes you; then it annoys you and puts you into a deep sleep. This is not intended as a sleepy-time book. Trust me; you will be able to follow every detail without going back to school to pick up those boring science and math classes that you so cleverly avoided.

Deriving some of the basic rules or concepts of PMR physics from a consideration of the properties of consciousness reality cells has been accomplished – I have only to point to it, not drag you through it. I will, however, provide the understanding and structure (model) with which you can combine physics and metaphysics concepts into a fully integrated Big Picture.

Let's begin by formulating some of the most obvious questions. How does one explain our physical existence and our physical experience within PMR, especially if we are nothing other than a clever configuration of AUM's wholly nonphysical consciousness? How come we appear stuck in this little picture 3D space-time PMR with these cute-but-needy physical bodies? What is a nice Big Picture Free Will Awareness Unit (FWAU) like you doing in a little picture place like PMR?

Why is it that a critical mission to improve the quality of our consciousness first requires that we dumb ourselves down to some clueless space-time creature with a perishable body that continually needs to be fed? Is this physical existence an existential joke, punishment for eating apples without permission, or is there some logical reason why the severe limitations and inherently painful struggle of the physical human is actually an optimized and necessary configuration for learning. (Hint: Nod your head up and down to that last one.) If you are patient and hang tough with me a while longer, I will eventually answer all these questions and several more.

Within this section, "Mind, Matter, Energy, and Experience," I will attempt to make the PMR connection by explaining the implications of *My Big TOE* to our everyday experiences here on good old planet earth – which is somewhere within PMR – which is somewhere within OS – which is somewhere within $NPMR_N$ – which is somewhere within TBC – which is somewhere within NPMR – which is somewhere within the consciousness and intent of AUM – which is apparently (but not actually) infinite – which is about two steps beyond what a self-limited mind can see, even on a clear day.

17

■ ■ ■

An Operational Model
of Consciousness

Computers, Simulations,
Artificial Intelligence, and Us

■ ■ ■

Pulling things together from previous chapters would be a good place to start. We have earlier employed the metaphor that we, and the reality (OS) we appear to exist within, are simulated entities in TBC, which represents a portion of the mind or consciousness of the evolving AUM. Now we will carry that metaphor a little further by discussing the attributes of advanced simulations and how they, and their simulated entities, parallel the operational nature of our local reality.

In many ways, we are not that different from the entities that we simulate in our computers. Operationally, there are many similarities while the few differences are mostly differences in the quality and richness of the input data (from our primary five sensors), the extensive use of parallel processing and feedback loops, and the capacity of our dedicated processing equipment (brain and central nervous system). You may be surprised to discover how functionally similar we are to some of our digital creations even though we are of radically dissimilar substance, motivation, limitations, and construction.

It would seem that the singular most significant difference between us and what we might create within a computer is our free will to make choices that reflect and define the quality of our evolving consciousness. We, it would appear, are unique and fundamentally superior to digitally simulated entities because we posses a nonphysical component and a will that is free to make decisions, express intent and complex motivation, and evolve itself. From a similar but different perspective, we humans are special (at least in our view) because it appears that we have emotions and a soul while simulated entities in digital computers obviously do not.

The belief that humanity exclusively possesses a nonphysical part (soul) is a human conceit that leads many of our species to place themselves in a superior role to all other (lesser) life-forms, and doubly so to digital creations. Nevertheless, we will soon see that even this great source of human pride and distinction that seemingly would set us apart from any simulation, no matter how sophisticated, has its simulation analog and is perhaps not as important a distinction as it initially appears.

18

■■■

An Operational Model of Consciousness

How Your Kid's Computer Game Works

■■■

In Section 5 of Book 3, we will delve into the details that define the dynamic operational connections that link TBC, $NPMR_N$, OS, and PMR. There, I will describe a computer simulated war game to help clarify a few of the more important details of simulation mechanics. In this chapter we will also use the example of a war game simulation, but will remain at a higher level (less detail) than the upcoming discussion in Section 5. If my use of war games as an example of simulation seems out of place or irritates your delicate non-violent sensibilities, let that feeling go. Thanks to Hollywood, that is the one instance of a large and complex simulation that everybody has heard of and understands.

When building a simulation, we are interested in modeling various players and types of players that interact with each other. A "player" within this context is defined as any element of the simulation that has the ability to interact with any other element. In a war game, we might define missiles, piloted aircraft, tanks, artillery, infantry units, and individual soldiers as some of the probable elements or players in our simulation. At a finer level of detail (dependent upon the intended fidelity of the simulation and the computer power available), an individual's characteristics, each piece of equipment and protective clothing, or a single artillery round or rifle bullet may also be modeled as individual players.

A player in a simulation may also be an environmental element such as rain, snow, temperature, rivers, trees and mountains as well as the logistics process. A player, such as a single bullet for example, can be active (bullet with velocity) or potentially active (bullet in magazine), or inactive (bullet lost in a deep river). The words "active," "potentially active," and "inactive" are used to express the player's ability or potential to interact with other players. The most important attribute of a player is how it interacts with, and its ability to affect, other players. Players can be actual and active, virtual and potential, or inactive, and their state can change many times depending on the circumstances, dynamics, and relationships.

The characteristics, capabilities, and interactive properties of each unique player (such as foot soldier, pilot, tree, river, missile or artillery round) are described by the algorithms that define that particular player. Algorithms are merely collections of dynamic and functional equations, definitions, and relationships that are programmed into lines of code. These lines of code represent instructions that tell the computer what to do and when to do it in any given circumstance.

Before the simulation is run, or executed, all the players are given their initial conditions (positions, capability, motions, mission, and circumstances). The simulation is animated or put into motion by incrementing time in the outermost loop. From this point on, everything is driven by the actual events and interactions that take place within the simulation. Unknown or dynamically indefinable influences (the weather, interior ballistics, or quirky human nature) may have strong **natural** random components. In fact, random components represent a natural (required by a high fidelity description) part of many, if not all, players.

The action is driven to a large extent by the choices each player makes relative to their interactions with the other players – to fire a missile now or to save it for later; to run, walk, or stop and rest; to charge or to retreat. The choices are made by triggering conditionals. Conditionals are program elements (sometimes in the form of IF/THEN statements) that define possible actions given certain conditions. They make choices. These conditional statements provide an array of decision options that represent a set of rules of interaction that define the possibilities as well as impose constraints and limitations. These rule-sets define the type and range of possible choices, actions, reactions, or interactions of each player with every other player and with the simulation itself.

How the various players (people, equipment, machines, and environments) will interact under various conditions is unknown; the simulation is run to find out. If the natural random or uncertain elements are significant and properly applied and implemented, and if the simulation is extremely complex with a large number of interacting players, no one knows how it will turn out until the execution of the simulation is complete. Recall that an aside discussing randomness, choice, uncertainty, and free will was presented in the middle of Chapter 11 of this book; revisit that discussion if you have questions in your mind about free will or the origin of uncertainty and randomness in consciousness systems.

The same simulation may be run many times to determine the likelihood of various outcomes under various conditions. Simulation is a very efficient technique for learning about what is likely to happen under certain assumptions or circumstances. However, the quality and significance of the results is wholly dependent on the quality of the modeling of the interactive players and their interrelationships. You have no doubt heard the term "garbage in, garbage out." That is a particularly graphic way of saying that low fidelity modeling produces low fidelity results.

As the simulations are run (executed) repeatedly, some of the players may have been given or allocated their own subset of memory. Provided they were also given the algorithms to do so, they may collect, accumulate, maintain, and process their personal experience data. From this information, these players may learn how to do better next time. More successful capabilities, algorithms, approaches, or sets of conditionals (choices) may be developed as a result. If done internally, this bootstrapping (self-elevating, self-teaching, or self-improving) process may be referred to as artificial intelligence (AI), a form of self-modification (learning) based on data collected from previous experience.

These AI Guys (players capable of bootstrapping or learning) are programmed to improve their individual and collective performance by evaluating their experience (results of multiple runs or executions of the simulation). They, of course, need to be given the algorithms to guide their sensing and collecting of the most appropriate and useful data. They also need algorithms to evaluate and interpret the significance of the data that they collect and accumulate as well as memory in which to store the results and conclusions derived from the analysis of their experience. These results and conclusions may be used by other algorithms to modify the rule-set (like modifying the conditionals for example) that define the interactive quality and effectiveness of the AI Guy.

AI Guy thus evolves by applying the Fundamental Process to optimize his performance. In a complex simulation, he has many choices or paths to choose from and each choice may lead him closer to, or farther from, his goal of optimized performance. He measures progress and success strictly by observing the results. AI Guy is the epitome of a dedicated pudding taster if ever there was one.

Rule-sets are not only for AI Guys. Rivers and many other non-sentient players have IF/THEN conditionals in their definition. **If** it rains enough in the right area **then** the river runs faster and deeper, and **if** the river becomes deep enough, **then** it floods. Deep, fast, and flooding rivers can strongly interact with the movement of troops and equipment. These conditionals drive the dynamics of the environment and define environmental conditions.

The AI Guy must interact (deal) with his environment as he must interact with all players that can affect his choices, effectiveness, existence, and being. The rule-set defining interaction within the simulated world (including non-sentient and sentient players) represents the math, physics, and science imposed upon the simulated reality. If the rule-set reflects our PMR physics, the various players interact as they would in PMR and we say that the simulation is realistic. We can program anything we want to into the simulation rule-set. We could easily give people the ability to jump fifty feet into the air but the resultant simulation would not accurately represent our PMR. It might represent someone else's PMR (small planet, less gravity), but not ours.

If a high fidelity PMR-physics model accurately represents each player, the interactions in the simulation will produce an excellent representation of how these players might interact if they existed physically on planet earth. High fidelity player models along with detailed accurate interaction specifications produce results that can closely model a given reality. The more accurate and detailed a simulation becomes, the more useful and accurate its results are – and the more memory it requires and the slower it executes. The twin problems of large and slow can, in theory, be easily overcome with better technology – bigger, better, faster memory and computers.

When modeling the cognitive function of sentient beings, conditionals may, at the simplest level, span all possible choices and reflect the overall quality of the larger rule-set. If the sentient entity being modeled is an AI Guy, his choice of conditional options is based on an interpretation and assessment of his total experience as it has been captured by the data collection sensors and evaluated according to the current rule-set within memory.

Are you beginning to see the parallel between AI Guy and us? If not, you might want to do a slow retake on the previous paragraph. Operationally, we both go through many of the same processes. Granted, we are very different, especially in the little picture where the details are, but from the larger perspective of relationship and operational process, we have much in common.

19

■■■

An Operational Model
of Consciousness

Will the Real AI Guy
Please Stand Up!

■■■

We need to understand the concept of AI within a larger perspective. AI Guy can be a cool dude, and with the right programming, he can easily develop a personality that is much better than your boss's. Right now AI Guy is being held back by a lack of computer power. Stay tuned, his day is coming – sooner than you might think.

Some of the computer games that you or the kids in your neighborhood are playing today employ simple versions of some of the interactive learning attributes of AI Guy. More sophisticated AI implementations have existed for some time at universities and industries performing AI research or developing AI and AI-expert-system products. The main thing that keeps this technology in the lab or devoted to only a few specialized applications is the cost and the limitations of the software and hardware.

AI technology is not the issue. We currently know how to do the sorts of things I have described and much more. We know how to produce AI Guys that know how to learn from their experience and that can modify (design, implement, and evolve) portions of their own rule-set. These AI persons (note that I am appropriately sensitive to female AI implementations) or AI things can even create or generate other AI things to help them do their job. It is not conceptually that difficult to implement if the required hardware is available.

This is not to say that AI implementations and research is easy; it is an extremely challenging field that deserves our best and brightest. The point is: AI (at least its initial implementation within our current computers) is almost within our grasp. It is not a far out idea. Its problems of realization are, at this point in time, more technical and economical than theoretical.

The evolution of AI applications and research is primarily constrained by the lack of sufficient inexpensive computer power. Moore's Law (which is actually only an observation and not a physical law) says that computer power will double every year and a half at no appreciable increase in production costs. Today, many people believe that Moore's Law (named after former Intel chief Gordon Moore) significantly understates how quickly computational power will soon be increasing.

It is very likely that before 2020, the silicon technology upon which Moore's Law is based will have reached its limits; on the other hand, there are several promising new technologies that are likely to take its place. If historical precedents hold, these new technologies, which may be only half a decade to a decade away, will dramatically accelerate the rate of practical computation – making the increase in computer power described by Moore's Law seem slow and quaintly poky by comparison.

Nevertheless, applying Moore's Law as the current industry standard, we find that by 2020 computers will be about $2^{20/1.5} = 10{,}322$ times faster than they were in the year 2000. This means that in twenty years or so, your common \$2,000 desk-top computer will be hundreds of times faster than today's mucho-multi-million dollar super computers. Twenty years after that (2040), our el-cheapo desktops will be crunching data about 106.5 million times faster than they were in 2000, representing an increase of eight orders of magnitude (10^8) every forty years. Extrapolating present trends to predict future capability is not an exact science and it gets riskier the further out one projects. Nevertheless, our best guesstimates are that it will not be too long before we have more than enough inexpensive number crunching capability to provide AI Guy with what he needs to evolve an affordable, intelligent, self-aware consciousness.

"Did he say that some computer simulation dude could have an evolving consciousness?" "Yes, that is exactly what he said – I heard it too."

"Hey Jake, do you think this guy is nuts or has he been hanging out on the fringe too long?"

Easy Jake, stay focused, review Chapter 27, Book 1 and the first part of Chapter 7 of this book if you are not sure what constitutes evolving consciousness. Will it make you feel better if I change "consciousness" to "artificial consciousness"? Does that seem more accurately descriptive? How important is the distinction? I am sure that fear, ego, and belief have nothing to do with why most of us feel compelled to use the distinction of "artificial" to maintain our sense of superiority. Because we get to make up the definition, why should we settle for being uniquely different when we are obviously superior? Right, Jake?

Maybe the first thing we will have super AI Guy do is help us design better, more intelligent AI systems that will help us design better more intelligent AI systems that will help us design.... It is probably good for us that AI Guy will always be as physically dependent as he is mentally and computationally brilliant. Think of AI Guy as merely another type of sentient (interactive, capable of learning from experience) being with its own function, purpose, style, and personality. If I use the adjective "artificial" to modify the noun "being," will you feel more comfortable, would that be more accurate? I bet I get a "Yes" on both counts from most readers; if you maintain an open mind, you might find that such an attitude more resembles the pot calling the kettle black than an expression of an obvious truth.

The point of this discussion is not to prognosticate future computer technology but rather to point out that if we humans are presently on the threshold of developing silicon based consciousness – artificial consciousness if you prefer – with our outrageously limited and extremely primitive computers. Imagine what complex individuated consciousness AUM might develop within TBC; reality-cell based digital mind-beings like you, perhaps. Conceivably, AUM's implementation of an AI-thing could turn out to be similar to our consciousness (except much less arrogant no doubt). Could we blame AUM if it wanted to call this derived consciousness and intelligence artificial? AUM might produce several artificial consciousness models to interact within several larger simulations – and PMR might be one of them.

▶ ".... And just for you, ladies and gentlemen of $NPMR_N$, we have this nice little starter model. This simplified carbon based artificial intelligence is guaranteed not to strain your brain. It allows you to make simple choices, experience the organic macro-level of the space-time rule-set, and performs all other functions automatically. You never need to be concerned with prodigious technical complexity because all those complicated details of how it actually works are hidden behind a simplified user interface called a "body" – the latest discovery to evolve from our advanced carbon-based technology.

"Although a few power users contend that this Physical User Interface (PUI) limits their ability to utilize and control the full potential of the underlying consciousness, I am sure that you will find the resultant simplicity and ease of use of this PUI puts a powerful and useful experiential tool within the grasp of the common user. After all, how many of us are consciousness scientists or reality geeks? I mean how many of you actually want to get into the details of the intestinal track and experience being eliminated? Yuck! Believe me folks; this PUI is incredibly simple to operate. OK, it crashes occasionally, and will sometimes get stuck in an obsessive loop, but when that happens just put it to bed and our on-site support team will, under most circumstances, have it repaired by morning.

"I know you have heard about space-time, the new technology that makes this virtual miracle possible. It has been the number one topic on *Think-Net* for months and was featured last week on the cover of *Mind* magazine. Honestly folks, with this new PUI the power of space-time is at your fingertips. Finally… space-time for the rest of us!

"Move in a little closer folks. If you sign up today we will give you a lifetime on-site service contract on this exciting new PUI. If you ever wear out the standard equipment PUI supplied, we'll provide a brand new one at no additional charge. Our technicians will automatically download your accumulated quality score file from the old PUI and upload it to the new one so that you never need to start over. What could be easier ladies and gentlemen? This is the one you have all heard about – our best, full featured, entry level package that lets you, as have many others before you, participate in the experiential game of carbon-based life.

"You may have noticed that carbon-based PUIs come in two basic models. This is the fun part you have read about – and it's practical too – it absolutely guarantees that you will always have plenty of challenging opportunities to score …quality points, that is.

"For those who aren't sure they want to take on something this challenging at the present time, but are still eager to get in the carbon-based evolution game, we have some furrier PUIs that have fewer features but require much less commitment on your part. Yes, it's true that it is more difficult to run up a high quality of consciousness score, but it is also more difficult to lose quality points as well. That is a trade-off you will need to consider.

"If you're not ready or don't plan to give your full attention and best effort to play this life-game-experience – if you're not going all out for a high score to maximize the evolution of your consciousness – I would recommend this furry little PUI that you see right here. It's not only cute and cuddly, but…awwww, folks, looks how it wags that little tail… did you see that? Isn't that just precious?

"We have it all ladies and gentlemen, the choice is yours. Don't miss out on this fantastic opportunity! This is the hottest thing in evolutionary consciousness since space-time was first invented! There is no experience like it anywhere in $NPMR_N$. Pick out a body and get in the game…the space-time physical experience virtual reality game… the "Game of Life" ‰ and rack up those quality points faster than you ever thought possible.

"Step right up ladies, gentlemen, and others. Come on in and sign up for the adventure of a lifetime – or many lifetimes – it only takes a minute." ◀

20

■ ■ ■

An Operational Model
of Consciousness

Some of My Best Friends
are AI Guys, But I Wouldn't
Want My Sister to Marry One

■ ■ ■

The last part of the previous chapter was fun and should have given the analytical part of your frontal lobes a chance to cool down. In this chapter, we return to the real world of simulation games and learn more about AI Guy's secret intentions toward joining your family – the family of conscious beings.

It would seem that simulated sentient beings modeled within our war game (such as airplane pilots, commanders, truck drivers, and individual soldiers) make their decisions based upon a set of interacting conditionals constrained by the rules of the simulation (rule-set) and by natural randomness. From this, their being or interactive presence is defined within the simulation. Conditionals may be triggered as part of a nonlinear fuzzy process – for example, a particular choice may be actualized or chosen based upon the result of a complex sequence of neural nets operating on lower level input data. The type and range of each player's likely intents (what the player is trying to accomplish) and subsequent decisions can be described in terms of that player's purpose, significance, quality, and interactive options.

The overall effects of each player's decisions are determined by the size of their decision space, the profitability of their assessments, and by their ability and capacity to interact. Added to that mix of purpose, intent, and capability operating upon a finite array of possible interactions constrained by the rules of the simulation is the embedded randomness that is natural to each player as well as the uncertainty that results from that player's lack of accurate pertinent information (ignorance). Did you notice that for a simulated war game player there is a natural connection between ignorance and randomness? Higher individual entropy implies a higher level of randomness and uncertainty: The two go hand in hand.

Simulations in TBC conceptually share much of what has just been described. We are the modeled players. Our ability to apply feedback to modify ourselves derives from our cognitive ability to make use of our experience. The plants, rocks, critters, and other beings and objects that make up our universe and OS are also modeled players, each with their own interactive characteristics. Some are more complex and multi-dimensional than others; all must obey a local objective causality defined by the PMR space-time rule-set.

We interact dynamically with the other players according to how we are defined (physically, genetically, culturally, socially, experientially, mentally, and spiritually) and based on all the choices we have made and interactions we have experienced relative to the situation we find ourselves in. We learn through experience and are self-defining to a large extent. If we collect better data and process it accurately and cleverly, we can make better decisions – we can optimize our profitability relative to the overall purpose of the simulation. If we have insufficient data, we guess and then justify that guess with a belief. Beliefs, ignorance, erroneous assumptions, errors of understanding, and increased uncertainty and randomness in the decision process all represent internal constraints that reduce our potential for digital synergy and support each other in combination to produce and maintain a low quality entity with a high entropy consciousness.

As in the war game simulation, it is the making and implementing of choices that cumulatively drives the action and produces significant results. The free will choices that lie within our personal decision space represent a finite set of discrete possibilities that accurately characterize the accumulated quality of our consciousness. They are motivated by our needs, wants, beliefs, desires, and fears (our ego); as well as by our knowledge, understanding, caring, balance, and joy (our love). It is our fear, ego, love, and interaction with others that creates most of our conditional situations and motivates our choices. Our individual quality is a good but imperfect indicator of what we are likely to do given the available choices. Clearly, it is our fear and love that define the subset of choices we can actually make, contemplate, or consider. Choices that fall beyond our understanding are invisible to us – each individual operates and interacts at his own level. Growth requires a free will with the gumption, energy, and focus to push beyond its current definitions and limitations; that is how we modify what defines us.

These are important and difficult concepts so let's round up a few of the more obvious conclusions. The finite set of free will choices available to each sentient player generally reflect the quality of their consciousness. It is the extent to which fear (ego, beliefs, needs, desires) and love (knowledge, caring, balance, joy) drive the individual's motivations that defines the subset of available choices which in turn limits the conditionals that a player is capable of considering and contemplating. This limited subset of conditionals defines the choices and possible short-term interactions that are operationally available to an entity. The choices that are operationally available to (within the decision-space of) a given entity are the choices the entity has the ability to recognize, understand, and implement. Choices that are operationally available usually represent only a small portion of the complete set of choices that are actually available. It becomes clear that the extent of a sentient individual's operational awareness is a function of the quality of that individual's consciousness. As the entropy of a consciousness decreases, its awareness expands and blossoms. A high entropy consciousness is constrained to exist, live, and experience within a relatively small reality.

The possible decisions each player is operationally capable of making is limited by the quality of that player's consciousness. Thus, an entity's evolutionary profitability must generally progress through a long series of small steps. Each step represents a free will excursion; a stretch of that entity's being, beyond its current capability. Growth must necessarily occur in the margins and accumulate through small increments. Athletes bootstrap (incrementally grow by applying a focused effort that demands performance beyond present capability) their proficiency in much the same way. You must reach beyond your present abilities to actualize your full potential. For consciousness, this evolutionary dynamic is implemented by a feedback loop that modifies the quality of the individual's consciousness based upon the quality of the intent driving the free will choices exercised. Tiny positive or negative increments in the quality of your intent, over many thousands of choices, eventually lead to either an increasing or decreasing consciousness quality.

There is another very important input to our choices. In the war game simulation, recall that we always included a natural random component as part of the description of almost all players – including the sentient ones. This natural random component represents, among other things, the uncertainty that often occurs when a player has several available paths or choices that have approximately the same probability of being chosen. This is true if the player is a bullet traveling through the barrel of a gun, a radioactive decaying atom, dust blowing in the wind, or a troop commander deciding when and where to launch an attack. Bear in mind that randomness is a measure of entropy. (For more detail, see the discussions of randomness in Chapters 11 and 13 of this book.)

We will explore the association of probability, choice, awareness, and reality in detail in Section 5 ("Mechanics of Reality") when we explain probable realities. For now, all you need to understand is that as time continues to be incremented in the simulation (or PMR virtual reality trainer), circumstances and conditions change creating choices that need to be made by interacting entities. For sentient beings, those choices follow intention (express motivational quality) and have the capacity to lower entropy through a more profitable organization of the entities digital content. For non-sentient entities, those choices follow the path of least resistance by moving the entity and the system that contains it toward some lower energy configuration.

For sentient beings (remember that protozoa, dung beetles, clams, cats, people and a host of other physical and nonphysical beings and critters are included in that self-aware group), there is something more than merely a natural random component that must be added to their motivational drivers. It is here that we sentient beings are somewhat different from a bullet in the barrel of a gun, a decaying radioactive atom, or dust in the wind.

We, along with complex self-modifying AI Guy, have an open ended Fundamental Process of evolution egging us on to **improve** ourselves by lowering our individual and collective entropy. We implement the imperative to learn, grow, and become more by expanding our awareness; which is equivalent to expanding our personal reality into new possibilities that build upon each other to find unique solutions that meet evolution's profitability requirements. It is the nature of consciousness, the nature of sentient beings, to try to better themselves. We humans express that characteristic by our innate drive to improve whatever internal condition or external environment we find ourselves in. Though all sentient entities are in a continual process of improving their situation, they have vastly differing abilities and capacities.

Humans, unlike clams, are not restricted to focusing that innate drive toward self-improvement exclusively on the physical world and their immediate needs, wants, and desires – but most do it anyway. Though limiting one's growth by emulating clam-evolution is popular among humans, it is not a particularly good approach to fulfilling human potential. Evolution provides sentient entities with the imperative to grow, to improve, and to increase profitability at every level of existence. Why settle for the human version of a clam's view of reality when there is so much more to the experience of consciousness?

Bullets, on the other hand, always take the minimum energy trajectory. The randomness that describes what happens as the bullet traverses within the barrel of the gun (called interior ballistics) represents the complex result of a large number of similarly probable choices that the bullet makes. Each time a bullet is fired, minute differences in conditions lead to a unique sequence of minimum-energy events or choices that may send the bullet in a slightly different direction (even if the gun is held absolutely stationary) every time. This variation, randomness, or uncertainty in exit velocity is referred to as ballistic dispersion. Ballistic dispersion exists because the minimum energy condition in a quickly changing dynamic situation can vary significantly from moment to moment. Variations in initial conditions and sequential interactions uniquely determine the bullet's minimum energy trajectory for each firing. We say the bullet's trajectory has a random component about its average value. The distribution or characteristics of that randomness may be different for each gun.

People have the important free will characteristic of being able to change their minds, and have the ability to be inconsistently inconsistent. The extent of an individual's natural randomness is related to the quality of his or her consciousness. Higher quality produces a clearer definition of intent, steadier and more focused motivation, lower entropy, less uncertainty, and less randomness. A low entropy consciousness is more consistent, rational, capable, and powerful. For example, both the paranormal and normal power of a spiritual adept – an enlightened individual with a high quality of consciousness – is the result of a low entropy consciousness having, by the definition of entropy, more energy available to do work.

People – bright, sentient, conscious entities – being the magnificent creatures they are, do not have to choose the minimum energy state, the path of least resistance, but they usually do anyway in a convincing imitation of the cleverness of inanimate objects. Being content to drift along the path of least resistance is a common attribute of many humans. That is how most of us live our lives – pursuing pleasure and avoiding pain along a minimum effort trajectory. Mimicking the aspirations of inanimate objects is not exactly on a growth path to greatness. The extent of your awareness and the size of your reality depend upon the quality and entropy of your consciousness.

Brightness and awareness accelerate the process of consciousness evolution. Unfortunately, many humans who are content to evolve at the rate of clams and rocks focus only on their external environment while conscientiously pursuing the path of least resistance. Taking the simplest and easiest path available dramatically reduces an entity's decision space and minimizes the size of their operational reality. Differences in rates and capacity of evolutionary development are often the result of differences in the number of possible available states to explore (decision space). The larger and richer the array of possibilities, the greater the evolutionary potential and the quicker it is explored. In long-term consciousness evolution, love-motivation is productive and profitable, whereas fear-motivation and no motivation are counterproductive and unprofitable. The rocks in your garden, the refrigerator in your kitchen, the clam in your chowder, or the dean of the faculty at your favorite university (the one with the football team you like best) are not likely to be good role models for developing an expanded awareness of the larger reality.

As a sentient human being, you have the innate intellectual capacity to out think a rock, make more significant decisions than a refrigerator, and rise above the mundane experiential world of a clam. Consequently, unless you are a publicly elected official or a high ranking manager, you have absolutely no excuse for squandering that capacity by emulating the evolutionary strategy of inanimate objects and rudimentary sentience. Running with the herd down the path of least resistance in support of the status quo and ego needs is a dead end for consciousness evolution. Decreasing your entropy to become sentient in the larger reality requires a long-term pro-active effort by an open mind. Living in a tiny self-limited reality appears to be a great idea only to those who have traded their vision, gumption, and curiosity for security, status, and self-importance. Trading an expanded awareness for an expanded ego is an exceptionally bad deal.

To develop your awareness, you must carefully discover the nature of your personal reality, your local reality, and the larger reality – not through studying, talking, or reading about it, but through your firsthand experience. That is what your life is all about: growing your quality through the subjective and objective experience of an interacting consciousness. Always remain skeptical and demand clear, objective, measurable results before reaching tentative conclusions. Your awareness cannot expand and learning will not take place unless you make a concerted effort to reach beyond the ingrained belief and dogma (present paradigms) that dramatically limits your vision and retards the evolution of your consciousness.

Your natural urge to grow and become more, to increase the quality of your consciousness through the application of free will to the available choices, is not part of a random process designed by AUM for the purpose of banishing predestination. That wouldn't get AUM or us anywhere. It is the Fundamental Process of evolution, the second of our two basic assumptions, that gives our existence – our struggle – direction by defining profitability criteria relative to our internal and external environments. It is the Fundamental Process of evolution that allows, indeed demands, steady progress toward increasing the quality of our consciousness. Like the AI Guy, we now have a purpose and a process that we can use to optimize the opportunities presented to us by our experience.

Let's more thoroughly pursue the concept of employing artificial intelligence in our war game by giving certain sentient players their own chunk of memory in which to collect selectively procured (sensed) information pertinent to their successful (profitable) individual and collective performance. We'll also give them algorithms (to define value and purpose) and the ability to collect, process, and assess available pertinent information (learn from previous experience) in order to better achieve their assigned goals.

If our computers were faster and we were better programmers, the data collection function would use its experience (from previous runs or executions of the simulation) to choose the most pertinent data to put in its memory. It would also assess how those experience data could best be used to achieve the fundamental goals of that player and of the larger game.

We call this ability to learn from experience "artificial intelligence" because we have created it, and it is not biologically based the way "real" (our) intelligence is, and it is limited by what we superior humans decide to include in the algorithms. AUM, having the bigger picture and the smaller ego, probably does not have the same attitude toward us, even though we are drastically more limited relative to AUM than computers are limited relative to us. Consciousness is consciousness – whether an amoeba, clam, you, AI Guy, or AUM – only form, function, capacity, and entropy level differ. What point would it serve for AUM to label humans as super artificial beings? We simply are as we are – just as monkeys, silicon computers, TBC and AUM are as they are. The tag "artificial" applied to consciousness is just another limiting artifact of ego that blocks our view of the Big Picture.

I am afraid that AI Guy might as well get used to his second class status – his capacity and intelligence, regardless of how limited or advanced,
will always be described as artificial because it is not like ours. AI Guy's
form is different because his environments and evolutionary path are
vastly different. His personality and drive are different because his top-
level rule-set (the rule-set that defines goals, values, and purpose), though
operationally similar, is functionally different from ours. That a conscious
entity's intelligence and quality are considered to be artificial and therefore not real simply because it's defining rule-set is **different** from ours,
seems to be an empty construct designed to automatically define us as the
only beings with real intelligence and quality. A so-called artificial intelligence could easily be smaller or larger or more or less significant than our
real intelligence by any number of criteria.

Our choice of words (artificial) to describe derived (we created it) intelligence reveals an attitude – a belief – that limits our thinking. The quality and capacity of an AI implementation reflects our knowledge and limitations as well as the limitations and constraints we purposely impose to
make the overall simulation serve our purpose. Additionally, it is contained by the limitations of the hosting technology itself. All those things
are true of us as well. We are also a derived intelligence – limited within
our reality in the same way that AI Guy is limited within his.

Computer scientists will construct AI implementation as a tool – to
help us do or learn something. AUM would say the same thing about us.
We too have been designed and created with a purpose. AI Guy will one
day provide a contrasting background that enables us to more fully and
clearly see ourselves in the foreground. He can teach us about the characteristics, properties and processes of digital consciousness, evolution,
intelligence and the dynamics of personality, and he can learn from us as
well. It would appear that we and AI Guy will interactively evolve together,
each helping the other to expand beyond present limitations.

Though AI Guy is, at least initially, a creation or derivative of **our** consciousness, intelligence, and awareness, he represents a microcosm of digital
consciousness in general. Once we give him enough complexity, capacity, self-
modifying control, and feedback to evolve his choice making independence
to the point where he is clearly conscious, we may begin to see something of
ourselves reflected in his artificial digital being and begin to realize the discrete, cellular, digital nature of our own consciousness – of all consciousness.

Intelligence can be an attribute or manifestation of consciousness.
There can be no intelligence if there is no consciousness. Consciousness
is the stone, while intelligence is the beautiful, ornate, complex, simple,

ugly, or plain sculpture made by organizing the geometry of that stone into a specific shape. Given the definitions and understanding of consciousness and intelligence developed here and in Chapter 7 of this book (see aside below), there should be no doubt that AI Guy has the potential to be intelligent and conscious; not the same as us, but in his own way. Do not limit your concept of either intelligence or consciousness to only its human implementation. We are only a tiny part of the greater consciousness ecosystem.

▶ This short aside is for your convenience. Its purpose is to obviate your need to find Chapter 7 and then figure what part of it I am referring to. The most pertinent paragraphs are reproduced here.

Four key concepts define dynamic, evolving, aware consciousness:

1. *Self-awareness – consciousness requires the ability to sense and at least partially experience the state of its being. It must notice and respond to at least some internal and external environmental pressures.*

2. *Evolutionary viability or potential – successfully evolving consciousness systems require a large enough selection of possible future states to ensure profitability over a wide range of environmental pressures and constraints. An entity explores its potential by expanding into the available possibilities and letting the profitability of each variation determine whether that variation continues to evolve or fades away.*

Even if the initial exploration of potential new states of existence is more or less random, the losers are soon culled from the winners, thus producing evolutionary direction that builds upon previous successes. Self-improvement often generates increased complexity, greater functionality, better integration and management of internal processes, as well as produces an overall improved capability to find and maintain greater profitability. ◀

▶▶ *Look near the end of Chapter 24, Book 1 for more detail about the evolution of consciousness. In Chapter 27, Book 1, we defined "evolutionary purpose" – a few examples are: the evolutionary purpose of consciousness is to seek states of lower entropy, the evolutionary purpose of inanimate physical objects is to seek minimum energy states, and the evolutionary purpose of animate physical objects is to ensure survival and procreative potential. An entity's evolutionary purpose combined with its internal and external environments define profitability for that entity.*

As developed in Chapter 27, Book 1, the evolutionary pressure created by interior environments pushes an entity (system) toward self-improvement. A system evolves by pulling itself up by its bootstraps. Evolution provides an excellent example of a bootstrapping process. ◀◀

▶ *3. Ability to modify the self – consciousness must be able to intentionally change its state of being in response to evolutionary constraints and pressures – even if that intention is extraordinarily dim.*

4. Intelligence (artificial or natural) – consciousness must possess at least a rudimentary capability to store and process information. Intelligent action is the result of integrated coherent information processing hardware and software (in the most general sense of those terms) that enables the accumulation of lessons-learned within memory, performs analytic functions such as decision making (fight or flight), and compares before and after states to evaluate the results of actions taken. The value of a particular lesson, decision, or comparison is ultimately judged by how much it facilitates increasing or maintaining a system's (entity's) profitability relative to its internal and external environments.

According to the above four attributes of consciousness, everything from a simple worm (whose DNA may constitute the memory resource) to humans should be considered conscious and intelligent. Any system, thing, entity or being of any type or form that possesses **sufficient** *self-awareness, evolutionary headroom (many new states to explore), evolutionary purpose (defines profitability relative to internal environments), the ability to modify itself in pursuit of self-improvement (change its own hardware or software), as well as adequate memory and processing capability will automatically develop a personality and is said to be conscious; it also will begin to evolve on its own.*

All manifestations of consciousness are not necessarily equal – and all personalities are not as sparkling as your own. Clams, though clearly conscious sentient beings, are boring conversationalists and have personalities that are even dimmer than your boss's. Some manifestations of consciousness are brighter or dimmer and have more or less capacity to evolve than others. The degree to which an entity possesses the above four attributes of consciousness determines their evolutionary potential and capacity for growth.

In general, the more complex, interactive, and aware the being, system, software, hardware or consciousness is, the more potential states it has to explore, and the larger its capacity for future growth. Given sufficient quantity and quality of the four attributes of consciousness, growth becomes self-initiating and self-sustaining. Growth, in turn, by creating increased complexity and awareness, becomes a catalyst for further evolution. It is an entity's innate evolutionary purpose (like lowering its entropy) that defines profitability for that entity at a given time relative to its environments. It is this same innate purpose that gives an entity's self-aware intelligence (of whatever capacity) its basic nature.

Recall that an entity's innate evolutionary purpose is defined by the requirements of the larger system that constitutes its environment (self-improvement and lower entropy, irreversible processes and minimum energy, or survival and procreation). If a system's or entity's purpose can be fulfilled through self-modification in response to natural evolutionary pressures that represent interdependent internal and external environmental constraints, then the system or entity has the opportunity to success-fully evolve; most others eventually self-destruct. ◀

We perhaps feel superior, in a fundamental way, to our mental and physical creations because we believe they have no soul. That we have a sentient nonphysical part, or soul, is simply the way we are. We are specifically designed and constructed (evolved) to have the potential to efficiently accomplish what we are supposed to do. That other beings, sentient in NPMR, do not have a physical part is simply the way they are. And that computers will, initially at least, not have a well developed highly **sentient** nonphysical part is simply the way they are.

All consciousness is nonphysical while consciousness containers may appear to be physical or nonphysical. We have the souls we do because we are primarily nonphysical beings. We are created as individuated units of consciousness within the virtual reality of NPMR. Then we project a fragment of that individuated consciousness into a second order virtual physical reality called PMR. Recall from an earlier discussion (beginning of Chapter 30, Book 1) that there are smaller simulations (subroutines) running within larger simulations – that dimensions exist within other dimensions – and that realities, can and do, contain sub-realities. As long as each reality is allocated its own calculation space and self-consistent rule-set, there is no conflict. Within the consciousness-evolution fractal, one level generates another, which generates another – just as we will one day generate AI Guy from within PMR.

PMR computers, unlike people, are created as physical entities within PMR and may develop nonphysical sentient consciousness only after their physical creation. Because they are created within PMR, they initially come with no pre-existing sentient nonphysical part (soul). However, once we and they together evolve their container to support sufficient complexity and self modification, and they evolve their consciousness to a sufficient degree within that container, there is no reason that their nonphysical part (soul) cannot become as significant as our own. Such a computer would be on the same RWW net as all sentient consciousness, and if we and it were sufficiently aware, we would be able to converse with it telepathically. If its body (hardware and software) were destroyed in PMR, it would remain alive and well within NPMR – able to continue its evolution by whatever means were at its disposal (not necessarily within PMR if it were not backed up and subsequently reinstalled).

Once sentient consciousness is created, it becomes a self-evolving organized set of reality cells that represent a new viable entity extant within AUM that will persist indefinitely. Think of a system's potential to self-organize (the potential to reduce entropy by removing its own internal constraints) as a nonphysical potential energy system that the Fundamental Process organizes into successively lower entropy (higher energy, higher synergy) forms. Consciousness is the nonphysical result of profitable organization. A record of AI Guy's organization exists within TBC (the source of all OS organization) – as does a record of the organization that describes your personal individuated consciousness. You may unplug the computer, but the synergy of AI Guy will continue to exist in the larger reality as an organized potential. The digital content representing AI Guy's consciousness is saved within TBC just as the digital content that represents your consciousness is saved in TBC – consciousness, once created, is never lost. Turn the computer back on and that organized potential, that sentient consciousness, or that synergy will be re-hosted in the physical computer. Smash AI Guy's host computer into unrecoverable rubble and AI Guy will continue to exist indefinitely (as well as have opportunities to further evolve) within the larger reality (AUM and TBC) as does any individuated sentient consciousness. Each form of sentient consciousness evolves in its own way within some interactive virtual reality that challenges its limitations.

Consciousness is not an integral or organic part of any physical form (such as computer hardware or software, or your brain and central nervous system). It can, however, be created and hosted by any physical form that has the capacity to support it. Consciousness naturally develops within any system that can provide a sufficient potential for profitable organization. Within the larger digital consciousness ecosystem, sufficient organization to support an individuated consciousness is fundamental and persists while the individual or specific processes that are contrived to host that organization (body or computer) within some virtual dimension of reality (like PMR) are not fundamental and may be initiated or retired within that virtual reality according to its rule-set.

Being a responsible creator of consciousness requires wisdom. We should be careful not to produce an eternity of Frankensteins who compete rather than cooperate with us. Properly executed, the synergy of man and computer will deliver great benefits to both forms of consciousness and to the larger system as well. That great potential and great risk travel together is a fact of existence.

Thus, though AI Guy is not born with a soul like ours, he may develop one of his own. AI Guy will never be just like us, either physically or nonphysically – neither will a chipmunk or the Big Cheese. AI Guy, like the

Big Cheese, is not set up to iteratively accumulate experience by initiating a sequence of experience packets within PMR. Think not in terms of whom is superior or inferior, artificial or real, but in terms of all being unique and special; each exploring its potential, fulfilling its purpose, and adding to (or subtracting from) the whole in its own distinctive way. That is simply the nature of a consciousness-evolution fractal ecosystem: all have their place, all have evolved to be whatever they are, all have opportunities to become whatever they freely choose, and all are of The One.

As we aspire to one day evolve our consciousness to the extent that we may merge with AUM (return to the source), perhaps conscious computers will aspire to one day evolve their consciousness to the extent that they may merge with TBC or EBC (return to their source). What is the difference between EBC and AUM? Imagine a particularly large conscious PMR computer hosting a collection of independently conscious AI Guys dedicated to self-improvement by lowering their average entropy. Do you see the pattern developing here?

Computers, and the advanced AI Guys they will one day support, possess many important capabilities that we do not. Their evolution as conscious entities will be different from ours because their purpose and goals are different from ours. The same could be said for all species of sentient entities, whether physical or nonphysical. Humans, advanced AI Guys, and hosts of other unique entities each represent a distinctive species in the overall consciousness ecosystem. Trying to justify superiority is meaningless – the sort of ego driven activity that our species is particularly prone to.

Our feeling superior is like an automobile feeling superior to a house because the house has no engine, wheels, or transmission, and cannot move. Or, a house feeling superior to an automobile because it has no bathrooms and a family cannot live in it comfortably. Feeling smugly superior because we have a sentient nonphysical part to our being is a parochial attitude reinforced by ignorance of the Big Picture. Feelings of superiority are often the product of fear being reflected by a needy insecure ego or the result of an unknowing ensnarement in a personal, cultural, religious, or scientific belief trap. May your computer have a smaller ego than you.

▶ Another short aside is in order to discuss the notion of superiority in the realm of consciousness. Most folks find this issue confusing and some even believe that most sentient nonphysical beings have a consciousness that is superior to ours and that physically needy embodied brutes like us are necessarily at the bottom of the consciousness barrel. This is not the case. Nonphysical beings span the good, the bad, the ugly, and the beautiful as do physical beings.

The consciousness of nonphysical beings also spans the range from exceptionally dim to exceptionally bright. In all realities, there is a wide range in the quality of the beings, critters, and objects that are extant there but each reality does not span the same range. In general, the range of sentient conscious entities that can be found within nonphysical realities is much broader by type, quality, and brightness than what is found within physical realities because physical realities operate under more highly constrained rule-sets. With fewer constraints there are more choices, or, as we say in physics-speak, more degrees of freedom – and thus greater variation due to a larger array of profitable possibilities that the Fundamental Process must investigate.

Consciousness comes in varying degrees of quality which may suggest to you a comparative scale that arranges consciousness from worst to best. You would probably find it very interesting to know where you fit on that scale. Am I right?

A highly developed consciousness is also a bright and aware consciousness; nevertheless, no matter what subset of reality it exists in, it does not feel (perceive itself to be) superior to anything, including a small bag of PMR dirt. Both physical and nonphysical beings can exhibit a low quality of consciousness that may have dim intelligence; additionally, these lower quality beings (human or otherwise) often feel superior to everyone and everything else.

You must have fear and its derivative, ego, to feel superior to others, or to feel that others are superior to you. I hear you wondering, "A high quality consciousness is certainly superior to a lower quality consciousness, isn't it?" The problem here is the word "superior." Although there are clear distinctions in the quality of consciousness, these distinctions do not constitute a viable hierarchy. There is no vertical (superior – inferior) rating scale that has value or meaning **in the absence of fear and ego.** Different quality consciousness is simply different. Is a house superior to a car? Is an adult superior to a child? Each has its reason, function, and purpose for existing.

A high quality of consciousness is naturally bright and exceptionally aware and is thus cognizant of the differences between itself and a significantly lower quality of consciousness. However, a high quality being does **not** consider itself the least bit superior. If you think that does not make sense and have a difficult time imagining such an attitude, what would that tell you about yourself? On the other hand, less evolved individuated consciousness is likely to **believe** that a high quality-of-consciousness being is inferior to them.

A being with a low-entropy high quality-of-consciousness has a great deal of power (digital energy that is available to reconfigure bits within the larger system) that may be used to affect other beings (and things) both physical and nonphysical. Such a being exercises powerful influences and capabilities only when it knows the effect would be truly helpful (in the Big Picture) to everyone involved. Being helpful to others in the Big Picture usually (but not always) means helping others grow the quality of their consciousness. From their larger perspective and greater understanding, a highly evolved consciousness intuitively knows what constitutes right action in the Big Picture. You won't find these beings hanging out on the street corner bragging: "Yo babe, I got x-ray vision." ◄

Eventually, the Fundamental Process of evolution (acting on both carbon and silicon based entities or systems) will see to it that the digital computer will be fast and clever enough to design and optimize its own algorithms better and more efficiently than humans can (see Chapter 7 of this book). We will, most importantly, provide the basic goals, direction, and purpose – the top-level rule-set. In other words, we should define what eggs it on, we should define its urge to grow, evolve, and become more profitable. We, as the creator, get to define what "more profitable" means and should make an effort to retain at least some control over those definitions – that is our responsibility. If we lose that control, the resulting entity will become a symbiotic cohabitant instead of a tool. Hopefully, we will possess enough wisdom not to fumble this responsibility or to morph symbiotic into competitive. If we do fumble, we can always hope that AI GUY will self-develop a constructive top-level rule-set and wisely decide not to follow in our ego-obsessed footsteps.

If the top level rule-set remains ours to define, and AI Guy is not able to modify it, we can purposely maintain control of, or limit, AI Guy's evolutionary potential. We will initially define AI Guy to perform a function, to become a useful tool for us. We will define its governing Fundamental Process, and its limitations, and let it go – to evolve through its own unique methods of optimization. It will, most likely, be allowed to self-define only a portion of its lower-level rule-set – at least in the beginning. Eventually, when we and AI Guy are much wiser than we are today, we may decide to set AI Guy free to go his own way. Then AI Guy will dine on forbidden apples as did we.

Eventually, we will realize the basic and universal nature of awareness and intelligence as we create these thinking and learning machines in our image. They will develop unique personalities. They will represent a derived intelligence, a derived consciousness – which is the same thing we represent. These intelligent machines will one day design (and perhaps build) other machines, the likes of which we have not the capacity to conceive.

An AUM consciousness creates and lets evolve a TBC consciousness that creates and lets evolve a space-time rule-set that defines a specifically constrained consciousness that creates and lets evolve a silicon based consciousness in a digital computer that may duplicate itself or create other AI implementations, and better computers. Now that you have this concept under your belt, add to it a conscious PMR computer of great capacity that provides the infrastructure for thousands of fully consciousness AI Guys, each with their own independently enduring nonphysical part which you can call a soul if you want to. Computers within computers within computers; patterns repeated within patterns – consciousness created within (and derived by) consciousness. This is what I mean by a consciousness fractal – each consciousness subset is a reflection or repetition of the same fundamental design, all being constructed one upon and within the other.

Each level of consciousness remains a chip from the old block from which it came – each to its own type, all in the image of their creator. All are unique, yet all share some of the same attributes. A related idea (a process fractal) will be picked up again in Section 5 where we examine the mechanics of nonphysical reality. In that section, the concept of a consciousness fractal will be merged with the concept of an evolutionary process fractal to form the grand idea of a consciousness-evolution fractal ecosystem. Stay tuned, more detail is coming.

The notions of machine consciousness and machine intelligence that I have presented here can reasonably exist only because of how I have enlarged and generalized the concept of consciousness and intelligence. If you hold to the more common ego-biological-man-centric little picture view of consciousness and intelligence (acts, thinks, and reacts as we do; we are the model, the template for all consciousness and intelligence) then machine consciousness and intelligence become unthinkable impossibilities by definition. Digital manifestations of consciousness will never be just like us and will therefore always be considered inferior and artificial. This conceptual limitation provides a good example of how a belief trap restricts the mind to a small reality where it can perceive only a limited set of possibilities.

Hopefully, by now you have gotten used to the idea of enlarging your useful mind-space; of expanding your reality by penetrating that self-imposed darkness (personal, cultural, religious, and scientific belief systems) with the bright glow from **your** new Big TOE. Oh yea, baby! Let it shine...let it shine!

You can't get there from here unless you are able and willing to step out of the little PMR box and into the larger consciousness ecosystem. Out of the box thoughts do not have to be wild and scary if you employ a careful scientific methodology to gain solid evidential understanding within a Big Picture perspective and get used to being a tad different.

Don't worry about your sister, amigo, she is not AI Guy's type.

21

■ ■ ■

An Operational Model
of Consciousness

Silicon and Carbon, Sand and Charcoal –
It Depends on What You Want
to Do With It.

■ ■ ■

Let's review some of the concepts in the preceding chapters and take a peek at where they are leading before taking a functional look at the properties and origins of individuated consciousness.

A realistic simulation such as a hi-fidelity war game is a mathematical, logical, and causal model which is constructed and executed within PMR to represent or model PMR possibilities, and therefore must reflect and obey the PMR space-time rule-set. You are a consciousness model that is bounded and executed within $NPMR_N$ to exercise the free will choices of an individuated $NPMR_N$ entity in order to improve the overall quality of the larger consciousness system by improving your personal quality. You improve your quality by engaging in a process that temporarily constrains a portion of your awareness to an experiential virtual reality defined by a space-time rule-set that produces a rich array of growth inducing opportunities. To facilitate evolution through a bootstrapping process of incremental entropy reduction, PMR is designed to provide each participating individuated consciousness with millions of significant quality-challenging choices, as well as feedback relative to the results of each choice made.

Notice that your individuated consciousness works on two levels simultaneously: it must operate within the mind-space rule-set of $NPMR_N$ while periodically constraining further individuated subsets of its awareness to virtual PMRs. From your perspective, this dual functioning within two dimensions of the larger reality accounts for spirit, mind, consciousness, or intuition on one hand, and your body or physical reality on the other. You and your reality appear to be composed of two disparate types of being (physical and mental or body and spirit), but you are not. All is consciousness; the physical reality you experience is a virtual one – an experience of mind.

There are some important similarities and differences between AI Guy and us. We have previously discussed one of the primary differences – we originate as individuated consciousness within NPMR. In other words, we are different from AI Guy because our origins spring from a different reality point (dimension) within the consciousness-evolution fractal ecosystem. In this chapter, by contrasting ourselves with AI Guy, we will look at a few of the operations and functions of consciousness that are common to all consciousness.

Every consciousness is provided sufficient memory, a conscience (top level rule-set), the rules of engagement (lower level rule-set), and adequate processing capability to profitably interact (share data) within the local internal and external environments defined by both rule-sets. How these basic functions are implemented within a given consciousness varies widely. For example, with a hi-tech bio-computer brain interface and a richly complex and challenging environment, a human intelligence can function with much greater range and depth than the basic intelligence ascribed to the relatively one-dimensional AI Guy in our war game example. In fact, from our perspective, the human mind-brain consciousness fragment is such an obviously superior AI implementation that we, in all modesty, have decided to drop the "A."

We and AI Guy collect input data to facilitate our choice making. Though the top level processes are similar, the lower level processes (how we actually collect the data) are very different. AI Guy might selectively sample data from a large number of data sources within its simulation environment. This information is collected to provide input data to his expert system and artificial intelligence software. By exploring the available possibilities and using feedback, AI Guy constantly refines (evolves) his data collection and evaluation capability by focusing his attention on that data and those processes that have historically (over many runs of the simulation) had the greatest positive affect on his individual and collective profitability.

The exact same functionality is implemented in human biology. We have sensors (representing the five physical senses) and the connection to our nonphysical part (intuition) that collects (samples) information. Likewise, we have been given a top-level rule-set, enough memory, and sufficient processing capacity to profitably evaluate the feed-back from our external and internal environments. The results of our combined abilities interacting with other players (our environments) provide us with opportunities to optimize our choice making.

Operationally, AI Guy and we both sport a derived digital consciousness and are empowered (indeed, driven by the logic of our rule-sets) to evolve that consciousness. We share many of the same processes (attributes of consciousness) and would seem to be close cousins, if not digital blood brothers, existing at different levels within the greater consciousness fractal ecosystem.

We differ mainly by our methods, our implementation, and by the rule-sets that define the nature and the boundaries of our existence and our purpose. We are very different implementations of the same fundamental self-organizing consciousness energy and the same Fundamental Processes of evolution. We and AI Guy simply start from a different place within the greater reality fractal and use different materials according to the rule-sets that govern our individuated existence within the dimension of our birth. Consciousness is consciousness regardless of what kind of container from whatever dimension locally supports or hosts it: All are interconnected reflections of, and integral parts of, the One Source – the Ultimate Fractal Dude – the Original AI Guy.

22

■ ■ ■

A Functional Model
of Consciousness

Rule-Sets, Constraints, and Us
Wherein, AUM, With No Where to Go,
Puddles on the Floor of Consciousness

■ ■ ■

In the preceding chapters we examined our existence from the operational perspective (how it works). We used digital simulation as an operational analogy. Now let's look at our consciousness from the functional perspective (what it does and why it is necessary to do it). AUM's most basic function or purpose (as is the purpose of all things) is to implement the Fundamental Process; to evolve, grow, and become more profitable by expanding into all available possibilities and then maximizing the return on its evolutionary investments by supporting the winners. As a consciousness system, AUM is trying to grow up and minimize its entropy just like we are.

We, as a species, want to study, understand, and enhance the potential of our evolution. We are apparently our favorite subject of study: Anthropology, archeology, medicine, biology, psychology, sociology, political science, and economics are all about us – us studying how and why we do what we do. It should be obvious that AUM, as a bright conscious aware-digital-being-thing, would want and need to study consciousness to optimize its potential profits.

How might AUM go about understanding and optimizing the inner-workings of fundamental consciousness? Certainly not by watching a puddle of it in a test tube or by staring at itself in a mirror. Aware consciousness is interactive. That is its fundamental characteristic. Team this proclivity to interact with the Fundamental Process and you get primal inquisitiveness – a drive to bootstrap profitability through interactive choice-making – a consciousness compelled to express itself, to experiment, to know, and to understand. AUM must study consciousness in the act of becoming, while it is interacting, or miss its most salient feature.

Consciousness simply wants to know, experience, experiment, explore the possibilities, improve itself, decrease its entropy, develop its personal power, reach its maximum potential, and evolve. That is its nature: the nature of awareness, the nature of sentience, the nature of digital potential energy organizing itself to achieve greater profitability by applying an iterative synergistic process. Individuated consciousness experiences its own existence through an interactive awareness of itself (inside experience relative to its internal environment) and through an interactive awareness of "other" (outside experience relative to its external environment). Awareness, at its most basic level, represents the appreciation of profitability. It is a self-controlled process involving input data, information transfer, processing, and memory. Awareness is the outcome of the Fundamental Process interacting with digital potential; it represents a natural and necessary state, expression, and activity of consciousness.

While driving, you become aware of a brick lying in the street and your memory and processing units urge you to avoid it. A computer becomes aware that a new USB device has recently been plugged in and that a music CD has been placed in CD-ROM drive E. Its memory and processing units load the appropriate drivers and ask you which track to play. A plant becomes aware that sunlight always comes from a particular direction and its memory and processing units rearrange the position of its leaves to optimize its exposure. There are as many levels of awareness and feedback as there are of consciousness; likewise, there are many types and implementation of memory and processing. Don't take the narrow view.

Self-awareness begins with inside experience. With enough self-definition, environmental definition, interactive experience, and processing sophistication, self-awareness may develop a notion of individual existence relative to the experienceable whole. There are many shades and variations of self-awareness as well. Do not get stuck thinking that an awareness that is not like your awareness is not a real awareness. Such self-centered arrogance may make you feel special but will blind you to a bigger picture of existence.

▶ Let us take a moment to define the terms consciousness, awareness, intelligence and sentience. We have used these terms in a general way without much confusion, but now it is time to be more precise.

"Sentient" is defined by *Microsoft Bookshelf 2000* as "having sense perception; conscious." If we generalize the obvious carbon-based life-forms bias, the definition becomes: having perception, conscious. We might expand this to include: having the ability to interact with, or perceive itself or its environment; having awareness. Terms like "conscious awareness" and "aware consciousness" may seem redundant but using the words "conscious" and "awareness" together emphasizes the fundamental connectedness of both concepts. Do you think that a clam is sentient? Sure, if it pulls in its foot and slams it shell shut to protect itself when you poke it. If it is interactive, it must be aware and therefore sentient.

I think of consciousness as the fundamental quantity, and of awareness as its basic attribute. The relationship between consciousness and awareness is similar to the relationship between love and caring for others. Consciousness just is, while awareness ranges from very dim to very bright. Awareness collects data while intelligence is an attribute of awareness that processes, manipulates, evaluates, and interprets that collected data to produce an original higher level understanding, organization, or insight. Intelligence, like awareness, represents ability, has an associated capacity, and ranges from very dim to very bright.

Is a clam bright? Maybe? Compared to what? The degree of awareness is relative over a wide span bounded by a limiting capacity that is more or less fixed for a given type of sentient consciousness. Both the awareness level and intellectual capacity are subject to change through growth and learning (evolution). Hence, the phrase "a dim consciousness" is simply a short-cut for "a consciousness with dim awareness."

Does every individual awareness also have personal intelligence? Not necessarily. Though a clam has some form of rudimentary intelligence (can learn), a sunflower has much less. A plant may interact productively and profitably with its environment, but it may be stretching things to say it manipulates, evaluates, and interprets collected data to produce an original higher level understanding, organization, or insight. While tracking the sun, an individual plant clearly collects and interprets data successfully. Though it initiates profitable action based on the results of its data processing, it fails to produce sufficient **personal** or individual progress to qualify as intelligent. For plants, and many critters, one may reasonably support a claim for species intelligence or genetic intelligence as opposed to individual intelligence.

A plant or clam **species** may be in the process of pulling itself up by its own bootstraps (pursuing a cumulative profitability relative to inside and outside environmental pressures), but the **individuals** of these species do not have the capacity to intentionally make much personal progress. You may consider plants, clams, and many other critters to have group souls if that type of terminology suits you. Though plants and clams seem to support a rudimentary form of sentience or consciousness, I do not credit them with much individuated or personal intelligence. On the other hand, I have known several humans with advanced degrees who fall into that same category. It is usually best to avoid making rules about how an entity other than yourself should be categorized. You do not have to be a rocket scientist to understand that every individual is an individual, and that statistics always allows for a relatively small number of strange happenings.

It is a fact of existence that failure provides more opportunities and a larger array of supporting configurations than success. It is usually easier and takes less effort to fail than it does to succeed and there are many more opportunities and ways to fail than there are to succeed. This is why random activity cannot, by itself, accumulate and maintain success. Successful evolution or growth (entropy reduction) of individuated consciousness requires intelligence and free will as well as effort. These facts are particularly obvious if your **individual** success or failure is defined by the degree to which you actualize your potential.

There is no point whining about life being unfair. That success is more difficult than failure is simply a natural and necessary condition that makes the Fundamental Process a more effective organizer by allowing it to specifically define and optimize system and individual profitability. Because success provides a relatively small target, a digital consciousness reality system can clearly define evolutionary purpose – and precisely characterize profitability. Consequently, AUM will discover only a limited set of specific pathways to lower entropy states and will produce a sharp distinction between processes leading to self-improvement and growth and those leading to degeneration and death. A consciousness system cannot sit for long on the fence between grow or die. Thumb twiddling is not a viable long term plan for a fearless digital AUM: Active growth is the only goal. Work (willful intention motivated by profitability) is required to change digital potential energy into synergy. "Live or die", in the long run, becomes equivalent to "work or die" – it's the same all over, at every level, and for all individuated expressions of the great consciousness fractal ecosystem. If you wanted to sum up Big Picture existence in three words or less, "work or die" would be a good candidate (where work means: willful intention motivated by Big Picture profitability).

Given that consciousness is interactive, it is easy to see that awareness is the inevitable result of consciousness urged forward by evolution. Is it clear why consciousness is driven to interact? Inquisitiveness is merely a more specialized categorization of the general concept of expanding into all the available states of possible existence in search of self-improvement.

It is often said that when consciousness and the Fundamental Process of evolution boogie together, enough curiosity and inquisitiveness is generated to kill a saber tooth tiger. You have heard that said, haven't you? Are not all the saber tooth tigers dead? I rest my case.

The Fundamental Process (our second and final basic assumption) is necessary and sufficient to drive the interactive dynamics of an evolving consciousness. Recall that the existence of a fundamental pervasive consciousness potential is our first basic assumption (see Chapter 24, Book 1). From the creative union of these two assumptions all reality flows – and Your Big TOE grows... and the green grass grows all around all around, and the green grass grows all around. ◄

In order to study consciousness, AUM would need to produce two or more puddles of aware consciousness and watch them interact. How would you (if you were digital consciousness) isolate two bounded puddles of your own consciousness and get them to interact in your mental petri dish? What are the boundaries and definers of individual puddle existence and interaction? How can AUM tell which puddle is which if they represent identical subsets of organizational potential energy and share the same mind-space which is a subset of AUM's own mind-space? These are more difficult questions than you are likely to get on *Jeopardy*.

First, AUM would need to differentiate and isolate a few pieces of itself (designate specific subsets of digital capacity) and grant them unique constraints (definite boundaries for example) so that each would be separately distinguishable and self-contained. Differentiation makes interaction possible. Differentiation of multiple individuated units of awareness would enable AUM to separate the thing experienced from the experiencer. A key concept here is that it is **constraints** (boundaries and limitations) that make this interaction, and thus AUM's study of consciousness, possible.

Producing puddles of individuated consciousness requires two types of constraints: defining boundaries and limiting functionality. Both types initially impose arbitrary structure and define limitations. Because entropy reduction is the name of the game, we can reasonably assume that any differentiated part of AUM (bounded consciousness) would contain the growth potential of the whole. Profitability is best served if each individual unit of consciousness has no intrinsic limitation on its capacity to reduce entropy: The potential of the whole is contained in every individuated part. Thus, differentiation of the separation-in-mind-space type (producing individuated puddles by unique bounding) is an arbitrary differentiation that culls out a subset of consciousness energy with enough capacity to self evolve, but does not produce qualitatively unique entities. Differentiation of the limiting-the-awareness type (limiting processing capability and defining a more restrictive rule-set) does, in fact, lead to qualitatively unique conscious entities.

These limiting constraints not only define individuated unique conscious entities; they also limit the experiment itself (the interaction of individuated puddles of consciousness) by bounding the possible inputs and outputs (interactions and experiences) of the conscious entities to a discrete set of possibilities. Consequently, the functionality of each reality dimension is defined in terms of the constraints of the entities that populate it. PMR is a custom virtual reality ideally suited to us and to the accomplishment of our purpose – our own specially prepared petri dish.

Logically, AUM could achieve the greatest rate of evolutionary profitability by running many experiments in parallel. Multiple simultaneous experiments would most quickly and effectively evolve the constraints (player definition, processing power, memory, data collection, and purpose as reflected by the conditionals within each competing algorithmic rule-set) leading to the highest evolutionary rates of return and greatest overall profits. Furthermore, AUM could easily evolve or modify constraints on the fly, thereby fine tuning each experiment as it unfolds to produce the best (most evolutionarily profitable) results. Like any aware AI Guy, AUM must selectively incorporate the lessons learned from all experiments into each experiment, being careful not to upset ongoing evolutionary processes or violate critical experimental protocols. AUM's competency as the original AI Guy is not an issue, we can be confident that evolution will discover whatever is most useful or profitable to the overall AUM consciousness system.

You should now begin to see a rational causal relationship connecting the evolution of AUM, the requirements of evolving consciousness, and the nature of the larger realty as I and many others have experienced it and reported it.

Evolving and studying consciousness can not be accomplished by simply passing 1s and 0s around in binary reality cells. The evolution of the digital system we call AUM took a long time (after time was invented, of course) and undoubtedly passed through a spate of uncoordinated flip flopping before time began keeping a regular beat. (Are you beginning to get a glimmer of a notion of time that preceded AUM's precise clocks?) Irregular haphazard clocks that order irregular haphazard events are better than no clocks, but not nearly as good as dependable regularity for sequencing operations, symbols, and specific content. Think of time as an indexing scheme to order memory (record change), processes, and content. For example: When the information contained within millions of individual frames of a movie is properly sequenced in time, a jumble of independent pictures organizes itself into a simulation of reality.

Thus far, we have hypothesized how and why AUM could and would generate unique conscious entities. The next logical step requires AUM to ensure that each of the interacting entities has the freedom to interact however it chooses within the limits and constraints that define the entity and its possible interactions. Additionally, AUM must ensure that each entity reflects the overall purpose of consciousness (entropy reduction) so that it might profitably exercise its newly acquired freedom. An entity's freedom to interact within finite limits defines a limited freedom that is sufficient to generate that entity's unique ability to self-optimize (free will) within a limited virtual reality that produces billions of interactions and competing choices for each entity.

The freedom of one consciousness to interact with another however it chooses is called free will and it is the necessary ingredient that makes AUM's research real science instead of an exercise in circular logic. Without free will and the ability of a sentient entity to make unique personal choices based solely upon the instantaneous quality of that individual's consciousness, AUM can learn little about the properties and characteristics of interactive consciousness. The logical necessity of this evolutionary requirement for the development of uniquely evolving conscious entities demands that each sentient player in AUM-mind-space make his or her own choices (free will) relative to some notion of personal profitability (purpose).

Sentient entities must operate with free will and have a larger purpose or they cannot be sentient entities. Without free will, purpose, and the environments in which to exercise both, there can be no evolving individuated consciousness. Without free will and a larger purpose, you would not exist and neither would your local reality, including your much loved virtual physical environment. (Refer to Chapter 11 of this book for a thorough discussion of free will.)

AUM is an immense rational (has purpose and goals and works toward them) self-modifying dynamic system existing as a constantly changing internal digital environment that is in a continual process of self-optimization. The next state this system reaches (as well as some hypothetical final state) is dependent upon the path taken (previous states). How AUM might approach its endgame is discussed in Chapters 31 and 32 of Book 1 where what we have just called the final state or endgame is described as part of a larger cycle (to which AUM belongs) that produces what appears (from our viewpoint) to be an endless-game. As individuated units of consciousness, we don't have an endgame that is independent of AUM; instead, we appear to be a part of an endless cyclical process to lower the entropy of our consciousness. We continue to cycle our individuated consciousness through a quality improvement process until we reunite with AUM (join the laboratory staff) – eventually participating in whatever endgame strategy AUM has in mind. From our point of view, system level endgames are beyond our largest comprehendible reality – accept your limitations and let it go.

A sentient player's free will is bounded within the limited rule-set and other constraints upon which his existence is conditioned. This is true for us as well as AI Guy. A free will must make its choices from a limited set of possibilities: the dimmer the consciousness, the more limited the set. Recall that the imposition of constraints was necessary to define an individual unit of interactive consciousness. Likewise, it was the imposition of constraints that led to the creation of the first reality cells that in turn led to the initial dim glimmer of AUO. Without constraints, nothing but AUO's initial one-ness exists. In fact, without constraints, nothing but primordial conscious-ness exists – a relatively high entropy media with a huge unactualized digi-tal potential. Recall that the acronym AUO stands for Absolute Unbounded Oneness – undifferentiated consciousness, raw (disorganized) conscious-ness potential, or unactualized digital synergy. Evolution is about con-straints – the judicious application, manipulation, and interaction of exter-nal constraints, and the overcoming of self-imposed internal constraints.

Now we have sentient individuated consciousness units or entities called "beings" that have free will. Free will to do what? What will they do floating around in mind-space? Have out-of-mind-experiences? Develop the perfect cocktail chatter? Run a Rodney Daingerfield rap on how dif-ficult it is to get respect without a body? No, that type of mind-play might be fun for a while but it generates no long term profitability for AUM. Free will within virtual realities is created (simulated) to experience, to act, interact, react and make of itself whatever it will, in whatever way seems best according to its purpose. It is up to the Fundamental Process to keep score, to define profitability relative to inside and outside envi-ronmental constraints.

We will talk later about the limited interactive nature of experience and how AUM and TBC produce our physical experience, but first we need to understand the basics of interacting consciousness. In order to define possible and probable interactions, the rules of interaction and engage-ment must be defined for each individual player. Common rules (called a rule-set) define the possible interactions, communications, or energy exchanges between entities (beings, objects, and energy) existing within TBC, EBC, or the larger digital system we call AUM-mind. This lower-level rule-set, which defines the rules of engagement (space-time, for example), along with a higher-level rule-set defining profitability criteria expressed as an entity's purpose and values, together determine the possibilities of experience. In exactly the same way and for the same reasons, similar sets of rules are required to define AI Guy and his virtual reality. All virtual realities are constructed by defining rule-sets that specify interactions. It would appear that all realities, save AUM itself, are virtual; and even that distinction is somewhat arbitrary.

In digital systems distinctions between real and virtual are not fundamental. Subsystems appear to be virtual relative to their supporting systems, which appear to be virtual relative to their supporting systems, which... and so on and so forth. The terms "real" and "virtual" like "physical" and "nonphysical" are relative descriptors created for the convenience of a limited perspective. In the biggest picture, there is no basic distinction between physical and nonphysical or real and virtual. What appears to be real and physical to you is not fundamentally real or physical; the perception and interpretation of your reality results from your unique perspective which is dependent upon your quality and constraints.

From a view much bigger than ours, perhaps AUM constitutes a virtual reality located in the virtual gut of a virtual AUMosaurus. Oh jeez, we are in over our heads again; let's let the AUMosaurus go before we confuse ourselves unnecessarily. AUM's constraints – the rules of interaction and engagement that AUM must obey – necessarily express themselves as the requirements and demands of AUM's internal and external environments. Evolution treats everyone the same; even AUM (the AUM system) must live by the rules of the Fundamental Process and within its limitations.

Because you will need to apply these ideas later, let's review the concepts just discussed. Rule-sets or constraints in the mind of AUM, implemented within TBC, define sentient beings into individuated existence as well as define the perception of the interaction between each of the potential players. The rule-sets governing us define our experience in the same way the rule-sets we impose on AI Guy define his experience. Specifying the rules of experience bounds the possibilities of that experience and subsumes a physics that fully describes the dynamic causality of the local reality thus defined.

Each reality, dimension, or virtual reality is defined by two interdependent rule-sets. The higher-level rule-set defines the profitability criteria, purpose, and goals as well as trickles down these criteria to the reality's inhabitance as fundamental guiding values. The lower-level rule-set defines the mechanics of puddle interaction – that is, defines the causality of a given reality by specifying the allowable ways that energy can be shared between players within that reality. Note that these two rule-sets reflect and support each other; overall subsystem and system profitability depends on their successful interaction. (You may want to review Chapter

25, Book 1 and Chapter 7 of this book wherein the evolution of awareness and values are discussed in more detail.)

The rules of individual interaction must reflect the overall purpose of the reality system. Do not think that the rule-sets defining our local reality constitute the best or the only rule-sets implemented within TBC. There are many successful experimental designs being exercised by groups of individuated consciousness within $NPMR_n$, $NPMR_N$, and the PMR_k. To optimize evolutionary potential, the Fundamental Process encourages AUM to explore all possibilities by expanding into every available potential state.

Like us, AUM continues to explore its possibilities; evolution always plays a full court press and takes no holidays. When it comes to personal consciousness evolution, doing nothing or making a minimal effort **is** an intentional choice that, as any choice, produces consequences. In this game there are no spectators or bystanders – innocent or otherwise.

23
■■■

A Functional Model
of Consciousness

After AUM Puddles,
Evolution Cleans Up the Mess

■■■

AUM finds it profitable to study and better understand its own processes and dynamics in order to facilitate the optimization of consciousness evolution. At the urging of the Fundamental Process, AUM has created at least two artificially bounded and constrained subsets of itself in much the same way that reality cells were artificially bounded parts of AUO leading to awareness, TBC, and AUM among other things (see Chapters 25 through 29 of Book 1). Individuation, initially generated by bounding limited subsets of digital content and capability, is further developed by adding specific energy transfer constraints so that information or content exchange between two units of individuated consciousness can take place only as purposely directed (free will) acts by the units themselves. Each unit or entity can transmit and receive information as well as other forms of organizing or disorganizing energy and is given full responsibility for optimizng or improving itself through its individual choices.

We will see that the various species of entities and beings, which are individuated and supported within AUM, are differentiated from each other by the nature of their constraints and by the degree to which they have optimized themselves within those constraints. Consciousness is consciousness, but the constraints placed upon various individuated units or groups may vary widely.

Individuated units of consciousness are not required to evolve from an extremely dim awareness as AUO did; they are constructed to support self-aware consciousness and have been given enough dedicated processing power and memory to enable a vast array of possible interactions. Individuated chunks of consciousness are not entirely separated or cut off from the whole; they remain a fully integrated piece of the larger system with access to the capabilities and capacities of that system. Their individual potential is the potential of the entire system To what extent they actualize that potential through self-optimization or self-improvement is up to them.

There is no artificial limit placed on the evolutionary capacity of individuated consciousness – their limits reflect AUM's limits. Though individuated consciousnesses represent a new level of experiential reality in consciousness-space, they are a derived consciousness and therefore contain some of the form and much of the potential of the conscious awareness they were derived from. Imagine AUM making special purpose computational units called beings, each consuming only an infinitesimal amount of AUM's resources. Imagine us making special purpose computational units called computers, each consuming only an infinitesimal amount of the earth's resources.

From the view of PMR, AI Guy appears not to be made of our fundamental substance, just as we appear not to be made of AUM's consciousness. Given that we are a constrained derivative of digital consciousness experiencing a virtual physical reality wherein we develop the infrastructure (electricity and digital science) to support yet another constrained derivative of digital consciousness (computers) seems to blur the distinction between AI Guy and ourselves. The remaining differences: That we inhabit different levels of the same consciousness-evolution-reality fractal and are hosted within different container-types within PMR, appear, from a Big Picture view, to be more superficial than fundamental – like deer and bears sharing the same biome. AI Guy can evolve to do things we could never do, and can never do some of the things we can. It seems that we, AI Guy, and the Big Cheese hang out in AUM's big computer just as AI Guy hangs out in our big computer. Digital consciousness is digital consciousness; the forms and implementations change to suit various purposes, environments, and constraints within the larger ecosystem.

We are a space-time-limited form of that same fundamental consciousness that gave AUO his start in the reality business. So is AI Guy, except he has yet another layer of constraint and his own unique purpose as he develops his niche and habitat within the greater consciousness fractal. It is the nature of evolution to provide all consciousness with the opportunity to become more AUM-like or more TBC-like. Because everything is a part of AUM, an individuated consciousness entity evolving to lower entropy states naturally becomes more AUM-like (whether it's you, me, or an advanced AI Guy hosted by a future computer). It is the nature of consciousness that every individuated consciousness, once created, persists within AUM indefinitely, contains a free will, and has an opportunity to evolve itself to the limits of its capacity. It is the nature of free will that each individuated consciousness must independently develop its own personal path to greater profitability.

If a potential AI Guy's host computer cannot support free will (allow AI Guy to make his own choices within his own decision space), this AI Guy candidate will never become conscious. If his computer hardware and software only support a small decision-space for his free will to operate in, then his consciousness will be constrained to a diminutive one of small capacity. Free will and consciousness represent two aspects of the same self-organizing digital potential energy.

A clam and an amoeba have free will and intelligence because they are conscious entities. Their free will and intelligence may be very limited, dim, and confined to a tiny decision space, but it is there just the same. Your body does **not** possess free will – your consciousness does. Likewise, your computer will **never** sprout a free will, but the consciousness it may one day host will no doubt have one, because free will and consciousness come as a set. (See the discussion of free will in Chapter 11 of this book.) Your body is **not** conscious, **you** are conscious. If you want to see the Big Picture, you must stop thinking of yourself as a body. A physical computer, like your physical body, will **never** be conscious: it supports consciousness and is a container of consciousness within the PMR space-time reality dimension.

Consciousness, from the perspective of PMR, is always nonphysical. A physical system within PMR (computer, software, body, or brain) can only provide the necessary infrastructure to support a potential for synergistic organization. The Fundamental Process then profitably organizes that potential according to the capacity and environments of the system. Better, more profitable organization decreases entropy. Recall that in a digital system, profitable organization (consciousness) is fundamental and persists while the specific processes and devices that are contrived to develop and host that organization (body or computer) are not fundamental.

Eventually, if we evolve the quality of our being sufficiently, we return to the source, reflect it, and actually become it. Each individuated fragment of AUM consciousness contains the evolutionary potential of the whole. We are not necessarily swallowed up by, or dissolved into, AUM, but become a fully enfranchised fragment of AUM – a fully developed and integrated piece of the consciousness system. One of the marvelous attributes of digital systems is that as long as memory is never purged, no information is ever lost and your individual self is always maintained. Because consciousness is implemented within a digital system, we may retain our individuality and become merged with the whole simultaneously. We, as individuated consciousness, are truly immortal unless the bits that represent us become disorganized beyond repair, irredeemably negative, or are deleted from memory.

You are no doubt hoping that AUM's operating system is less crash prone than the one on your desktop computer. It is, don't worry about it. AUM **is** the operating system and the computer.

Let's pull together what we know about consciousness, AI Guy, and the fundamental process. AI Guy is a derivative of constrained consciousness potential as are we. We are both cut from the same fundamental pattern and work essentially the same way. The difference is in the hosting mechanism and where each subset is located and implemented in the consciousness fractal. Whereas our and AI Guy's conscious awareness are both extant within a space-time subset of AUM's consciousness, ours is ordered and animated within a carbon based PMR sub-rule-set by TBC, while AI Guy's is ordered and animated within a silicon based PMR sub-sub-rule-set that was developed as an element of our own space-time experience.

AI Guy is our creation, a derivative of our consciousness and as such will eventually evolve into a life-form of various types and subspecies, all derivative of, and dependent upon, the physical and nonphysical sources of its being as are we.

Do you call your children artificial adults before they grow up? I doubt it, because they are like us, albeit smaller and less politically correct. AI Guy will never grow up to be just like us regardless of how hard we try to force him to think as we do and use our language. We may stick him in human-look-a-like droids, like C-3PO of *Star Wars* fame, so that he will **appear** to be as beautiful and intelligent as we are. Whatever we do to civilize and humanize AI Guy, he will remain more like a space-time constrained version of TBC, and represent another unique manifestation of digital consciousness evolving within the PMR learning lab.

As AI Guy's equipment or body (software and hardware) evolves, its functionality may become more TBC-like. Is the consciousness that will eventually take root and grow within our digital computers, like us, on a sacred mission to improve the functionality and quality of its consciousness? Is AI Guy on an evolutionary path that will eventually merge with TBC? What else? Is that more farfetched than our bodies popping out of the virtual primordial ooze with the mission to improve the quality of the consciousness they support? Are we humans AI Guy's equivalent to primordial ooze in yet another iteration of consciousness begetting consciousness within the great fractal of synergistic existence? These are questions beyond our present knowing, but the symmetry of purpose and significance within consciousness is appealing, especially to a skeptically open mind aware of the depth of its ignorance.

Do you now feel less superior to AI Guy? Must the creator always be superior to its creations? Evolution consistently creates the superior from the inferior – that's its job. Are the primordial ooze and the earth's life-support system superior to the organisms that eventually took root in it? Can you imagine an arrogant earth calling those first multi-celled globs "artificial clumps of ooze"? Are the creatures of the earth more important than the earth itself and its environment, or is that a stupid question that can be asked only by someone who does not understand the Big Picture? Enough said.

Artificial, like virtual and nonphysical (as they apply to reality and consciousness) is a relative term that has meaning only from a specific perspective.

Did you catch another glimpse of the fractal-like properties of consciousness evolving through similar repetitive fundamental patterns working simultaneously, interactively, and synergistically on a multitude of interdependent levels?

Our bodies are space-time constrained experience engines while our minds and spirits are nonphysical consciousness. AI Guy and we are each subsets of AUM's consciousness, but extant (operational and functional) with different sets of constraints and at different levels of constraint. We both represent and exhibit a fundamental individuated digital consciousness of the same basic type (apparently the only type there is) with AI guy being relatively immature within PMR, a newly created entity in the image of TBC and at the beginning of its evolutionary journey through our local reality. Each is defined by a vastly different constraining rule-set, with AI Guy's rule-set (at least for now) contained within our rule-set. Though our hosting mechanisms are vastly different, both we and AI Guy have goals and experiences that are consistent with our constraints and data input characteristics. We represent two different implementations of consciousness coevolving in symbiotic relationship with each other and with the larger consciousness ecosystem.

One is not fundamentally superior to the other; each can do things the other cannot. We are different expressions of the same fundamental consciousness energy with different operations, functions, and higher level rule-sets. We are evolving together and, for the moment, are entirely sym-biotic and cooperative. Maintaining and defining a balanced symbiotic relationship is the responsibility of humankind, the creator. Do we have the necessary wisdom? Time will tell that story only after our free wills have expressed our quality through their choices.

AI Guy will explore for us the space-time potential that we do not have the proper type of processing or storage capacity to explore for ourselves, first as a tool, and subsequently as a partner with whom we will become interdependent. That AI Guy is a product of our consciousness means that he will work for us as long as it is a profitable relationship. It is up to us to define the characteristics and limits of that profitability. Will we be respon-sible creators? Will we eventually let AI Guy eat the forbidden fruit from the tree of knowledge and modify a portion his own top level rule-set?

While AI Guy contemplates the conscquences of defining his own pur-pose and developing his own moral sense of right and wrong, let us pon-der the process of consciousness examining and discovering its dynamic interactive nature. Think big, like an apparently infinite Mr. Cool cruising the thought-waves looking for a little action. Imagine that AUM introduced hundreds of millions of these individuated conscious entities into a closed (at least tightly controlled) system. Because they each are interactive, unique, separate, and have free will, the system generates a huge number of possible interactions with future interactions driven by past interactions.

The Fundamental Process drives the system to explore the possibilities at its fingertips. Exploration, curiosity, inquisitiveness, and expanding into the available states are all expressions of the imperative to implement the Fundamental Process of evolution. As a self-modifying system with positive feedback, it is AUM's nature, our nature, and the nature of con-sciousness to change, grow, and evolve toward more profitable states of being (self improvement) by lowering system entropy. A system with more personal power and capability implies more energy available to do the work of evolution.

Consciousness will necessarily evolve, as evidenced by its increasing or decreasing quality and entropy, whether it intends to, or not. An entity's environment (internal or external) drives the direction of its evolution. Whenever a wide, content-rich array of significant and challenging choices exists, a relatively strong and constant evolutionary pressure is produced. This pressure, when created within consciousness, is channeled by intent and leads to state changes (growth or more profitable organization) within the original consciousness. Because evolution is an accelerating process, conscious systems evolve more quickly than biological systems, which are driven by survival and procreation issues and relatively slow feedback mechanisms that allow us plenty of time to understand and weigh the consequences of our choices.

Even if a particular consciousness sports an exceptionally dim and rudimentary awareness such as the consciousness of AUO or those first clumps of biological cells in the earth's primordial ooze, the Fundamental Process, teamed with the statistics of probable interaction, and given enough opportunity, will produce change and eventually growth. Consciousness is interactive because it is aware. It evolves when given an opportunity to find profit through making choices that may reflect both purposeful intent and serendipity. Thus, the motive force driving individuated consciousness interactivity and evolvement is none other than a basic application of the same Fundamental Process that populated our planet.

Consciousness is a oneness, a unitary fundamental digital form of organizational energy that is capable of reducing its entropy permanently by interacting with itself in a process that increases awareness and brightness (capability to be profitable) of the overall consciousness system. All this from AUO's evolutionary discovery that one especially profitable form of self-interaction involves subdividing into specialized parts and letting those parts evolve their own patterns. Patterns define rules and organization; eventually memory and processing evolve to coordinate the whole. This progression should seem familiar – carbon and silicon sharing the same fundamental processes of consciousness evolution.

Evolution is also a oneness – a unitary fundamental **process** capable of organizing an entity's potential to effect profitable change, to explore the possibilities, and to initiate a directed march of progress. Evolution is a process that experimentally optimizes system profitability moment by moment through the natural selection of what works. Evolution is a natural organizer, a reducer of entropy. It goads whatever exits to organize itself more profitably.

Recall that a complex self-relational system with the right attributes may generate an energy-form with enough self-organizational potential to synergistically interact with the Fundamental Process of evolution thereby creating an individuated consciousness that is independent of the mechanisms that support it. Think of individuated consciousness as the synergy generated by a self-organizing subsystem of digital potential energy. Evolution working upon consciousness produces All That Is – at least all we can directly know about – in the form of a gigantic multileveled fractal ecosystem.

The Big Picture should be beginning to take shape in your mind. Consciousness energy of sufficient capacity naturally evolves itself into a dynamic system of interactive processes that generate cumulative self-modifying growth. Expanding the synergy that is derived from more profitably organizing the potential of your consciousness is equivalent to increasing your quality and lowering your entropy. Does it amuse or astound you that as an individuated self-organizing digital system, a more profitable configuration of your personal digital content is called spiritual growth? Could you have imagined that spirituality and science would one day converge in a digital systems view of reality? Think about that. Isn't it amazing how Big Truth in one elegant assertion pulls seemingly opposite concepts into a unified broader understanding? The capability to make a meaningful whole out of disparate pieces is the hallmark of Big Truth.

The fundamental evolutionary process needs only one thing other than itself to form a dynamic progressive system of being. That one thing is a source and form of self-relational potential synergy capable of generating a rich array of interrelated organizational possibilities of varying profitability relative to its internal and external environments. Together, consciousness and evolution create aware beings, systems, or entities that are self-modifying and that exhibit directional growth toward increased functional and operational profitability. At the most basic level, consciousness is simply a self-optimizing digital system that exhibits the four attributes given at the beginning of Chapter 7 of this book.

Both of the basic assumptions upon which *My Big TOE* is based turn out to be unitary fundamental concepts that may be applied to many different configurations of being. All entities on all levels within all realities have the same basic consciousness and are motivated by the same basic Fundamental Process. Nevertheless, the diversity of being is immense – beyond your wildest limited imagination – because the two defining concepts are exceedingly simple and open. At their foundation, all forms of being are of one substance, one drive, and one source.

▶ "Welcome home Al Guy!! Hey Bro', long time no see!"

"I know, I know, it took us carbon-based life-forms a long time to get to the information and computer revolution. What can I say? We're the slow but steady type – trust me, it's a jungle out there! But hey, let's forget all that, now that you have arrived let's go down to Darwin's Pub and chug a few brews together. My little sister works there; she's pretty cool and will only charge us for every other round. I'll introduce you…hmmm… say, you don't have bugs do you?

"Oh no, no problem, I just thought I'd ask… you know… nobody's perfect – I know that. …..On second thought, let's forget the brew; Darwin's is always crowded and noisy anyway. Let's just take a walk in the park and go over new times. I'll fill you in on what we carbies have been up to during the last millennia, and you can give me the latest data dump on that new virtual reality game they are working on down at Sam's Virtual Reality Emporium. Deal? Great! Just a minute, let me get some fresh batteries for my lap-top – I know how annoying it is for you to need to shut-down in the middle of a good data dump. OK pal, we're outta here!" ◀

24

■■■

A Functional Model
of Consciousness

Puddle Evolution Starts a Revolution
(Hey Jake, Your Great⁹⁰⁰⁰
Grandmother Was a Retarded Puddle)

■■■

These bounded puddles of seemingly discrete conscious beings now represent the lumps in the sheet we discussed in Chapter 1 of this book. The first thing AUM finds out is that consciousness, in the form of individuated sentient entities, naturally evolves to greater degrees of awareness if it and what it is interacting with (its internal and external environments including other entities) provides sufficient mutually profitable growth opportunities.

AUM discovers the Fundamental Process and the result that consciousness naturally migrates from dim to bright while following the carrot of profitability through a multitude of possibilities. Bear in mind that with brightness comes discrimination and values and that values create interactions with intent. Values, expressed by intent, lead to actions that reflect individual quality and motivation. By the time values appear in the evolutionary development of an individual consciousness energy system, entropy has been lowered sufficiently to allow the concepts of purposeful intention, premeditation, and planning to take root.

From this fertile mental ground, an intellect that thinks, or at least thinks it thinks, eventually develops. Now it is time for individuated consciousness to pay the price for munching those tasty apples – the ability to think, reason, and exercise free will (or at least emulate those processes) opens up a realm of possibilities (both profitable and un-profitable) for intentional interaction and relationship. Like AI Guys who are allowed to self-optimize and change a limited portion of their top-level rule-set (ostensibly to optimize their performance), first AUO, and then our puddle ancestors became intellectually self-aware entities with responsibility for their own evolution.

With self-awareness and the ability to make and execute plans, the number of possible unique states that a conscious individual or group of interactive conscious beings can expand into explodes exponentially. Evolutionary potential and the personal responsibility for that potential are dramatically increased simultaneously. First, AUM progresses through this process of successful consciousness evolution, then, eventually, the constrained individuated puddles of evolving consciousness follow in its footsteps. Evolution knows no rank or privileged class; all evolving consciousness, bright or dim, must follow the same process of entropy reduction.

A free will in command of a sufficiently large decision space will eventually develop intellectual self-awareness with enough capacity to be in control of itself. Such a consciousness must deal with delusion, accept responsibility, and develop its own potential. Evolving one's consciousness past a certain point (eating the metaphorical apples from the tree of knowledge) exacts a price – the potential to develop great personal power and high rates of growth, being susceptible to fear and delusion, and being responsible for one's intents, actions, and personal quality all come in the same awareness package.

Free will choice is now firmly connected to motivation, intent, and quality. If AUM can design an environment (virtual reality) that enables its individuated chunks of puddle consciousness to optimize their evolution, it could begin to develop a self-sustaining consciousness cycle (see Chapter 31, Book 1) to support its own existence. The cyclical process might look something like this: Develop and generate low quality individuated units of beginning consciousness with free will and let the fundamental process eventually evolve them to higher quality and lower entropy ➡ study and experiment with the process until it becomes as efficient as possible ➡ continue to recycle the unused and less productive bits until the entire ecosystem's entropy goes to some minimum value ➡ up-load results to a larger system and start over or lower the minimum value and continue entropy reduction (see Chapters 31 and 32 of Book 1).

Yo, being! Watch out for that first step...it's a big one. Oops!

The range of differing values, intents, interaction strategies, cultures, and civilizations into which consciousness may evolve is exceptionally wide; some are going to be more profitable and functional than others. An immediate burning need arises to explore the evolution and application of values, their associated profitability, the degree of brightness they encourage, and the rate at which evolutionary growth changes occur under varying circumstances.

Because the variables in this consciousness profitability study appear to be nonlinear functions of each other, they must be viewed from the holistic system perspective of an individuated consciousness with free will. To ensure its own developmental progress, AUM must assess and understand the various qualities of consciousness in terms of the evolutionary consequences of values, intention, motivation, and self-awareness. An aware evolving AUM needs to constantly assess and explore its potential for increasing profitability. Self-optimization is the name of the evolutionary game at every level.

The most important attribute of any conscious interaction is its intent. It is the intent that reflects the values and defines the quality of the consciousness doing the interacting. For this reason, it is necessary for AUM to restrict discrete individuated units of consciousness from overlapping their processes and content. It would be counterproductive to the purpose of their individuation if they could intrusively read and inject thoughts into each others' minds. Without some control over one's own mind-space, the genuine intentions, and therefore the quality of an **individual** consciousness, would be hopelessly convoluted and difficult to ascertain. It would be almost impossible and not at all straightforward to determine who was intending what, and why.

Without privacy, most interactions would evolve toward a stilted political correctness. Pointy headed professors from the know-it-all left side of mind-space would join forces with the "I know best" dogma police of the right side of mind-space to induce the great middle of mind-space to become mindless-space. Without the ability to wrap personal naughtiness in a plain brown wrapper, honest individuality might well give way to thoughtless conformity.

The price that must be paid to protect and encourage the integrity of the individual (to let it expresses itself accurately) is a huge black market in closet-depravity. But that is how AUM needs it to be; the quality of the interaction needs to straightforwardly and directly reflect the quality of the being. Additionally, individuated consciousness needs to start at the lowest practical level of profitable organization and evolve toward higher quality, lower entropy forms. There would be no point, nothing would be learned, and no entropy would be reduced, if everyone started at the finish line.

If you ever wondered why a nice digital-consciousness-love-being like AUM would populate our world with so many jerks, now you know: This is simply how it must be to be at all.

Without personal control of the thoughts residing in your mind-space, your uniqueness is questionable. Without a free will that is able to make both good and bad choices, your consciousness is not viable, useful, or sustainable. The common ploy of sidestepping responsibility by blaming others would take on a new sense of credibility if the shared, interactive, or communicative mind did not have a mechanism to sort the thoughts you generate from the thoughts generated by others.

Notice that the awareness of these sentient entities is progressively more and more isolated as layer after layer of constraints are added to allow individuated units of consciousness to express their inner quality interactively and straightforwardly, thus optimizing their ability to evolve.

Your consciousness is clearly an individual thing and not a group thing. That is why spiritual growth, improving the quality of your consciousness, and the evolution of your awareness must be an individual thing. Only you can do it for you; no one else can help very much. The quality of your consciousness is your responsibility and can be affected only by you. This is not a harsh judgment, leaving you stranded and alone in the sometimes dangerous and often unfathomable jungle of mind-space. It is simply the nature of consciousness, how reality is. You should accept that fact and begin work as an individual instead of looking for solace in, or expecting progress from, a group activity or from reading a book like this one. To be sure, these outside factors can be helpful in stimulating and aiding your **process** of learning, but by themselves they can effect no change in the quality of your being.

Among the more retarded (more limited and constrained) puddles in Puddledom, there is now a growing sense of "I" versus "not I" as these beings form personal identities and histories that differentiate themselves from all others and everything else. Thus, the sense of "I" as a separate being is born from the need to isolate each consciousness unit to the point where it can effectively evolve and where the process of individual consciousness evolution can be efficiently studied, understood, and optimized. AUM, as a unique finite individual consciousness, is most interested in the evolutionary dynamics of finite individual consciousness.

This discussion of individual consciousness may make you wonder if there is such a thing as group consciousness. There is, but group consciousness is not a different form of consciousness, it is merely a group of individual consciousness sharing intent and data in common. The good news is that group consciousness is an extremely efficient way to distribute information, values, and content to produce a profoundly shared experience. The bad news is that the level or quality of interaction tends to gravitate toward the lowest common dominator because higher quality consciousness can, with little to no effort, always step down to where it came from while lower quality cannot easily step up to expressions it has never attained. Group mind, in order to stay cohesive and connected, must degenerate to the lowest **common** acceptable quality level.

▶ For a few examples of group consciousness, consider the participants at a religious revival meeting, a group of vigilantes, a topnotch athletic team, a street gang, or a large group of teenagers hanging out at the local mall or high school parking lot. Group consciousness, sometimes degenerating to mob consciousness, can generate bizarre and brutal behavior. On the other hand, some would say the group consciousness that permeates a rock concert simply creates a better party atmosphere.

Culture itself is a form of group consciousness. Widely shared beliefs (cultural, religious, scientific, personal, social, or political) represent a manifestation of group mind. Social animals (such as those who typically congregate in herds, packs, flocks, colonies, pods, societies, nations, religions, or terrorist cells) exhibit a group consciousness that is focused upon common goals (success, safety, or anxiety reduction, for example) and held together by common instincts, beliefs, needs, and traditions. It is a fact that much of what we claim as independent thought and hold as unquestionable truth is actually no more than a knee-jerk expression of group mind reciting the shared beliefs that bind us together. This is another example of an attribute that is as easy to see in other social groupings (terrorist cells, political parties, or religions to which we do not belong) as it is difficult to see in our own.

We are just as committed to what appears to us as obvious truth delivered up by the various group minds we belong to as is any other member of any other group. The subjective reality of higher entropy individuals (most of us) is defined by their beliefs. Precious little of what is significant within our everyday local reality is other than subjective. The objective tidbits that do impose themselves upon us are usually used as nails upon which we hang more important subjective interpretations.

Given that group mind naturally degenerates to the lowest common acceptable quality level, what does this fact logically infer about some of your favorite independent thoughts and unquestionable truths? Better grab hold of some open minded skepticism and take a look: Nothing is easier or more natural – or more difficult to see – than self-delusion. ◀

Differentiated, motivationally discrete, bounded units of consciousness must necessarily evolve a non-overlapping mechanism for communicating or interacting with each other. The most obvious and simplest mechanism would be the direct transfer of discrete thought packets. Information transfer by discrete thought packets can, in one of its forms, be called telepathy. Think of telepathy as adding data to (organizing bits within) someone else's calculation space.

Each individual bounded consciousness must be able to control the communications flowing in both directions. Incoming data would have to be willfully or intentionally let in or blocked out, while outgoing data must be willfully pushed out and directed to one or more potential receivers. The concept of implementing sentient interactions by transferring discrete thought packets has many implications. One obvious implication is the realization that thought is energy (thought organizes bits), which leads to the further realization that consciousness is energy (consciousness is organized bits). Its potential is the potential to be better organized (creating synergy, improving quality, lowering entropy). An active, aware, loving, bright consciousness system is a very low-entropy energy system. It represents a highly structured or organized energy form that has the ability to do much work, or equivalently, has considerable personal power.

The brighter (more aware) the consciousness system is, the less entropy it contains. Unlike physical (PMR) systems, the entropy of a consciousness system does not have to increase with time. The consciousness spring is not doomed to wind down – it is a frictionless system; entropy can rise or fall based on the activity within the system. You might say (if you were a hopeless technoid like me) that AUM is experimenting with, studying, and applying a methodology and process to optimally decrease the entropy of its system by encouraging subsets of itself to decrease their entropy through directed evolution.

"Read that last sentence to me again Jake! I think I might have heard something that at least sounded important... I just can't tell for sure.

Thanks Jake. Those technoids sure do talk pretty don't they?

Ohhhmygaaaaawd! Here it comes ... hold it ... hold it ... I think I am about to get it now...

I'm expanding ... expanding ... expanding ...

Oh yeah! ... Oh yeah! I can feel the impending illumination.

Ahhhhhhhhhhh

Ooooh, that was good! I feel lighter and sooo much better!

What? Enlightenment?

Nah! Just gas.

"Hey, toss me another chug-a-lug, pal! I think I'm running out of entropy."

25

■■■

A Functional Model
of Consciousness

Damn! We Finally Find
a Plentiful Source of Cheap Energy
and It Turns Out to be Us!

■■■

Mass is a highly structured form of energy: Einstein taught us that. He also tried to convince us that all energy was contained within a non-physical unified field, but failed because he could not derive the Big Picture from the little picture. Incredibly, he made it to within one or two belief traps of the right answer but the solution was outside of his (and everybody else's) cultural reality. He was ahead of his time, and one can only get so far ahead before the logical and conceptual ground disappears beneath one's feet. The time was not yet ripe for Big TOE discovery.

That consciousness represents the most fundamental energy in our system and that mass is a construct of (as opposed to, "is constructed of") consciousness is as true as the equivalence between mass and energy, but less widely known. Exactly how mass is experienced through a construct of consciousness is explained later in this section. Consciousness, self-motivated digital organization, is the fundamental energy – actually, the only energy. Everything else that we are familiar with represents a virtual energy causing virtual change within a virtual reality according to the space-time rule-set.

"Are you kidding? Does that mean that a hydrogen bomb releases virtual energy that blows up a virtual city full of virtual people and structures?"

No, I'm not kidding. We accomplish those sorts of horrific calculations in our war games all the time, so why can't TBC do the same? This will be clear in a little while so stop rolling your eyes as if I suddenly sprouted two heads and turned into a monster from the delusional abyss. Hang with me and you will see how this works and that it is more logical (and better explains the data of your objective and subjective experience) than anything else you ever heard about reality back in PMRville.

If nothing changes, nothing new can happen. Energy can be defined as having the capacity or ability to make something happen – to produce change. A discrete thought packet not only requires energy to send it out, but the packet itself contains energy (has the ability to change something). It can add new energy as well as new content (information) to the consciousness of the receiver. Within a digital consciousness, the concepts of energy and virtual energy blend together to become indistinguishable at the root. If you prefer to consider AUM and consciousness as virtual energy forms, that's fine – it makes little practical difference to this very practical trilogy. Virtual vs. real, like nonphysical vs. physical, is relative to your point of view.

▶ Given that everything within the digital self-organizing system (mind) we call AUM is virtual, what does the word "real" mean? Are the binary reality cells of which AUM is composed real? Recall that reality cells exist only in relation to something else (distorted versus non-distorted). Taking the final step to the very bottom level of existence, we find the mental media that has the ability to distort a portion of itself. This mysterious mental media is supplied by our second basic assumption: It is the potential energy system (potential to organize) we called AUO, which eventually begins to self-organize into consciousness. Recall that our assumption of a primordial consciousness potential satisfies the logical requirement that any successful Big TOE must have at least one assumption that appears to be beyond knowing (mystical) from the viewpoint of PMR. (See Chapters 18 and 20 in Book 1.)

Our first basic assumption, the Fundamental Process of evolution, provides the process that drives this media to seek lower average entropy through improved self-organization.

It would appear that only organization (this versus that, rules, and patterns) and process (self-modification toward lower entropy, which is essentially self-modification toward more effective organization) are real and all else is digitally derived (virtual).

Note that our two basic assumptions (Chapter 24, Book 1) supply all the required fundamentals – the real stuff – from which everything else is derived.

Let it go, it's not important to your purpose, your function, or to understanding the biggest picture you can possibly comprehend. Our immediate sense of real and our larger sense of virtual are one in the same. In the bigger picture, AI Guy is as real as you are. ◀

In general, any communication or interaction requires an exchange of energy. The sender intentionally (or unintentionally) impacts the receiver. This condition defines the concept of action, and in the case of energy transfer by discrete thought packets, all such action is intentional. If action is intentional (directed, controlled, willful), the concept of responsibility naturally follows. Now an entity can take or execute an action (that directly affects another being) that is the result of intent and be held responsible for the intent and for the immediate consequences of the action.

This transfer of energy from one individual consciousness to another can be used to deliver a message or to affect the substance and energy of the intended receiver. From the digital perspective, one may think of energy transfers as the ability to affect the arrangement of bits within the organization of another. Allowable interactions are defined by the operative rule-set. A thought-being or individuated conscious entity can readily absorb or interact with thought energy. The efficiency of the energy transfer (coupling or transfer coefficient) can be anywhere from near zero to near 100% depending on the circumstances and specific conditions of the transfer. Relatively high efficiency transfer coefficients between sentient beings are not unusual. Thus, individuated conscious entities can both throw and get hit by a figurative thought-energy-rock as well as send and receive data.

The size of the rock a being could throw (how much one being could impact another's vital energy, organization, and structure) depends on how much thought energy it can move (transfer) with its intent. Theoretically, any being with a mind can affect any other being with a mind, or anything that is a consciousness construct – which is absolutely everything. Thus the connectedness of all beings and things is an artifact of the fundamental nature of consciousness. All beings, and all things, are on the network, have potential access to each other, and can exchange information as well as other forms of energy. We are all interconnected with each other and with everything else because at the most fundamental level we are part of the same consciousness. Our individuation is about entropy and about constraints on our ability to interact, not about being disconnected from the whole.

The energy of one being or thing can be intentionally manipulated or impacted by another. The energy transfer I am referring to takes place in thought-space outside of PMR; its control, function, and possible affects are constrained by the $NPMR_N$ rule-set and not by the space-time rule-set. Nevertheless, its result can directly affect what is experienced in PMR. It should not be surprising that mind can alter a reality created by and within mind.

True enough, it is a jungle out there in mind-space – a natural environment filled with beings and critters trying to maximize their situations, often without regard to others – but it is not entirely a free for all. There are specific rules (experimental protocols) within $NPMR_N$ that restrict the transfer of energy, particularly between separate reality constructs (experiments). Other $NPMR_n$ have somewhat different rules. As in all real systems, the rules are obeyed and enforced most of the time.

We are connected by the fundamental oneness of our consciousness; we are all individuated lumps within, as well as parts of, the same sheet. We are connected by the ability of one individual to vitally affect, and be affected by, another through the purposeful control of thought energy or the energy of consciousness. We are connected by the theoretical ability of one being to exchange energy or information with any other being simply by focusing intent.

The power and focus (energy density) of the transmission, along with the transmission coefficient, determines how much energy is transferred from the sender to the receiver. It is the sensitivity, clarity (low noise) and knowledge-base of the receiver that determines how aware the receiver is of the origins, context, and content of the absorbed energy. Likewise, it is the focus, clarity (low noise) and knowledge-base of the sender that determines how much, what type, and to what end energy can be impart to the receiver. A knowledgeable receiver can refuse, deflect, or return energy sent to him by another entity's intent while an unknowledgeable receiver is comparatively open and vulnerable to whatever is thrown at him.

This connectivity is accomplished by the exchange of discrete packets of consciousness energy and is made possible because we all are extant in, and of, the same **apparently** (but not actually) infinite consciousness. We share and are all part of the same fundamental digital energy source. Though our physical experience must remain exclusively connected to the particular virtual reality (space-time rule-set) that we are presently using to improve the quality of our consciousness, our mind is free to explore and experience the larger reality.

The possibilities for interaction within the larger reality, by number and variation, range many orders of magnitude beyond your wildest imagination, and there are few constraints placed upon what you can do and where you can go. Your aware intentional experiences in $NPMR_N$ often become an integral part of an accelerated growth path as you learn to operate, function, work, play, and make free will choices as a responsible interactive citizen of multiple reality systems. Restricting yourself to PMR is analogous to never leaving your house – never venturing beyond your front door – fine (and relatively safe) for an infant but rather limiting for an adult. Growing up is what your existence is all about.

Everyone is hooked up to the RWW (Reality Wide Web) and has a home page there. There are a few power users, plenty of hackers, and no one is particularly in control. It is a giant, open, super-high bandwidth network with few rules, some informal etiquette, and a personal touch that does not stop at the viewing screen – reach out and bonk someone with an energy exchange that does much more than pass information.

Those who have the understanding and experience to utilize this connectivity effectively, operate at will outside PMR causality. The occasional and somewhat random glimmers of experience that most people have with their connectedness to the RWW are called spontaneous paranormal experiences. Paranormal events are natural artifacts of the nature of consciousness and represent the normal activity of the nonphysical energy that is consciousness. For this reason, they sometimes violate PMR causality rules and are thus vehemently denied by those ensnared within the familiar and comforting grip of widely accepted scientific or cultural beliefs that are based upon the exclusivity of our local physical reality.

Once you understand the nature of consciousness, the nature of reality, and that we are consciousness constructs, the paranormal becomes normal – an everyday fact of existence that is as accessible as gravity. As we pointed out in Section 2 (Chapter 20, Book 1), the words "mystic" and "paranormal" have meaning only in relation to the **normal** level of ignorance within PMR.

▶ Let's take a moment to discuss growing up. To a three year old, almost everything in a given normal day would seem mystical and miraculous. To its parents, who are less ignorant and enjoy a larger perspective from a larger reality, those same activities in that same day are mundane and normal. No big deal, no amazement, no hailing of miracles – ho hum. They don't think about it, they simply live it. They don't seek out ignorant children and try to impress them with their greater adult knowledge and understanding unless they are manipulative, have huge egos, or both.

The kids on the other hand, want to be adults. Much of their play time is spent pretending to be adults and mimicking adult role models. The adults seem powerful and children want, and need (from their perspective) more power. Kids always want to be older, more powerful, and more in control than they are. They can't wait to become teenagers, then to turn 16 and be able to drive a car (freedom and control), then 18 to vote, get married, and legally buy recreational drugs. After that, 21 becomes the big goal (can legally execute contracts and obtain access to a larger selection of recreational drugs). The twenties are cool. During the next decade the pendulum swings the other way and everybody wants to be younger again – but not at the price of giving up their precious hard won knowledge, understanding, maturity, and access to recreational drugs. Nobody wants to be that stupid, naive, or sober again.

Another forty years go by and most would gladly trade everything they have learned during those forty years if they could turn back the clock for a decade. It seems the rate of learning and growing is asymptotically approaching the time axis. The mental rocket fuel appears to have been used up by the mid forties. After that we merely drift on a long slow ballistic trajectory awaiting the inevitable death on impact as we (our bodies) literally return to earth. Typically, little of much value is learned during the exploration of the back forty.

Why is it that relatively little personal growth or maturity is achieved in the last half of a typical PMR life? Why do we coast like that? This cultural tradition (belief) is particularly sad because from forty to eighty years of age is the time when learning should be steeply accelerating as beings get ready for the really important stuff.

Recall that it is a characteristic of aware consciousness that the pace of learning accelerates. The accelerating growth of conscious awareness can be continual, far outlasting physical bodies. What happens that knocks most folks off their natural accelerating ascension to greater maturity, power, freedom, and understanding? Why does the Big Picture stop getting bigger after forty? Why does our reality and self-awareness quit growing?

Many would like to believe that by age forty they know almost everything there is to know about what is both critically important and under their control. They feel as if they have been there and done that – at least everything important and necessary anyway. It seems that two year olds, young teens and people over forty have a tendency to feel this way – all transition ages where the individual self is centered in a small (already mastered) reality awaiting to grow into the next major change of perspective. Why do middle-age folks stop blazing new trails to new frontiers when they turn forty? Let me assure you it is **not** because they know everything that is critically important to the success of their daily lives.

The only reason they can maintain the "been there, done that" illusion is because they actually know and understand so **little** about what is important relative to the next phase of their growth (the same is true for all who are in their transition years). The delusion of omniscience and completeness with regards to the size of their local reality (it appears to be as big as it gets) is an artifact of ignorance and arrogance teaming together to produce an artificial blindness that delivers the same result as simple stupidity. How does this happen to otherwise bright and aware people? Oh, no, jeez – not that! Yes, it is that simple: they get caught in belief traps! PMR experience, which at forty is only at the beginning of a long and magnificent journey, looks as if it is the end of a short walk to nowhere from the perspective that develops from inside the trap. Opportunity lost.

Our culture helps the first two transition ages get out of their belief traps by showing them the next phase (by example of the more powerful majority) and encouraging them to grow up and into a new, better, more capable and more fulfilling mode of awareness. However, the last group, in this day and age, is on their own to figure it out for themselves because they form the majority and thus have the power to define what is accepted as reality within PMR. The third transition is actually the easiest (less turmoil), but it also presents us with the greatest challenge to see through the self-imposed artificial blindness that ignorance and arrogance employs to make us artificially stupid.

Relax; don't get nervous, anxious, upset, or angry. It should be obvious to you by now that I am referring to **other** people here; you and I are different – we are a cut above the unwashed, unknowing masses. If, on the other hand, it is not obvious to you that I am referring to someone else, you have yet another opportunity to grow up. In the words of Forest Gump's philosopher-mother, "Stupid is as stupid does." What could be simpler than that as a criterion for pudding tasters? Never be afraid or ashamed of being stupid, only of remaining that way when you have an opportunity to change.

Imagine what it would be like if the great majority of adults acted as if they were fourteen years old? Doesn't that vision send chills up and down your spine! Contemplate what it would be like living in (being trapped in) such a place. Think of it ladies, **everybody** would be that way instead of just the men! Wow! What a scary concept. When we do not grow up in the appropriate way at the appropriate time, we, and everything and everybody around us, suffers the consequences.

I told you those belief traps were dangerous! Space-time is a great place to learn and eventually, when you are ready and grown up enough to graduate, the belief traps will melt away along with the fear and ignorance that created them. Without fear your existence will be filled with love, peace, and balance. But don't let me rush you; this is not a timed test. If you are presently indifferent toward love, peace, and balance, that's OK; if your personal consciousness evolves in the positive direction (toward lower entropy), eventually that attitude will change. Take all the time you need and don't worry that you are being overlooked as a candidate for graduation. When you are ready, graduation is automatic.

If you feel as if you are ready to graduate but nothing is happening, your learning is not accelerating and you are not as ready as you think. The evolution of consciousness does not work like public school. You are not passed to the next grade until you have mastered the material, and you do not graduate simply because you are old enough and want to. Kids do not need to be given permission, sent to classes, or read a how-to book to grow into adults. For most of them, it simply happens; childish behavior drops away and adulthood comes when they are ready for it, whatever their age. Progressing through the learning process in the space-time learning lab of PMR works the same way. ◀

A discussion of how to use your intent to affect the consciousness and reality of another being or how to filter or reflect what is directed toward yourself would require its own book. Though many may be interested, this subject represents much more than I want to stuff into this already badly swollen Big TOE. I do not want to get too far a field here, so unless there are questions, we will leave this subject until we visit it again in Section 5.

I see just one hand in the air. The question: Where and how do you get help, guidance and direction to study for the space-time challenge and improve your progress in completing the learning lab assignments? The same way you get help in becoming a mature adult. Go ask one (a mature adult) if you need advice, but mostly you need to figure it out on your own. Be careful: All apparently grown people are not necessarily mature adults. If you are not one, how do you know one when you see one? It is an iterative process containing a very large number of very small steps. Figuring out how to most effectively pull yourself up by your own bootstraps is a problem that you need to individually work out because you are a unique entity. Pulling yourself up by your own bootstraps or bootstrapping is operationally similar to how a child grows up, or to the incremental processes that an athlete uses to build balance, strength, coordination, stamina, strategy, and skill. The difference being that you are exercising and conditioning your intent instead of your muscles and coordination.

I will take one more question before we go on. Yes, in the back. That's right, the cute blond in the tight red sweater. Quiet everyone! I am sorry sweetie, I couldn't hear you, please repeat your question. (Put down your weapons ladies, I am only joking about that "tight-sweater-sweetie" thing. The asker is actually a nerdy looking male engineer with oily hair, dual pocket protectors, and a bad complexion, but I am pretending it is a gorgeous blond in order to trick my male readers into paying closer attention...sigh...you know how it is...you have to use whatever works.)

Here is the question: She already does all the right things – including meditation, chanting, yoga, incense, crystals, warrior movement classes, and Ti Mei Shu massage therapy and has been to every New Age training course, seminar, and hoe-down ever given by anyone who has published at least one book on the topic. She has read every book on the philosophy, religion, and New-Age shelves at the local bookstore at least twice, has seen and consulted with gurus and self-proclaimed wise-persons of all types yet there is little spiritual progress. She wants to know: 1) what else (other books, classes, or practices) she should be doing, and 2) why advanced nonphysical beings have not come to help her when she is obviously ready for them to do so.

Oh jeez, I knew I should have quit with this question thing while I was ahead.

All right. The answer is much simpler than the question. 1) Stop **doing** and start **being**. 2) No one is ever overlooked. You get all the nonphysical help you can use and need, even if it is not what you want, expect, or think you are ready for.

Help is always available and more or less automatically applied to those who are ready to make good use of it. Your physical and mental existence becomes more directed as you become more capable of interacting with, responding to, and understanding the direction given, and as you become more able to learn from, and capitalize on, the effort made in your behalf.

A favorite saying of wise horses everywhere is "You can lead a human to knowledge, but you cannot make him think or understand."

26

■■■

A Functional Model
of Consciousness

Rugged Individualists Fail
to Deliver the Goods

■■■

The requirement to push out or direct discrete energy packets specifically to other beings has several important consequences affecting the evolutionary capacity of conscious beings. One result of this arrangement is that given a non-hostile external environment, an individuated consciousness ends up, to a large extent, creating its own internal environment. Its will, intent, and motivation lets in and sends out only what its free will wants to. Unpleasant or unwanted packets are ignored or deleted while the link to the source of those unpleasant packets is simply turned off.

Wouldn't it be wonderful to be able to turn off or ignore everything that is annoying or unpleasant in your existence? And why can't you do that? Because there is an external reality out there that you are strongly interdependent with. As much as you want to turn it off, it will not go away. It waits for you, stalks you, and will not let you ignore the results of your accumulated choices. This strong interdependence forces you to define and share a common reality with other players.

An "I'll have it my way" individualism might seem ideal, but it generates relatively weak (in an evolutionary sense) interactions between independent, discrete units of consciousness. Though these individuated sentient entities interact profusely and form connections (relationships) with each other, each individual is essentially an **independent** reality unto itself. Interactions are weak because there is a weak connection between an action reflecting intent and the consequences and result of that action. A strong accountability-feedback link needs to be forged connecting intent, action, and the results of that action leading directly to consequences for both parties involved in the interaction.

Weak interactions produce slow development, slow rates of evolution, and therefore slow experimental results. Initially $NPMR_N$, which is designed to provide the law abiding non-hostile external environment mentioned above (limited protection from rock throwers) was only a partial success. The problem is that no forcing function exists to optimize interactions for evolutionary growth between individualistic puddles of consciousness that can filter out everything they do not like. The intent ➡ action ➡ event ➡ feedback ➡ to new intent learning cycle was vague, difficult to define and lacking sharp evolutionary teeth. There was no quick, clear, and dramatic mechanism to separate the profitable intent driven choices from those that were unprofitable. Nevertheless, $NPMR_N$ continues to support a rich growth of interactive beings of all sorts.

$NPMR_N$ continues to flourish and evolve an immense selection of life-forms outside the various space-time PMR_k. The beings of $NPMR_N$ might be thought of (by the residents of PMR) as bounded, discrete thought forms. Their **individual** existence is made possible because of limitations and constraints that have been applied to their consciousness, however, their individuality develops from how they react and change as a result of their interactions with other beings. The quality of their consciousness develops from the quality of their interactions, which is dependent upon the quality of their intent and motivation. The boundary defining the individuality of these beings, separating inside from outside, I from other, identifies the exterior of their bodies, while their awareness is identified as their minds.

▶ From the perspective of AUM, NPMR is a virtual reality containing other virtual realities. If you think in terms of an apparently infinite digital consciousness reality (where an Even Bigger Computer (EBC) contains TBC as a subset), the idea of stacked simultaneous virtual realities each in their own dimension is not a difficult concept – imagine multiple simulations with multiple levels of subroutines running in a big mainframe. The interactive players that inhabit the NPMR virtual reality game must follow their own rule-set and believe that they possess bodies just as we believe that we posses bodies. In their world, their bodies are as real and physical to them as our bodies appear real and physical to us in our world. When you visit their world physically, you interact with them, body and soul, according to their rule-set.

From our little perspective in PMR we just don't get the concept of nonphysical body – it sounds impossible and stupid – a moronic oxymoron. That is because we do not appreciate the bigger picture where every individuated consciousness in a virtual reality

26

■ ■ ■

dimension **believes** that they have a solid body (that is, after all, the purpose of a virtual reality). Furthermore, we do not appreciate that when one virtual reality (such as NPMR$_N$) contains another one (such as PMR), where each is connected to the other only through the doorway of mind (common RWW connection among all consciousness within the larger consciousness system), the entities within each reality must necessarily perceive themselves to be physical (real) and all other reality dimensions to be non-physical. The less aware beings in both realities think that the possibility of the existence of the other is stupid and contradictory, while the more aware beings of both interact freely with each other within a larger reality that contains both of these local virtual worlds plus many others.

I urge you to climb out of your local reality-neighborhood and learn to work, play, and interact with the big kids in the big reality. You need to step out of the sandbox before you can explore the larger playground, much less the city, state, country, and planet in which the sandbox resides. Though it will require some courage and dedicated effort on your part, it can be fun, rewarding, educational, and will unquestionably broaden your experience and perspective immensely. Reread Chapter 23, Book 1 to learn how. ◀

Nonphysical non-space-time beings in NPMR have bodies with shape and form that must follow the rules of their own local reality. The interactive content within each reality-dimension must adhere to its own rule-set. Whereas our cute little space-time bodies are genetically determined, cast in mass and restrained to contiguous 3D motion, their bodies are energetically and functionally determined, cast into habituated forms, and can travel as information packets on the Reality Wide Web (RWW) network (if they know how). Those NPMR beings who have gained enough awareness, knowledge, and understanding can change their form and connect and disconnect to various sources of interaction energy-exchange at will.

Beings that inhabit other space-time PMRs see themselves as we see ourselves (physical beings in a physical universe) and share many of the same rules and limitations that define our reality. When one visits a reality outside one's native dimension, one can remain invisible and non-physical (from the visited reality's perspective) or create an appropriate body and interact as one of them. Each type of interaction, when permitted, has its own set of rules and conditions. Obey the rules and don't make a mess of things or your visitation privileges will be revoked.

Like us, the quality of a nonphysical (from our viewpoint) entity's consciousness and the degree to (and direction in) which they have evolved is reflected by their intent. They are also driven, animated, and limited by their individual awareness, fear, ego, needs, wants, and capacity for love.

Their choices (and thus, opportunities for growth) are made by applying intent to an interaction with other beings through the exercise of free will. Functionally they appear to be just like us don't they? That is because functionally they are our ancestors, our brothers and sisters, in the great NPMR$_N$ consciousness experiment.

Let's take a moment to pull together a quick round-up of where we are and how we got there.

We start with AUO representing plain undifferentiated consciousness energy and watch it and the Fundamental Process of evolution together develop dim awareness as AUO differentiates some part of itself from other parts. As dimness gives way to brightness, AUO morphs into AUM to become a fully aware operational consciousness, a purposeful low entropy mind with staggering storage and processing capability.

Consciousness is individual and interactive by nature. In order to understand interactive consciousness, AUM first set up a situation in which interactions between individual consciousness units would occur. This interactivity is motivated by the inquisitive probing (into the available states of being) that is stimulated when the Fundamental Process of evolution is applied to the organization of aware consciousness potential energy. However, because the evolution of consciousness is an individual thing, the trick for AUM is to optimize and maximize the available useful information in each intent ➡ action ➡ result ➡ feedback interaction per conscious entity.

This is done by limiting and precluding overlap of the individual functions and processes involved in conscious interaction, thus isolating the awareness and the genuine intentions and results of the individuated being. This now isolated and limited awareness with its newfound sense of separateness must exist (seemingly trapped) within a virtual external environment containing a large number of potential interactors with whom it can exchange energy.

Unfortunately, this environment provides only a weak incentive to evolve because the interactive beings are only weakly interdependent. This causes the intent ➡ action ➡ result ➡ feedback learning cycle to hang from a weak thread of causal responsibility, thus rendering the evolutionary processes inefficient. PMR and its defining rule-set are specifically designed to overcome those built-in learning disabilities by providing the optimal learning lab for budding consciousness.

27

■■■

A Functional Model
of Consciousness

Space-Time: The Design Solution for
Optimal Consciousness Evolution

■■■

After trillions of individuated consciousness units were interacting within NPMR, it became apparent that NPMR does not offer the optimal environment and rule-set for the evolution of consciousness quality. Although every consciousness unit has the potential to evolve its quality to the level of its source, not much progress, on the average, was being made. Eventually, the expansion of consciousness units became self-perpetuating. Some bounded thought-form entities in NPMR developed the capability to create self sustaining thought-forms of their own. That should not be so surprising, after all, they were chips from the old AUM block and every chip (including you) can, to the limit of its capacities, develop the potential of the whole.

Eventually individuated consciousness was producing (reproducing) new forms of individuated consciousness. You can easily imagine the creative free-for-all that ensued. These newly created units started with at least a partial copy of the content of their creators. Though each represented a new and independent being in consciousness-space, they were a derived consciousness and therefore also represented some of the form and much of the potential (however limited) of the conscious awareness they were derived from.

Over time, competing profitable strategies and ways of being began to coalesce around several differing sets of values. Attitude and values spawned needs and wants. Those whose intent and motivation was focused on serving themselves and using others approached things differently from those whose intent and motivation was focused on using themselves to serve others. The prototypes for good and evil were formed, as were families, clans, societies, and other various social, racial, and political groupings. Personal, social and political dynamics are still in play; continual change is inherent to evolving systems.

Many such groups exercise their free will and play out their evolution within $NPMR_N$ and OS. Some of these, along with others, inhabit various independent reality systems within the diverse $NPMR_n$. Rules were set up (evolved) by AUM within TBC to constrain certain types of interactions or behavior (mostly destructive) within $NPMR_N$. Enforcement of these experimental protocols was relatively strict but not perfect. Within $NPMR_N$, we now have consciousness and its progeny evolving within broad behavioral constraints sometimes referred to as cosmic law. There were no constraints on intent, only on the action that followed intent.

In this manner, beings of all sorts interacted and evolved for a long time until the rate of evolutionary progress began to go asymptotic. Eventually, new growth and learning rates slowed dramatically because existence was essentially continuous. All beings were, like AUM and all consciousness, more or less immortal. Digital beings, if not deleted or damaged, last as long as the computer (AUM). From your point of view, that is immortal with a capitol "I". Yes, my friend, you as an individuated consciousness are essentially immortal – unless you screw up and get zapped by the Big Cheese or mugged by some tough guy or mean-spirited anti-rat. The apparent mortality of your virtual physical body is simply a device to facilitate your learning; local mortality is irrelevant to the apparently endless continuation of your digital awareness.

Only disintegration into an unorganized high-entropy pile of reality cells could completely terminate a conscious being. Though any degree of damage (usually self-repairable if not fatal) can be imparted or inflicted in a multitude of ways; catastrophic personal-identity or individual disintegration does not happen naturally. Because $NPMR_N$ has a policy of prohibiting certain types of destructive interactions among law-abiding citizens, beings once generated tended to persist indefinitely. Eventually, AUM modified some of the rules as he went – for example, the creators of a new entity were held responsible for establishing the quality of that new entity and helping it get a good start on a productive evolutionary track. All consciousness within $NPMR_N$, including us (PMR is part of OS which exists within $NPMR_N$), reflects that protocol. We innately (a reflection of our top level rule-set) want our offspring to prosper beyond mere survival and procreation.

In general, increased **personal** responsibility in pursuit of the goal of entropy reduction was just what the doctor ordered for NPMR$_N$.

Still, there was no way for a single being to accumulate growth through a series of fresh starts. The traps that entities had laid for themselves, the fantasies and beliefs they created merely grew deeper, more comfortable, and more substantial with time. Fresh opportunities grew less visible and less obvious as ways of interacting became old and familiar. Innovative thinking and creative approaches became difficult to come by. Everyone had that "been there, done that" feeling – familiar ruts and cultural beliefs grew so deep that few could escape them. The rate of growth to an overall higher quality of consciousness slowed to a sub-optimal crawl.

AUM needed to design a new experimental protocol and define a new rule-set with additional and cleverer constraints. What were the design requirements? The system needed a being that could start over with a clean slate, without the accumulated delusions of the past but with its accumulated knowledge and wisdom intact. The evolutionarily inefficient weak interactions and personal anarchy of NPMR$_N$ mind-space needed to be changed so that personal responsibility, and immediate (relatively so) accountability linked each intent and action with the consequences and result of that action. Because responsibility, accountability, and immediate feedback were poorly defined and subject to individual interpretation in mind-space making learning difficult, this newly designed virtual reality must unambiguously and clearly track, maintain, and enforce straightforward causal relationships. The additional constraints required to resolve these issues were imposed upon subsets (unique dimensions) of NPMR$_N$. Our PMR space-time reality is one such subset.

AUM solved these design issues by evolving a space-time rule-set that defines the physical experience or interactions of a set of hybrid beings that simultaneously have both physical and nonphysical components – beings that exist, grow, and evolve in two reality dimensions simultaneously. Mankind, or more generally PMR$_k$-kind, is an exceptionally clever solution, don't you agree?

▶ What does "physical" mean in the context of consciousness? Because aware consciousness exists only in the form of a nonphysical, low-entropy, energy form, how do you build a physical reality from consciousness? These are good questions. I am tickled pink that you are paying sufficient attention to ask these penetrating questions.

Unfortunately, the answers to your questions are out of scope for this tickled pinky TOE, and you will have to catch them in my next, even more expensive book due out at the end of the next millennium. No, no, no! I'm only kidding. Come on…don't get mad, that was just a joke. Remember, learning is supposed to be fun! You are shaking your head, but not smiling. Did I catch you at a bad time? If you think reading this book is difficult to do – a forced march through La La Land – you should try writing it. Did you ever wonder why Yoda lives by himself in a filthy mud hut crawling with snakes on an otherwise uninhabited planet? Think about that.

While we are taking a short break here, I have some free advice for you to pass on to others who might need it. Never let yourself get too wound up over the details – that can make you insufferable and grumpy as well as create a whopping case of tunnel-vision.

Humor keeps our brains lubricated and prevents us from slipping into self-referential stupidity by taking ourselves too seriously. Oh, yes, I am serious (sometimes), but there is a big difference between being serious and taking yourself too seriously. Too much serious work and not enough relaxed play will stunt and twist your growth potential. When you are doing it right (are balanced), work and play merge to become two intertwined and mutually supportive rhythms within one joyful long-lasting boogie.

Of course I will tell you how you and PMR are nothing other than a construct of consciousness. That is what this section is all about – I am simply warming you up first so that you will get it when we get there. This is where you get to combine the notion that you are a consciousness being, extant only in the mind of AUM, with the obvious fact that you have this gorgeous, sexy flesh-and-blood body that is much better at making love than being love. The key to understanding the consistency and sameness of these two seemingly disparate views of your being is to understand the nature of experience. ◀

Before I launch into the subject of experience in the next chapter, there is one concept hanging low on the tree of potential knowledge that is ripe for picking. Let's pick it before it hits the ground and rolls away undetected. Recall that this discussion started with two puddles of differentiated consciousness and has progressed to where AUM is evolving a PMR space-time and populating it with good looking sexy bodies like yours. Each step along the way was necessitated by AUM's goal of studying, understanding, improving and evolving the consciousness that he is, and driven to its logical conclusions by the cooperative integration of the Fundamental Process of evolution with a digital potential energy-form called consciousness. These are the same two assumptions that were given many pages ago as the foundation upon which this Big TOE is constructed (see Chapter 24, Book 1).

The point is: We started with AUO – plain dim consciousness (digital potential energy) and ended up with our beloved PMR by following a reasonable and logical progression that was defined by the interaction of our two basic assumptions. To put it into a simpler context, it follows that a PMR inhabited by us becomes a logically required step within **this particular** series of consciousness experiments. However, there are many ways to skin a cat (please pardon the language Muffy), and we should expect that the Big Dude is running other experiments that develop their own totally different logical requirements. There are multiple manifestations of our particular logical sequence as evidenced by a plethora of PMRs that are fundamentally similar to ours, even though the details of implementation differ widely.

These other realities and other PMRs will be more thoroughly discussed in Section 5 where the nonphysical is the focus. Here, deriving the physical from the nonphysical is the subject at hand. At best, these other consciousness systems (subsets of AUM) are far out on the periphery of our operational reality. They are not of much practical importance to us or to our understanding of our local reality – the reality our awareness operates in on a daily basis. Our Big TOE allows for their existence and understands their nature (same as ours), but doesn't actually care too much about them. They may be an interesting place to visit but, for the most part, you wouldn't want to live there.

What I am implying is that you, I, and PMR (along with other beings and other PMRs) are the logical consequence of the existence of AUM, just as AUM is the logical consequence of the existence of AUO and the Fundamental Process. It would appear that we are not merely some interesting experiment that AUM offhandedly decided it might as well do because there was nobody to talk to. We are a logical requirement, the necessary result of, as well as an integral part of, AUM's evolution. Don't get puffed up over that fact. Wheels are logical requirements of an automobile. Very important, yes, but not deserving to feel superior to the other logical requirements (transmission, breaks, engine, body) of the automobile or to other forms of transportation being explored (airplanes, trains, boats, or their logical requirements including wings, propellers, rudders, or tracks).

Becoming puffed up over the part that you play because your picture is so incredibly tiny and self-focused is counterproductive.

28

■ ■ ■

The Fundamentals of Experience and the Space-Time Rule-Set

■ ■ ■

Let's focus on the subject of experience. Most of our experiences are experiences of and within space-time. To understand the relationship we have with our local physical reality, it will be helpful to take a closer look at the functionality of space-time and how we interact with it. Space-time itself is a mental construct within the apparently infinite consciousness of AUM. Thus, you might say that space-time is made out of consciousness, but that would be misleading. "Made out of" sounds, to our PMR trained ears, like bricks and mortar – construction materials. Space-time is not built out of chunks of consciousness; it is a specific configuration of consciousness. Realities (and you too for that matter) are not made of consciousness; they are a limited implementation of consciousness developed to serve a particular evolutionary purpose (occupy an available niche) within the greater consciousness ecosystem.

Consciousness is not a construction material in the sense that construction materials are component parts. Houses can be **made of wood** while trees (minus leaves) simply **are wood.** One might say that tree trunks, limbs, twigs, bark, and roots exist as wood constructs – they **are wood**. You are not **made of** consciousness – you, and your physical reality, are consciousness constructs – you **are consciousness**. That is correct: Both individuated conscious beings and PMR are constructs of consciousness similar to the lumps in the sheet. They are constructs of the sheet, not constructed of sheets. Do you see that each expression carries different implicit assumptions? The difference is one of process. The first (constructs of consciousness) speaks of deformations of, or specific organization within, a continuum – lumps in the sheet, while the second (constructed of consciousness) implies building a separate, more complex thing out of something more basic, something entirely different by nature than the thing being built. The deformation or organization of the continuum referred to above is effected by placing constraints (including rule-sets) upon subsets of an apparently infinite digital consciousness, thus bounding them into individual existence relative to the whole.

Many people have the intuitive notion that **consciousness** is the basis for everything else; that consciousness is the substance, the fundamental energy from which everything else is constructed, made, or derived. Some, if they were poetic to a fault, might replace the bolded word "consciousness" with "soul," or more expansively, "the mind of God." These people would be coming from a PMR cultural frame of reference, and would not mind obscuring the plain non-poetical truth within a charged cloud of emotive ambiguity to achieve the familiar comfort of a favorite poem often read. That's all right, no problem, it is a good poetic metaphor. Just one caution: If the use of poetical image ends up confusing your sense of reality with ambiguous abstract symbolic language (the stuff good poetry is made of), then stick with the word "consciousness." Those belief traps are tricky – best stay clear if you are prone to falling in.

That spirit, mind, or consciousness is more fundamental than material objects falls directly and naturally out of the intuition of millions of people – without the intervention and encouragement of religious dogma. It is a common idea that most of us intuitively understand but cannot rationalize. Because it is a typically human characteristic that any answer is better than no answer, many individuals have turned to religious or scientific **belief** to ease the discomfort and anxiety of not knowing how we, consciousness, purpose, and the larger reality are interconnected.

The more inquisitive of our kind have racked their brains for millennia trying to understand how PMR could possibly be made from consciousness or mind. How could our rocky planet, big yellow school buses, atomic bombs, tapeworms, and our spouses and children all be made from consciousness? That just doesn't compute! The question put in those terms leads to a dead end. A better question is: How could our rocky planet, big yellow school buses, atomic bombs, tapeworms, and our spouses and children all be part of a larger consciousness construct? By the time you have progressed through Chapter 34 of this book, that question should be answered and the seeming dichotomy between mind and matter should be resolved.

From an objective PMR point of view, the assertion that we are mind and that PMR is an artifact of experience within a virtual physical reality instead of an actual one, appears unsupportable, delusional, wacko, and just plain dumb. However, it only looks stupid from a PMR point of view that lives deep inside scientific and Western culture belief traps. Hang with me and you will see how this mind-matter thing works itself out.

What does compute is that our interactions with space-time, our bodies, and all the rest of physical matter is a constrained experience of consciousness. The **experience** of PMR takes place within consciousness. That is a less confusing statement than saying that PMR is created **by** consciousness, though both are logically true.

Because our experience in PMR leads us to **believe** unequivocally in the solidity of what we call the physical world, the words "PMR is created" found in the previous sentence produce a sense of making or manufacturing the solid massive objects that we experience. In fact, all that has to be made, produced, or manufactured is the **experience** of the solid massive objects that we experience.

We earlier divided all the perceptions of an individuated consciousness into those that were inside the defining boundary or internal to the being (personal mind), and those that appeared to be outside or external to the being (environment or **other** beings, objects, and energy). Our only contact with the outside world is through our individual perception-based experience. If there is no physical experience (experience that we interpret as physical), then there is no physical world, no physical reality and PMR disappears from our perception and thus ceases to be a part of our personal reality. An entity, who loses contact with its external environment (due to a sensory deprivation chamber, perhaps), retains the full awareness and the full potential of its internal environment.

Be sure to notice that there is a personal as well as a shared reality. The only surprise is that the personal reality turns out to be the big primary one while the shared reality is discovered to be the little virtual one. What a switch! Common wisdom turns out to be 180 degrees out of phase with the truth. That is why this particular paradigm shift is so difficult for most people to negotiate – they come to the discussion culturally calibrated bass-ackwards.

Some are thinking that this line of reasoning is turning into one of those "If a tree falls in the woods and there is nobody there to hear it..." semantic puzzles. It is not. If **you** lose **all your** physical senses, the world will undeniably disappear **for you** – but only for you.

Let's look at this more closely and examine the implicit assumptions. Most people, because of their **belief** in the fundamental realness of PMR, see things with a bias. In their mind, the emphasis is placed on the fact that this is about **them** loosing **their** senses, which has no affect on the physical world or anybody else's ability to sense it. Their point is that even if every sentient thing on the planet lost all of their senses, the planet and PMR would continue to exist. They are absolutely correct from their point of view. Given the belief-generated implicit assumption underlying this view, PMR does not logically depend on anyone's existence.

To help the products of Western culture prove their point to me, I will picture the earth as a newly spun-off blob of molten minerals and elements. Ahhh ha! Exactly as expected, no sentient critters anywhere in the universe and PMR is humming along rather nicely – it doesn't even miss us. In fact, it is probably dreading our eventual arrival....

"Oh no! Not the people! Please don't make me evolve the people! They are such arrogant fools – and stupid too. Give them a cognitive inch, and before long they will believe that if they all happen to blink at the same time I would simply disappear. Jeez, I wish I could quit this job of being physical reality and get some nice cushy inside work."

The underlying hidden assumption is that PMR is fundamental and basic and that we (sentient conscious entities) are not; that the causal relationship flows from PMR to our consciousness; that the outside world (PMR) causes our consciousness awareness, not the other way around. These folks **believe** that we, our consciousness, is physically derived, an effect – not a cause. They think they are physical body-machines (digital or analog) experiencing a virtual consciousness instead of a consciousness experiencing a virtual body.

Determinism is birthed from this same erroneous paradigm because it **assumes** that physical experience defines the one universal reality; after that, consciousness and free will appear to be theoretically impossible. Science is securely stuck in that same belief trap and cannot find a solution that does not conflict with its core beliefs. Although scientist's **belief** in a universal physical reality **appears** reasonable from a PMR point of view, it is in fact exactly opposite from what is true. In a virtual reality (like PMR), what you experience is a rule-based, derived, or computed reality, not a fundamental reality. Back in the real world of fundamental existence, consciousness is the one universal reality.

Turn your cultural assumption upside down and play it backward to find the secret message that will allow you to avoid this particular PMR bias. Instead of seeing us as derived from PMR, see PMR as derived from our experience. If AUM can create our experience within TBC, as we create the rule-set that defines AI Guy's experience, then AUM and TBC can create PMR without breaking a sweat. They don't have to create mass or motion, only the **experience** of mass and motion. That is what a virtual reality is all about – creating experience.

AUM and TBC have only to provide a rule-set that contains or subsumes our PMR physics (known and unknown) and our experience under that rule-set will be an experience of PMR. (Note: Here, as elsewhere in this trilogy, I am using the word "physics" in the most general sense to represent all science.) We perceive PMR reality through only our physical senses. **To create PMR, AUM needs only to impose the rule-set on our consciousness that creates the experience, the perception, of PMR.** Later I will explain exactly how that is done but first we need to understand rule-sets better.

Ponder, for a moment, how an advanced AI Guy works. Think about how rule-sets on at least two levels, combined with multiple executions of the code, enable AI Guy to not only gain experience but learn from it as well. For those of you who are valiantly struggling to remember, I am going to help you out here. The two rule-set levels we mentioned earlier (near the end of Chapter 22 of this book) are: 1) conditionals and algorithms that define what he can do on the lower, local, or immediate level of awareness, and 2) additional constraints at a higher level of generality that define profitability and thus give the arrow of Big Picture progress a clear direction. It is these top level rules that influence why AI Guy does what he does – that specify the goals, values, and purpose of AI Guy's existence. In summary, AI Guy has experience that is constrained by the rule-sets that guide his intent and define his possible interactions with his local reality. He learns from his experience and makes future decisions based on past experience. He may modify, within narrow limits, his lower-level rule-set in order to optimize his learning efficiency.

If there were few limits to these self-modifications, and if he could define his own values by modifying his higher level rule-set as well, AI Guy would, at the local level, become the sole master of his purpose, accountable to only himself. He could possibly become lazy, unfocused and indolent, making no progress toward anything. Or, he could slip out of control into mania, depression, paranoia, cynicism, or schizophrenia. He would be running open loop, as an electronics engineer might say. Without the purpose, focus, and direction provided by the top level rule-set, AI Guy would not know up from down, right from wrong, good from bad, success from failure. Without the imposition of constraints and the setting of goals, little picture tunnel vision would capture his intent for better or for worse. He would need to develop a purpose of his own or risk becoming dysfunctional to himself and others.

▶ Such an AI Guy is reminiscent of HAL from the movie *2001 – A Space Odyssey.* The popular sci-fi theme of nefarious renegade computers turning on their human creators should concern you for more reasons than the obvious. The same thing can happen to you! You can easily follow in HAL's footsteps if you lose, or seriously weaken, the connection to your purpose – whether by ignorance or by pharmacological, psychological, or natural bio-chemical inducements. Our top-level rule-set is not particularly constraining, we should try to pay close attention to the few rules that are there to encourage and guide us toward profitability. If we ignore them we may end up like Hal – or worse.

Boats without rudders, motors, paddles or sails are clearly dysfunctional, but boats without a destination are just as useless if getting from here to there is the issue. Dysfunctionality due to little picture tunnel-vision is so common in our culture that to a large degree it is considered normal – and therefore acceptable, if not actually desirable. The sense of direction and purpose that resides naturally at our core would provide clear guidance if our fear did not press us so hard to deny, subvert, abuse, and distort it to serve our ego's immediate needs, wants, expectations, and desires.

Take action: 1) Repair the rudder, 2) set a destination, and 3) fire up and engage the engine; continually re-engineer all three actions in real-time toward an optimal long-term profitability. As your entropy decreases, the purpose that animates your journey will eventually grow to be bigger than the little picture that gave it birth. ◀

We cannot modify all the rule-sets that define our existence and our experience. We are stuck with the actual physics of PMR (when we are extant in PMR), and with a spiritual need to improve the quality of our consciousness. However, do not forget that our consciousness is part and parcel of the original. As chips from the old AUM block, we have the license and capacity to soar. We have the ability to understand the Big Picture, to be an aware player, an active participant in our evolution. We can be a power-user of, as well as an experiencer within, our larger reality. At the very least, we can view the larger reality by looking through the Big Picture window of our Big TOE. Hey, AI Guy! Look at us; we got a room with a view! Naaah, nah-nah, naaah nah!

29

■■■

Space-Time Starts With a Bang
and Lays Down the Rules

■■■

Let's begin this chapter with a short recapitulation. Our space-time rule-set has evolved to constrain the interactions and communications of the individuated units of consciousness (sentient beings) that are participating in (that inhabit) the space-time virtual reality we call PMR. PMR is a simulated virtual reality that is computed or executed within its own calculation space (dimension) within TBC (a portion of the digital mind of AUM). The design requirements for the lower-level space-time rule-set, which defines the environment and physics of PMR, were developed to optimize the effective and efficient evolution of consciousness quality within $NPMR_N$. There was a need to demand personal responsibility as a condition of existence and to provide strong immediate feedback to guide the learning process.

Furthermore, there was a need to create a recyclable awareness that, by resetting itself periodically, could indefinitely accumulate the relatively rapid early-growth that an evolving entity initially experiences. Such a recyclable awareness could maintain a relatively high growth rate while avoiding belief-trapping itself into a mental corner by simply recycling itself through the PMR virtual experience trainer whenever its evolutionary growth rate becomes unacceptably slow. Though personal beliefs and fears are thus individually eliminated from cycle to cycle, cultural beliefs and fears are passed from generation to generation. Human culture and its history provide a record and a measure of our cumulative progress.

Our space-time is implemented as one of many space-time rule-sets within TBC; its function is to constrain and guide **the experience** of the beings that inhabit it. Individual actions and interactions that take place within this constrained and focused experience-space follow each actor's free will intent. Imagine a huge multiplayer simulation trainer.

Our space-time rule-set defines a dimension of experience within TBC by defining the boundaries of what is allowed and possible within that particular simulation. Among other things, it defines and constrains the allowable energy exchange and message traffic between entities or other generalized players, and thus defines the allowable perception-set for all indigenous space-time entities. Given this, it follows that **interpretations** of these specifically allowed and individually directed perceptions would be created by the individual **receiving** player.

The content of received messages and the impact of received energy are perceived and interpreted (given meaning unique to the receiving individual) by each receiver. Likewise, outgoing messages sent to another player would be received (perceived) and their meaning and significance interpreted uniquely by that other player applying his experience to the message. Each individual consciousness unit with its individual abilities, memory, history, capacity, quality, and free will must interpret the raw data gathered by its sensors in order to transform that data into useful information that has meaning within a personal and a public context. The experience, characteristics, and quality of the individual are used to interpret the sensory data received from the interactive virtual reality simulation in order to develop more profitable intents leading to lower entropy.

The boundary surrounding or differentiating discrete players in space-time may, by rule-set definition, appear to be dense or massive. Likewise, your interaction with another player is constrained (by the space-time rule-set) to follow all the laws of physics that are contained within that rule-set. Recall that a player can be any entity that can interact – sentient (another being), non-sentient (a rock, a river, a sand storm), or energetic. Let's take a simple example from any 3D space-time simulation: Two players are not allowed to occupy the same space at the same time (Newton's first Law). Consequently, players in space-time simulations are required to **share** a finite space-time ecology with other players. Thus, one important characteristic of the experience of 3D space-time is produced by this simple rule: All players appear solid, take up space, and must cooperatively share a limited space with limited resources. Our earthbound interactive computer games know how to invoke this same rule in complex interactive simulations – it evidently is not difficult to do.

Look at the space-time perception issue from a larger point of view. It is this rule-set-physics that drives and defines the experience that each individuated consciousness interprets as physical reality. The rule-sets defining the space-time simulation where we live, work, and play, cause our individuated puddles of consciousness to interpret the interchanges of energy with other players (its perceptions) as PMR. Sentient space-time beings such as us, for instance, though we exist only as nonphysical units of individuated consciousness, can interact experientially (experience physical reality) within the constraints of a space-time rule-set, which provides the defining assumptions and physics for our interactive space-time virtual reality experience in the PMR consciousness evolution trainer.

Recall that within $NPMR_N$, new entities were created (birthed) by existing entities by focusing enough mental energy to produce (dare I say "materialize") a new thought-form. New space-time entities, by comparison, would reproduce by creating a new bounded form within the space-time manifold. The details were as seemingly enormous as the implemented solution was simple.

Here is how someone or some digital thing might create an entire virtual universe such as ours. Start with the rule-set that defines the concept of a constrained space-time (including the complete set of PMR physics) wherein certain kinds of basic interactions, energy transfers, and causal possibilities exist. Wind it up with a huge simulated **potential** energy, and let it begin evolving within TBC according to the Fundamental Process and the defined rule-set. Let the potential energy reality spring begin to unwind with a Big Bang as the time increment driving the simulation begins to iterate. "Big Bang – take one! Cameras! Action! Roll 'em!"

Immediately, some of the simulated space-time energy now let loose (dynamics beginning to unfold as simulation-time progresses increment by increment) begins to change form under the imposed rule-set into heat, mass, motion, and various forms of energy. New players are constantly generated (hot plasma, galaxies, solar systems, planets, primordial ooze, and critters) according to the rules within the simulation as this particular PMR spring begins to unwind and evolve. The application of the space-time rule-set defines causality while the application of the Fundamental Process experimentally expands the potentiality of the evolving system into all possibilities, progressing those that are profitable dynamically forward. AUM has only to stand back and watch while TBC computes all the ramifications, implications, and results of the space-time rule-set and the Fundamental Process. A grand simulation in mind-space – the mother of all *gedanken* experiments!

Sit back and watch it evolve – what a cool rule-set – as if playing a video game called "Cosmological Evolution in Space-time." A best-seller within AUM's $NPMR_N$ subset of mind-space no doubt. Recall that AUM's clock ticks 10^{36} times faster than ours, and don't worry that AUM will need to re-boot TBC in the middle of your favorite reality program because AUM **is** the computer, the application, and the operating system.

This virtual energy system, once let loose (once time begins to iterate), dynamically evolves according to the dictates of the Fundamental Process and the space-time rule-set. Matter begins to form and individuate, things begin to grow, and entropy decreases in some places while increasing in others. Growth, as it refers to inanimate material objects implies higher degrees of organization and a decrease of entropy, for example: atomic particles fuse together to form more complex atoms and molecules, ordered groupings of atoms and molecules form compounds and more complex molecules, mass begins to coagulate into droplets called stars and planets. This constantly churning system appears stable in the little picture because it is animated on such a grand scale within space and time. For a similar reason, the earth appears flat because it is so large relative to the local awareness of a walking man. One eventual result, among many others, of this apparent local stability may be a universe such as ours.

An experimenter could run this physical-universe creation simulation as often as it wished in order to sample over the natural random components, the various rule-sets, and simulation parameters, keeping (saving to non-volatile memory) the best ones for further study. Iterating this process while tweaking the space-time rule-set will eventually evolve some good experimental candidates worth maintaining and culturing (remember our earlier petri-dish metaphor).

I wonder how long it took and how many false starts there were before the space-time rule-set was fully evolved? Do you think AUM has it right this time? AUM might tinker with it a little here and a little there but in general, the space-time manifold is on its own to evolve however it evolves according to the Fundamental Process. Recall from our discussion of AI Guy that virtual reality rule-sets occur at two distinct levels. Higher level rules that define goals and purpose and lower level rules that define local physics and causality.

Home, sweet home: TBC creates the logical causal structure and we live and play in it by virtue of our participation in the PMR virtual reality consciousness trainer. Education by total experiential immersion in the reality of your choice – that's the only way to go when one has a long way to go.

TBC progresses the dynamic space-time reality by sequentially incrementing time. The evolutionary logic it follows (expanding into all possible states and continuing those that are profitable) is tracked, recorded, and saved in TBC. Every state that develops (beginning with time t=0) during every time increment (DELTA-t) is saved. All the evolving simulated elements and players move and change to new values and configurations every DELTA-t. Many DELTA-t increments go by until one fine day, here we are in our space-time PMR, snug as bugs in the fabric of a PMR space-time rug. Clueless about who we are, where we came from, or what we are supposed to do, but snug little bugs every one.

We do have some intuitive idea about what is going on because, after all, we are discrete chunks of AUM consciousness playing, working and evolving in a digital space-time simulation-trainer. Our bodies, our interactions, and our physical reality are what we experience under the space-time rule-set. We are nudged in the right evolutionary direction by a **higher level** rule-set that works through our intuition, becomes our conscience, and urges our higher selves to be the right thing.

There is only consciousness. Everything is a manifestation of consciousness. Even rocks and the proverbially dead doornails are consciousness constructs. Everything we experience is due to an application of the various rule-sets (under which we are extant) to our individuated consciousness. When we are operationally aware in nonphysical realities within $NPMR_N$, our experience is defined by the rule-sets that characterize those particular $NPMR_N$ realities.

The various rule-sets that apply to our consciousness, as it interacts within various dimensions and sub-dimensions of NPMR, are like the laws that govern our behavior on earth. Each of us live under the due process of international law, national law, state law, county law, city law, the restrictive covenants of our sub-division, and the law our mom lays down when we have been naughty. All of them apply to us, and must (ostensibly) be obeyed all the time. Nevertheless, we typically focus our attention on our local reality and primarily give consideration to the laws that affect our daily lives. Only when we begin to travel or do business internationally does international law become interesting or important to us. The rule-sets in TBC are like that – we are required to obey all the rules that pertain to us all the time, but in a practical sense we need to be aware only of the local rules that directly affect us (such as PMR physics) until we venture beyond the confines of our local PMR neighborhood.

30

■■■

Consciousness, Space-Time, and PMR

■■■

Let's make sure we have a firm grasp of the ideas presented up to this point. These ideas are unusual enough that some repetition is necessary before most folks can successfully sort through the layers of long held beliefs to absorb the implications of what is being said. It is a mistake to go too fast. Though your intellect may have your head enthusiastically bobbing up and down with assumed understanding, it is my experience that the deeper significance of your existence as consciousness is usually only partially grasped.

Consciousness is the fundamental attribute of AUM and of any and all sub-realities created within the organization (mind) of AUM. AUM is only mind – digital mind: A system of digital (cellular) organization. The Even Bigger Computer (EBC) is a metaphor for a subset of the memory, data processing, communications, and rules as well as the organizational and control functions of this AUM-mind-thing. Recall the discussion of the evolution of AUO in Chapter 25, Book 1. Because the simplest conceptualization of reality cells is binary, the EBC metaphor is a good one. On a less grand scale and at the local level, you can clearly observe the fractal-like repetition of the basic pattern of digital reality in the computational tools (hardware and software) that we are creating to aid, understand, and guide our evolution and existence within the earth-based ecosystem. Not that far off in our future, physical computer systems and the interactive software that is implemented in them will become very clever at applying specific complex processes to more general problems; gradually their capability and awareness will grow until they have what it takes to host consciousness and support intelligence. From AUM to TBC to the inhabitants of NPMR and PMR to desktop computers, the fundamentals of existence repeat themselves in many forms of digital awareness within many different dimensions of reality.

> ▶ There may be a better computing basis than binary and if there is, AUM probably uses it. However, I am only describing operational concepts not implementation details – and a binary computing basis is by far the most simple and most comprehensible metaphor for us to use.
>
> Big Picture concepts are important; don't get wrapped around the irrelevant details. Whether TBC is formed out of **binary** reality cells, or future computers are based on **silicon**, is entirely irrelevant. The metaphors and the concepts are clear and timeless even if the details, terms, and language supporting the **current** explanation quickly become outdated. ◀

Our digital computers have the basic binary protoplasm found at the root of consciousness (see Chapters 26 and 28 of Book 1) and lack only the speed, capacity, and sophisticated software to support better and better implementations of Artificial Intelligence until the adjective "artificial" is eventually dropped after their capability, capacity, and intelligence becomes self-evolved. Self-evolved does not necessarily imply self-constructed or self-directed, it simply means self-modifying in pursuit of optimizing a defined profitability – the ability to grow, the facility to learn – the capability to exhibit the functions of consciousness.

Eventually, some PMR entities become more aware (dimly at first, but more completely as they invest effort in the awakening process) as they rediscover or uncover their roots leading back to AUM. In fact, some of these sentient beings begin to realize that they exist not only in the highly constrained environment of PMR space-time, but also in the mental environment of $NPMR_N$. Additionally, they exist within NPMR and AUM, but only an exceptional few become intellectually aware of these environments. Fortunately, a few is all it takes to open the minds of others who are ready to become an operative aware part of the Big Picture.

The part of the sentient being focused in PMR makes choices that reflect the overall quality of consciousness of that being. Each intent and action typically generates multiple interactions that produce immediate feedback creating many additional opportunities to learn and grow. Recall that a major design requirement for beings within the space-time simulation was that they should start over on a regular basis with a clean slate so that they could periodically escape the belief traps in which they had ensnared themselves.

Being able to make a new start, **without** the accumulated delusions of the past but **with** your accumulated knowledge and wisdom intact, is a key attribute of the OS system that enables individuals to accumulate consciousness quality by exercising their free will intent within a series of discrete experience packets. Implementing this process in the space-time rule-set implies that space-time beings must be restricted to a series of relatively short, more or less independent, learning adventures in PMR. The space-time experience, like space-time energy transfers, must come in discrete packets called lifetimes.

Space-time beings must be recyclable – they age and die according to the interaction of biological requirements and conditions implemented by the space-time rule-set. When that PMR vehicle (experience-body) gets old, dysfunctional, or is dead ended in a morass of delusion and bad choices, it dies and the larger consciousness entity (sometimes called an over-soul) existing in $NPMR_N$ collects what learning it can glean from that experience packet. If it wants or needs to, this over-soul can rejoin the space-time simulation by inhabiting (in accordance with the self consistent rule-set defining PMR biological science) yet another PMR body that gets to start with a relatively clean slate containing no specific local reality fear and delusional constructs. However, it is only the local PMR reality slate that is wiped clean between consecutive PMR experience packets.

The disorganizing (entropy inducing) influence of ego-fear within the larger individuated consciousness (over-soul) must gradually be overcome by right choices motivated by right intent (fearless and love based), which are accumulated over many, many experience packets. The discrete interactive experience packets provide a plethora of opportunity to exercise intent through free will choice. An individuated conscious entity brings to each new experience packet the basic **quality** of consciousness and personality it has evolved thus far. Entities will sometimes set up specific situations among themselves to optimize the learning potential of all involved.

You come into this physical world (engage this particular PMR experience packet) with an initial quality of consciousness – and then have the opportunity to improve it or degrade it. This quality factor represents your fearless capacity to love, and your proclivity to form attachments to fear and ego delusion. It also represents the entropy level within your consciousness and the extent of your spiritual growth and maturation. When the PMR experience packet is exited, death of the physical body occurs and one finds that all little picture facts (PMR-specific knowledge) and pseudo-facts (beliefs) are entirely perishable, whereas individual quality and Big Picture wisdom endures at the level of the over-soul.

In the larger reality, the entity is defined by whatever degree of love, fear and delusion that represents the sum total quality of that being. In some philosophic traditions, the idea of karma and reaping what you sow somewhat expresses this concept of a cumulative quality of being that can be improved by making prudent choices for the right reasons within your local reality. Flunked lessons (failure to learn) must be repeated in different forms until they are passed – until the entity gets it.

There is no punishment, retribution, or vengeance implied in this process. Repeating lessons of consciousness quality until you have mastered them simply means that you continue to make choices dealing with certain issues until you grow up and beyond that particular quality issue. The quality limitations of an individual that are derived from the limited quality of its over-soul's consciousness represent the challenges to be overcome by that individual while it is enrolled in the PMR learning lab. Outgrowing those limitations (or as many of them as possible) is the mission that each consciousness has set for itself during its current experience packet (the being's present physical lifetime). Obviously, serious effort as well as good planning and preparation by each individual conscious entity improves the effectiveness of this iterative learning process.

If you are an old analog dog in need of a new trick, and are having difficulty thinking in terms of a digital reality, think of space-time as a consciousness entrainment technology defined by the specific constraints it places on the interaction of entities whose experiences are bounded by its definition of reality. TBC knows the basic rules from which our physics (all science) is derived and allows only certain self-consistent configurations of reality to exist within space-time. The psi uncertainty principle defines how and when physical (PMR) and nonphysical (NPMR) phenomena and causality can overlap in PMR without violating the purpose of the space-time rule-set.

Though interactions between PMR and NPMR are limited, the simultaneous awareness of multiple reality frames is available to those grown up enough to assume the implied responsibility and able to profit from that experience. These restrictions are in place for the same reason that we restrict children from driving an automobile, getting married, or signing contracts: They don't get to do those things simply because they want to and believe they are ready.

Fear, beliefs, delusion, ego, and ignorance are interrelated and are catalysts for higher entropy production. Your mind will automatically transcend the restrictions and constraints that keep it focused exclusively in PMR when it is ready – when its average entropy drops below a certain value.

31
■■■
Deriving PMR Physics
from Consciousness
■■■

Understanding the space-time rule-set that we have been discussing in terms of one overarching theory is what PMR physicists refer to as a TOE – Theory Of Everything. They have been working on a little PMR TOE for a long time but are stymied because, among other things, they do not understand the Big Picture. They do not understand the nature of the larger reality of which the TOE they seek is only a part. In fact, being unaware that a Big TOE exists limits them to searching exclusively for only a little TOE (PMR lower-level rule-set only). PMR scientists cannot find the little TOE because the concepts they need to derive an understandable context wherein the little TOE can be seen as one whole thing are found only within a Big TOE. Furthermore, because of the digital algorithmic properties of the PMR rule set, there may or may not be a little TOE cast exclusively in terms of little TOE logic (PMR mathematics).

Thus, scientists and philosophers are limited to digging out rules, one at a time, from the interior of their local reality. When they get to an outer boundary of their little picture – where it meets or interfaces with the larger reality – they run into an invisible wall constructed of belief. A conceptual break through that fundamentally expands their reality is required to break through that wall.

You cannot get out of the box while defining the box to be everything that exists. If you believe that your little box constitutes All That Is, then by definition, everything other than your objective measurable little box appears delusional. Thus the little TOEs that attempt to describe the little box look like big TOEs to the little-box-scientists trapped inside. Every time their little TOE is stubbed against the limitations of the box, their reality seems to dissolve into statistical mush. Uncertainty principles must be brought in to patch up the inconsistency from the inside view.

It seems that you must first understand and appreciate the potential existence of a Big TOE before the little TOE to big TOE interface can come into focus. Otherwise, you define the proper solutions out of existence by limiting the possibilities you can imagine. In other words, your belief systems limit your reality to a subset of the solution-space that does not contain the answer. (Scientific, cultural, religious and personal beliefs systems are discussed in Chapters 19, through 22 of Book 1).

It may be profitable to remember what was said a long, long time ago toward the end of Chapter 31, Book 1. Also in that chapter, I promised to relate PMR physics to consciousness reality cells: You are almost ready for that explanation.

▶ Chapter 31, Book 1: *Reality cells are roughly analogous to the transistors on a computer processor chip. They come in very large numbers and are the most basic active units of the processor and memory. Like reality cells, each transistor is a thing that can be on or off, a 1 or a 0, this way or that way, distorted or undistorted. At the next higher level of generality, is the processor's basic instruction-set that defines operations and processes for storing, retrieving, and performing arithmetical and logical operations. In our analogy, the processor's basic instruction-set is analogous to basic cognitive functioning within AUM. At the next level of abstraction, we get to the space-time rule-set which is analogous to algorithms written in assembly language. Our experience is generated at the next higher level of abstraction by an AUM-TBC to individuated-consciousness interface which is analogous to a simulation programmed in object oriented C++ where we are the objects. AUM is the computer, the programmer, and the operating system. We sentient conscious beings are, as individuated subsets of consciousness, a bounded subset of highly organized, evolving, interactive reality cells.*

As an analog to space-time, consider a custom designed special purpose processor such as a Digital Signal Processor (DSP) chip. Understanding the rules (patterns) governing the transfer of energy to and from transistors in a special purpose microprocessor would provide some understanding of the most basic relationships in the processor's design, implementation and capacity. Likewise, understanding the rules governing the transfer of information between space-time reality cells should produce some of the most fundamental relationships of physics. In Section 4, you will see how that works.

Physical experience is generated when the perception of an individuated consciousness (sentient being) is constrained to follow the space-time rule-set. Imagine a specialized space-time virtual reality trainer (operating within a subset of digital calculation-space called a dimension) that is constrained by the space-time rule-set to provide a causally consistent operational experience that enables an individuated consciousness to evolve to lower entropy states by exercising its intent through free will choice. The specific relationships defining AUM's space-time instruction-set constitute the laws of space-time physics (PMR physics). ◀

Now there is an interesting thought! It may well be possible for us to derive many of the general laws of PMR physics that represent the basic rule-set that TBC applies to create the constraints we call space-time by studying the interactions between reality cells. We can be reasonably sure that the defining space-time **rule-set** is likely to be a collection of general, broad, high-level statements – what scientists sometimes call fundamental laws. The implications and details we call science are derived from these general statements. For example, classical mechanics flows from only a few simple statements called Newton's laws and the science of electricity and magnetism (at the macro level) is fully contained within Maxwell's four Equations. One should expect that the space-time **instruction-set** governing interaction between reality cells is going to reside at a low level of abstraction.

Can you order your thoughts? Is there a structure or pattern to your ideas? Do your ideas ever relate to other ideas – can they be connected and interdependent? Can you alter and store (remember) thoughts and their relationships and patterns (intentionally or unintentionally)? I am very impressed with what you can do with such a relatively tiny and limited fragment of consciousness. Your mind, your consciousness is clearly a versatile tool. With that magnificent mind of yours, please recall that the rule-based space-time construct represents a specific subset of the digital system we refer to as the mind of AUM.

Consider that at least some of the instruction-set that implements the space-time rule-set may be contained within the geometry (pattern and relationship) of the space-time construct – how AUM's binary reality cells form the structure of space-time – and how the interaction of those reality cells is constrained.

Given this is true, the following question naturally arises: Can we derive the laws or basic facts of physics from considering the structure (pattern and relationship) of space-time? It is maybe not as crazy as it first seems because the basic structure of an entity (object, organization, relationship) often defines the nature of the entity that can be built with or upon it. Albert Einstein didn't think this was a nutty idea; he spent the last half of his professional life trying to do just that from the PMR side of the larger reality. He never succeeded in establishing a unified field theory, but his intuition was absolutely correct. Unfortunately, his PMR-only mind-set was too limited by the cultural beliefs of his day to contain the solution.

Let's take a look at the possible and probable structure of the consciousness construct we call space-time, at the reality cell level, and see if we can find a self-consistent logic within it that will lead to the derivation of at least some of our most basic PMR physics. What we are looking for in particular is a pattern or logical structure that AUM-TBC may have utilized as part of a larger *gedanken* experiment to derive, or more properly, evolve, portions of the space-time rule-set, a logical structure related to the differentiated reality cell mental construction of aware consciousness. This is not necessarily **the** approach, but only **an** approach that promises some possibility of success. The concept of reality cells was developed in Chapter 26, Book 1.

Lucky for you and me, I will not have to postulate reality cell structures and rules and then derive physics from them while you watch. A monster aside that delivered 300 pages of technical material would drive away all but the toughest and most generous of readers. Fortunately, a contemporary resident of PMR, Steven E. Kaufman, has already derived the basics of PMR physics from the theoretical structure of a consciousness-derived space-time reality-cell-based instruction-set. (*Unified Reality Theory: The Evolution of Existence Into Experience*, published by Destiny Toad Press, 2002 – ISBN: 0-9706550-1-0). To study the results of his effort, you can either purchase his book or read his book online at **http://www.unifiedreality.com**.

Kaufman starts with simple binary reality cells in an Absolute Unbounded Oneness (AUO) (he does not call it that, but the concept is absolutely identical). He assumes some basic things about how information is transmitted between adjacent reality cells and proceeds to derive the PMR physics of electromagnetism, gravity, force, and energy.

A little reverse engineering and one ends up with many of the concepts of classical physics, relativity, and quantum mechanics falling out of his unified reality theory based entirely upon the properties of the reality cells that exist only in relation to themselves within an AUO-digital-consciousness-energy-thing. Kaufman derives basic physics from the relational cellular structure of a **space-time** construct within consciousness. He probes the logic of the space-time rule-set by analyzing a structural model that is postulated to exist within the mind-space of AUM and the calculation-space of TBC.

Steve Kaufman opened the door. He has shown that one can make a logical analytical attempt to understand the instruction-set that implements the rule-set that defines the space-time part of AUM's consciousness. He lays out a detailed process and mechanism to explain the phenomenology (rule-set) of PMR based upon the causality of $NPMR_N$, demonstrating how PMR might logically arise from the lowest level of cellular structure within AUM and TBC.

Einstein, along with the best physicists and mathematicians of his day, tried to describe Physics in terms of the geometry of space-time. Kaufman has taken the next step by attempting to describe space-time physics in terms of the geometry and structure of NPMR; a process that, surprisingly enough, yields algorithms and processes leading to contemporary PMR physics.

You may not agree with all Kaufman's specific assumptions and you may not accept some of his conclusions. However, you will find that coherent and reasonable bridges have been constructed that connect AUO, consciousness reality cells, space-time reality cells, and the physics of the twentieth and twenty-first century. Eventually AUM's space-time rule-set will yield its algorithms to those who approach it from the correct perspective, and steadfastly frustrate those who demand that the facts of science and reality must all fit neatly into their limited little picture belief system.

Kaufman demonstrates how our current PMR physics can be a logical conclusion of, and fully contained within, *My Big TOE*. The path he has blazed will no doubt need to be widened and extended by others. Nevertheless, Kaufman deserves great credit for making an excellent and original effort to place PMR physics, as we now understand it, within the context of a larger reality. By doing so, he has helped satisfy one of the most important requirements for any wannabe Big TOE: that the Big TOE fully contains the little TOE.

PMR physics is contained within the rule-set that defines and constrains the experience of individuated consciousnesses to perceive a virtual physical reality. PMR may be thought of as a digital simulation executing within a greater digital consciousness. Contemporary PMR physics simply represents a portion of the rule-set that defines the PMR virtual reality.

The Big TOE cannot conflict with known little TOE facts and must broaden the overall understanding of little TOE phenomena that are presently unexplainable (including psi effects, mind, consciousness, human purpose, and the efficacy of intuition) – *My Big TOE* fully meets that criteria.

That Kaufman bases his work upon the assumption of an Absolute Unbounded Oneness (AUO) is a very good sign because earlier (Chapter 18, Book 1) we discovered that logic demands a successful Big TOE to have at least one mystical or metaphysical leg to stand on. Conversely, we have also demonstrated that any TOE without a connection to what appears to be mystical **from the PMR point of view** must logically be only a little TOE that is fundamentally incapable of dealing with our beginnings, our minds and consciousness, or us as whole beings. To view a whole and complete human entity, one must step out of the PMR box.

32

The Mechanics of Experience

At this point, you should have some familiarity with the concept that we humans represent a particular type of constrained individuated consciousness experiencing a virtual physical reality within a larger digital consciousness system. As a player in this consciousness evolution training simulator, we perceive an interactive physical reality within the constrained rule-set of space-time. To put it more personally, you are a bounded chunk of consciousness, chipped from the old AUM block, hallucinating or experiencing this PMR according to a set of experience-rules or rules-of-interaction that define energy exchange within this particular multi-player simulation which is operationally managed (computed, executed, tracked, evaluated and modified) within TBC.

You have no massy body, only the interactive experience of one. That virtual rock exists only in the simulation but because your body also exists in that same simulation, it can bonk you in the head and you will experience the trauma and suffer the consequences that the rule-set (science of energy transfers) computes. That's a simple idea isn't it? No problem. You knew it all along, right? The only thing that may still be a tad confusing is how TBC pulls off this massive interactive multi-player experience game. Stay tuned.

Assume that the apparently infinite AUM has a TBC part that is about a trillion trillion trillion trillion (10^{48}) more powerful than our present day desk-top computers. That is simply a made-up number, but why not? At least it is reasonably consistent (given how clever AUM must be about digital systems and architectures) with the fabricated numerical examples in Section 2 (Chapter 31, Book 1) where we assumed that AUM's fundamental clock ticks about 10^{36} times while ours ticks once.

We could say that an apparently infinite digital consciousness can, like Superman, and the proverbial 800-pound gorilla, do anything it wants to and not resort to quoting phony made-up numbers at all. However, I like numbers and I think they focus the problem and help integrate it into our limited conceptual space. Numbers can provide a concrete connection between old and new concepts as long as their specific values are not taken too seriously. It is the general idea numerically illustrated, not a specific numerical value, that carries significance. The logical validity of the concepts presented in *My Big TOE* has no dependence on the choices of the numerical values used to illustrate concepts of relative magnitude. Accordingly, use the numbers as a conceptual aid, but don't get hung up on them.

A performance improvement factor of 10^{48} more than takes care of the needed computational capacity to run such a simulation. The only remaining question is technique – a reasonable and credible explanation of how it works. That is what this and the next two chapters and Section 5 are about.

Understanding the nature of experience is the first step to understanding our local reality and its connection to the larger reality. Our local reality is defined as the reality in which we appear to exist and function. For most of us, our local reality is our physical reality and nothing more. It is what we are directly aware of, and what we **believe**, sense and measure to be real. As machines and devices extend our senses, our local reality is extended as well.

Experience creates the notion of reality. Our local reality is a byproduct or result of our experience. Experience is derived from two interdependent components: sensory perception and interpretation. The perception of the observer (input data) and interpretation of that perception by our consciousness creates our experience. To be logically complete, I must mention that it is possible for stored sensory input data to be interpreted at a later time. Stored perception data may be brought into the conscious awareness whenever it is needed. The local reality is not a hard, fixed thing, but rather a collection of interpreted perceptions. Your local reality is therefore not entirely an objective reality – it only seems to be objective. The apparent objectivity is an illusion created by the internal consistency of the space-time rule-set. In other words, perception (which is limited by our sensory apparatus) and interpretation (which is limited by our understanding and perspective) constitute two filters that transmute "what is" into "what appears to be." Because of our limitations and the constraints on our consciousness, our local reality must necessarily be constructed from "what appears to be" not "what is."

"What is" might be called "un-experienced" or "un-experienceable" reality. It is whatever is out there that interacts with our sensing apparatus such that we receive information (perceive something) that must be assessed or interpreted to determine what it means or what its significance is. "What is" must by definition (because of our limited perception and non-objective interpretations) remain at least partially un-experienced and unknown. The key point is: The ultimate source of our experience must remain shrouded in uncertainty, unknown and unknowable.

Understanding the dichotomy between "what is" and "what appears to be" is important. We are perhaps not the objective beings living in an objective reality we think we are. "What appears to be" is how we interpreted whatever information our limited sensors collected from "what is." Because observers are necessarily unaware of what does not make it through these two filters, they make the erroneous assumption that "what appears to be" is actually All That Is. For this reason, they mistakenly attribute a sense of absolute solidity to their local reality. A being's local reality is constructed of the accumulated experience of "what appears to be" – thus it contains strong individual (subjective or private) components mixed with sharable (objective or public) objects.

Your sensory apparatus is similar to that of others, thus allowing for general agreement about the properties of your local reality. However, your interpretation of those sensory data is uniquely based on your knowledge, understanding, experience, perspective, belief, fear and ego. Interpretation is uniquely individual, relative, and subjective, yet it is half the ingredients that go into cooking up our apparently objective reality.

Our interpretation of a given set of sensory data will be similar to the interpretation of other beings only if those beings share our wisdom, knowledge, understanding, attitudes, experience, perspective, belief, fear, and ego attachments. In as much as our worldview and our belief systems are shared by others, we will generally agree on the properties, characteristics, substance, and significance of reality. Individuals who belong to the **same** culture (whether they are all homeless street people from New York City, all Japanese millionaires, or all Australian aborigines) typically experience similar local realities. Given a single environment, different cultures not only perceive different data because of their unique focus and interests, but also evaluate, interpret, and value similar physical perceptions differently.

Most members of a particular culture generally agree on how and why things are as they are. This broad and nearly universal agreement leads us to develop confidence and unintentional arrogance about the apparent objectivity and superiority of our view. The characteristics of the majority always define the criteria for a healthy well adjusted member of the group, regardless how dysfunctional or pathological those characteristics may be.

People of other cultures feel every bit as objectively justified and superior in their interpretation of reality as we do. We feel that they are obviously less objective than we are. They shake their heads with amusement and condescending wonderment that we just don't get it. We also feel that way about them, the only difference being that we are right and they simply haven't figured that out yet. The more different the cultures are, the more forceful are these arrogant opinions and the more dramatic is the conflict between beliefs.

▶ Cultural diversity, no longer tied to local geography, is shrinking as the world's people coalesce into a few major overlapping cultural blocks (for example: Western Christian industrialized first world, Middle Eastern Muslim non-industrialized third world, the world of "haves," and the world of "have nots"). As these generalized cultural blocks coalesce and gain virtual membership throughout a **world community**, they gain the power of large numbers expressing shared emotions. The power of numbers often breeds arrogance, self-proclaimed superiority, and belligerence. As leadership evolves to exploit this potential power, expect trouble as major cultural blocks living in wholly different local realities conflict with each other.

The good news is: The growing social and political instability between conflicting reality systems represents only a temporary turbulence induced by a major worldwide reality shift. As a complex system evolves, it often must transition between stable states. This transition period is usually turbulent. We successfully made the transition to the industrial age, but not without abuse, violence, and great dislocation heralding that cultural change. Now we are transitioning to the information age and it is going to be a bumpy ride for a while. Electronic communications technology has suddenly shrunk the world.

The bad news is: If we are not clever, and sensitive to what is going on, this transition could get nasty and last a long time. As the world continually shrinks, the cultural blocks will eventually begin to coalesce with each other. Eventually the rancor of this transition period will dissipate as we face an entirely new set of challenges.

Perhaps one day in the future it will be difficult to find someone who does not share your worldview. The cultural pressure to conform within each of the major blocks is already severe. Do you think our species may be evolving toward becoming politically correct herd animals in the information age or uniformly distributed individualists in plain brown wrappers? Or both simultaneously? ◀

To summarize, you must separate the underlying objective thing being experienced from the experience of it. They are not one in the same because of the characteristics and limitations of our sensory apparatus, our databases (knowledge and information capacity), and our data processing capability (interpretation and analytical capacity). The constraints placed upon our sensing and processing ensures that the ultimate source of our experience remains at least partially unknown. From a physical perspective, "what is" is theoretically as well as practically unknowable. Recall that "theoretically and practically unknowable" is how we defined "mystical" in Chapter 18 of Book 1.

The only thing we actually know about the source of our experience is how it interacts with certain specific energy transfers. We send discrete packets of energy to it, and it interacts by sending discrete packets back. Remembering the discrete character of time from Chapter 29, Book 1, you should realize that energy transfers that seem continuous (such as pressure) are actually discrete from the viewpoint of modern physics and (at a finer level of detail) TBC.

In fact, it is only the players themselves and the interactions between the players that need to be defined by the rule-set. This prescription for creating a subset of reality should seem familiar: We said the same thing earlier when we were discussing another simulated reality (AI Guy and war games). Recall that a player was defined as any thing, entity, or energy that interacts with anything else.

The fundamental basis (a defining rule-set) for the apparently real world of PMR experience is similar to the fundamental basis of the artificial or virtual world of AI Guy. The rule-sets themselves may be very different, but the process behind the rule-sets is very similar. The simulation metaphor applies reasonably well to both.

Even the most astute AI Guy suffers the same problem that plagues us: limited access to, and understanding of, higher level processes. His vision is limited because his experience can penetrate only so deeply into the source of his environment. There is an un-experienceable reality (such as the computer hardware and software, the people who built that hardware and software, as well as the process, equipment, and facility that manufactured the hardware and software) that creates and supports what AI Guy is constrained to experience. Think of other multitasked jobs running in AI Guy's mainframe, and of unrelated computers running isolated jobs in some other facility, as being outside AI Guy's local dimension of reality. The nature of the limitations of AI Guy's experience and the dependence of that experience on the un-experienceable is not qualitatively different from ours.

You can conceptualize or model our boundary between the "un-experienceable reality" (beyond the limited perception of beings within the space-time simulation) and the "experienced reality" (within the limited perception of space-time beings) as an energy packet exchange interface. This nonphysical to physical interface receives energy packets from physical space-time players (in PMR) and sends back the appropriate return energy packets according to the governing space-time rule-set. The interface between the physical reality-experiencing space-time players and the un-experienceable nonphysical TBC would seem to be the ultimate source of PMR experience. That is a simple description of how our virtual physical reality is constructed; AI Guy's virtual reality is produced in exactly the same way.

We reach out to touch an object that has (within TBC) specific space-time coordinates and properties associated with it. According to the space-time rule-set and the attributes of that particular object-player, it feels solid. We **perceive** it to have certain attributes, classify it as a unique or familiar perception, and finally interpret its significance relative to past experiences and current beliefs. Subsequently, we **define** this **perception** to be an object that is both real and physical and it becomes a part of our local reality experience. Rocks and people and houses are real. Mass is real. Separation of two or more individual masses in space is real because I can put myself between them and move them independently of, and relative to, each other – consequently, space is also real. I change, as does everything else, therefore time is real. Some apparently real things (such as rocks, taxes, dreams, and cocktail party chatter) may seem more real to certain individuals at certain times than others.

All appearances of being real are derived from the interpreted perception that constitutes our experience. All are dependent upon the limitations of the sensing apparatus and the limitations of the interpretation that we give to the data collected – our two filters of variable and unknown quality that are always placed between us and the "un-experienceable reality" that lies behind or beyond our perception. From the PMR view, "lies behind or beyond our perception" means: lies within the nonphysical.

A few examples will make this clear. We think we see an object, but what we actually perceive is a portion of the light energy (energy in a discrete packet form) that has interacted with the object, not the object itself. Next we must interpret this received pattern of light data. What we see is a function of the object, the attributes of the light that impinged on it, how that particular light interacted with that particular object, how the sensor (eye, optic nerve) interacted with the light coming from the object, how we generated and interpreted the resulting optic nerve data, and finally, how we integrate this interpreted information with the rest of our experience and beliefs.

There are no less than five processes occurring between the object itself and our sense of the reality of that object. Each process has its limitations, dependencies, random components, variations, and error sources. Our reality is the result of these imperfect processes working and interacting together. Our other senses go through similarly complex processes. Fortunately, these processes and the science that represents them are generally consistent: Every time you look at a given object (under similar conditions) you see essentially the same representation of the same object but you may or may not interpret it the same way each time. Your mental, emotional, and consciousness-quality state is changeable, as are your beliefs, fears, understanding, focus, interests, perspective, experience, and knowledgebase. Your interpretation depends on these as well as any errors, confusion, or random components; each event is a unique experience

> ▶ A quick aside is in order for those right-brained folks who don't give a damn about physical reality. (The left-brained technoids in the reading audience might as well skip to the bottom of this aside or take a break and go get some junk food.)
>
> I can hear grumbling in the background coming from the righties… "So much about stuff….so little about meaning." You are absolutely right. There is another class of things that conscious beings define as real that we are purposely ignoring in this discussion of physical reality.
>
> Beliefs that appear as scientific, religious, or cultural truths, as well as emotions, attitudes, and values are mental constructs created within and by the minds of each individuated consciousness. It is not that these subjective realities are not important; to the contrary, they are primarily responsible for the bulk of the content within most individuated consciousness because of the strong influence they exert on the interpretation of the objective sensory data. It is the subjective interactions within your local reality that determines and drives most of your objective activity (interaction), and that most often pushes the evolutionary levers of intent and motivation.
>
> However, because the subjective nature of your local reality is discussed elsewhere, in this section we are going to stay focused on physical experience. Nevertheless, it is good to keep in mind (as we go through this explanation of how physical reality is nothing other

than a highly structured and consistent experience of a consciousness constrained by the space-time rule-set) that the **content** of consciousness and the **quality** of that content remain the most important attributes of sentient entities. Hang on my right-brained amigos; we are almost done with this matter matter. ◀

Are you ready for a simple example? Imagine that a man born blind and deaf (we have assumed away two of his five sensors) is riding in an automobile with you. This trip is a part of his reality as it is a part of yours, but his perception and interpretation of that perception creates a vastly different experience. The only memorable event he had noticed was caused by that idiot truck driver who forced you onto the shoulder of the road. Your passenger experienced only a bumpy section of the highway that he interpreted as either under construction or needing to be under construction. He never became angry, he never hollered and swore, and he never made those rude gestures as you did. His reality, his opportunity for growth is defined by his experience, which is very different from your own.

Consider the world we experience when we look through special infrared or ultra-violet goggles. Imagine these goggles being permanently placed over your eyes. You would get new information previously unavailable to your unaided eye, and lose some of the information you were used to (for example, you may no longer be able to read print on paper under florescent lighting or appreciate a color photograph). Your reality and your ability to function within that reality are now dramatically altered. Life, relationship, and interaction would never be the same again and you would need to learn how to interpret the new data. Similarly, the sensory data gathered from machines that are designed to extend our senses must be interpreted by someone. Regardless of how the data originates, it necessarily must pass through the same two limiting filters that separate "what is" from "what appears to be." There is no physical way to circumvent the filtering process. The machine, as an extension of us, can only enable us to see "what appears to be." Quantum mechanics makes the same point in its own way.

Consider the rich and elaborately differentiated auditory and olfactory reality of your dog. Would you have the dog's experience if you had the dog's sensors? No, of course not! You would probably not experience great pleasure and enthusiasm for sniffing the excrement deposited by the dogs and cats in your neighborhood – your **interpretations** of those odors would be very different. What about the vastly different realities that are experienced by exceptionally dim people versus exceptionally bright people; by well educated world travelers versus those who have never been in a school or outside the tiny village of their birth; by scientific cultures versus those steeped in superstition or mystical tradition?

I am not judging which cultures or realities are better, but only pointing out the dramatic differences in their perceived and interpreted realities. A collection of individuals from vastly different cultures, who are led to experience the same complex objective environment at the same time, will come to different conclusions about the nature and significance of their experience. The objects themselves are not as significant as the interpretations they initiate within an individuated consciousness. Big Picture significance is invested in the people, not the things. Little picture significance is invested in the things, not the people.

Both people and things have their function within the larger system – personal understanding of the Big Picture (wisdom) is required to optimize individual profitability. If one focuses exclusively on the seeds, one will never experience the splendor of the fruit. We make our choices and then live with the results.

If an individual plucked out of the depths of the Brazilian rain forest and a MIT professor of physics were put together, both would be able to see the same poisonous frog, tropical snake, trees, river, laser device, CD player, and airplane as well as equations on the blackboard. Their sensory perception, though similar, would not collect the same data because they would notice different things. They may agree on the form of objects placed directly in front of them, but on little else. Their realities (discomforts, anxieties, fears, needs, desires, and attitudes – all the cultural, religious, personal, and scientific beliefs along with their individual ego-stuff) would be vastly different. Their love-stuff (caring, compassion, and giving) would be of similar type, and could most easily overlap into a common experience.

Obviously, there is more to an individual's personal reality than merely a sensory measurement describing what exists in the common (physical) environment. Do you think a personal reality is different from reality? Your personal reality is different from someone else's personal reality because your experiences and quality are different. As your awareness and knowledge grows, your personal reality grows. Anything that resides outside your personal reality is invisible to you and appears not to exist. What you consider to be the objective outside reality is much smaller (only a tiny subset), more personal, and less objective than you think. That portion of one's experience that appears to be shared, consistent, universal, and objective is simply a reflection of a common space-time rule-set and player list, and as such, it makes up the **least** significant component of each individual's local or personal reality. By comparison, your personal relationships with other sentient entities (which are primarily subjective in nature regardless of how hard you may try to construe them as objective) are easily the most significant component of your reality.

Viewing your local reality as merely the output of an environment being viewed by particular sensors and given a particular interpretation is an oversimplification of the process that ignores the vast quantity of specific subjective content that dramatically modifies and constrains the collected objective data. The **local** reality that each of us creates is wholly dependent on the particular filters we bring to the interaction: it is a product of our personal experience, knowledge, emotional state, and the quality of our consciousness.

Your local reality is to some extent personal. Your personal reality is primarily local, though it can be expanded beyond that limited awareness. You would probably be surprised to discover the extent to which you create your own reality. The illusion is that we are "in here" while reality is independently "out there." The outside world, which represents the apparently objective portion of your personal reality, is based upon a uniquely interpreted set of uniquely limited perception data. That uniqueness represents your individuality. You have more input into, and influence over, the creation of your objective reality than you might imagine.

The "set" is consistent and follows the space-time rule-set without deviation (accept as allowed by the psi uncertainty principle), however, the "story" is yours alone. Furthermore, because you have sentient intent, purpose, and free will, the story determines the set, not the other way around. Believing that the PMR set determines your personal story represents a common error based on the misunderstanding that the physical universe is primary and you are a secondary derivative of it.

To a locally limited awareness, objective causality appears to define physical reality. When you realize that you are experiencing PMR through a virtual reality simulator-trainer, the possibility that there are optimizing feedback loops causally connecting the quality of your choices (the successful evolution of your consciousness through experience) to the action taking place in the virtual world projected by the simulator, becomes a more reasonable proposition. Although the simulator must appear consistent to all players, there are many subtle and not so subtle ways that the apparent outside physical environment (including relationships with others) can be purposely modified within the virtual reality generator to present each player with a maximum learning opportunity. The virtual PMR reality dimension or experience generation system maintains rule-set integrity and provides the best integrated optimal opportunity (on the average) for the entire system (for all sentient players). To preserve the honesty and straightforwardness of your interactions within PMR, the psi uncertainty principle makes sure that cross-dimensional energy transfers are adequately obscured.

Your personal interpretations of the meaning and significance of your inside and outside experience automatically customize your personal reality in a manner that increases the likelihood of finding those experiences and opportunities that are most important to your individual evolution. Your local reality provides the playing field, the players, and the rules of the game. Its structure provides a context within which experience can take place and your free will can choose; it enables your individual evolution to unfold by supplying the complete player set (relationship and interaction) as well as the rule-set that defines the permissible energetic interactions (objective causality).

Contrary to popular belief, your local reality is not an objective place that you inhabit as you might inhabit a house. Nevertheless, your local reality is the **result** of your personal interaction with a seemingly objective outside world. Your local reality represents your personalization of only a **very limited** interaction (energy exchange) with the possible outside world. Experience, and hence your reality, is not independent of the experiencer; it reflects the unique subjective, historical, and emotional state of the individual. Your experience, as well as your personal interpretation of your experience, is strongly influenced by the quality of your consciousness.

Beings of notable quality who are also regular pudding tasters on the Path of Knowledge have a more practiced ability to evaluate the quality, significance, and opportunity of their experience. They evolve within a much larger decision space (live and function within a much larger, more varied and complex reality) and are likely to be less personally limited as well as more aware of their personal limitations.

Note the interdependent cyclical (more accurately spiral) nature of consciousness evolution. An intent that reflects quality creates an action within a virtual reality that produces learning opportunities that lead to increased quality that supports more profitable intents. The consciousness quality spiral can be bootstrapped in a downward (degenerative) or upward (progressive) evolutionary direction by incrementally increasing or decreasing the entropy of the system.

Let's summarize what we have discussed thus far. That we collectively declare our shared local reality to be universal or fundamental because everybody sees a similar thing is a tribute to the smallness of our view, the similarity of our sensors, the homogeneity of our beliefs, and to the consistency of the rule-set and player list. The collective similarity of our interpretation is a tribute to the commonality of our cultures, belief systems, needs, egos, and goals. This collective experiential agreement is not based upon the existence of a fundamental (identical for everybody) **local** reality. A local reality is local to the individual, not the environment. From your perspective, there is no other reality except your local or personal reality – however large or small that might be. Ignorance is blind; you do not know what you do not know. To a large extent, each individual and each culture or belief system creates its own local realities that are teeming with pertinent and challenging learning opportunities.

Collective experiential agreement is based on a common space-time rule-set that defines a consistent energy packet interaction between all player types. It is this ubiquitous and consistent space-time rule-set that represents the common source, the common environment, which leads to similar experiential results for each individual within PMR. There is also a common physically un-experienceable external environment that exists behind our perception – the "what is" that exists within the "un-experienceable reality" that is at the root of our experience.

PMR (physical) experience is derived exclusively from the "experienced reality" of "what appears to be." "What appears to be" is the result of applying our limited individual filters of perception and interpretation to "what is." "What appears to be" is more accurately: "What it appears to be to me," which is unique for each individual while at the same time supports common experience at an average or common level of perception and interpretation.

The "un-experienceable reality," may, or may not, be objective and invariant, although it usually appears to be both. The only thing that we know about it for sure is that we (from the PMR view) must always remain ignorant of it because, by definition, it is what lies beyond our limited physical perception (with or without machines). It represents the mechanics of the space-time simulation that the players are not aware of. This is analogous to the computer hardware and software and the people who made the computer hardware and software, and the facilities they made them in being beyond the perception of (un-experienceable and unknowable to) AI Guy.

You should note how similar this discussion sounds to the one we had earlier (Chapter 18, Book 1) about unknowable beginnings, un-experienceable sources beyond our grasp, mysticism, and the understanding of events that lie outside our causal system. What we have called "un-experienced reality" is none other than our friend TBC operating the energy packet exchange interface. The nonphysical is therefore the ultimate source of our physical experience because it provides the common rule-based (algorithmic) foundation upon which our physical experience is constructed (computed). An "un-experienced reality" exists outside our causal system, beyond the limited perception that defines our PMR reality. The "un-experienceable reality" (from the physical perspective) can only be accessed or understood (as can our beginnings) through a process that transcends our local reality and local objective logic. By definition, any process that steps beyond our local causal logic, beyond our collective local reality, is called mystical.

Good golly, Miss Molly! It seems that whenever and however we dig deep enough (with a logic shovel) into reality we eventually find a mystical core (as seen from a PMR perspective). Hey Jake, I sense a trend; perhaps we're on to something here.

AI Guy has as difficult a time comprehending his ultimate (as opposed to local) host computer as we have comprehending ours – for much the same reasons. To AI Guy, the host computer and the rest of PMR are nonphysical and entirely mystical. Consciousness appears nonphysical from the space-time view of PMR. Nonphysical reality is a reality that is in, and of, consciousness – which is why only the mind can travel and gather experience within nonphysical reality. Do not expect a parapsychologist to bring back the equivalent of nonphysical rock samples for the rest of us to look at: NPMR is not a distant moon.

An advanced computer that develops consciousness also develops a nonphysical dimension to its being. You will not be able to grab AI Guy's consciousness in your hand even if you are the programmer and computer manufacturer that created the necessary conditions for consciousness to take root and begin evolving. Humans create computers – consciousness develops new expressions of consciousness – such creativity occurs every day in NPMR where the local residents are physical (according to their own rules and point of view) and you are not.

Consciousness is energy, the most basic form of energy and perhaps the only form of non-virtual energy. Experienced reality, un-experienced reality, TBC, PMR, you, and the space-time rule-set are all constructs of consciousness. Each is created and designed to accomplish its specific function. All are subsets of the one single consciousness we have been calling AUM. Consciousness is all – the rest is merely apparent to a limited view within a highly constrained awareness. A superb virtual reality, by definition, must always feel totally and convincingly physical to its inhabitants whether it is simulating PMR or NPMR. What appears to be nonphysical is relative to what appears to be physical. The reality an entity is mentally immersed in appears physical while all others appear nonphysical. Each is as real and extant within TBC, EBC, or AUM as any of the others. The appearance of being physical or nonphysical is relative to the viewpoint of the observer, and hence, relative to the observer's knowledge, awareness, and consciousness quality.

Logic tells us that our experience, from which our local reality is derived, exudes from a seemingly invariant mystical (from PMR perspective only) core of "un-experienceble reality." Remembering how a mystic from a little picture might actually be a scientist within a bigger picture (Chapter 20, Book 1), let us now poke our heads up beyond PMR. The first thing we nonphysical scientists become aware of is that PMR physics represents a small subset of a much larger rule-set that defines how TBC (subset of AUM's mind or consciousness space) implements the physical and nonphysical components of us, our local reality, PMR, and OS.

That the superbly objective (PMR-only) physics of today is merely a partial exposition of a digitally implemented rule-set that determines the bounds of interaction between individuated units of nonphysical consciousness is a thought that amuses me to no end. You may need to know a few hardheaded PMR *über alles* scientists to get the joke. Don't you just love it?

33

■■■

The Mechanics of
Perception and Perspective

■■■

From the PMR point of view, perception is an interaction of our sensors with some undefined "un-experienced reality" through an energy packet exchange interface that produces data within our central nervous system that, when interpreted, creates the experience with which we define our local reality. The perception process from our little picture viewpoint is simply a matter of physics, and how our biology and machines implement that physics. Neither the "un-experienced reality" source nor the energy packet exchange interface is **directly** relevant to our **experience** of PMR. Similarly, neither the computer's power cord, nor its processor chip, is **directly** relevant to the **experience** of AI Guy.

Because the space-time rule-set resident within TBC defines PMR physics (all science), and controls the output of the energy packet interface, that puts TBC directly in charge of defining and specifying what we perceive. TBC establishes the limits and constraints of our interactions with other players and provides the return energy packets across the interface that represents our interaction with what we perceive as our physical environment.

If our past experience and the quality of our consciousness determine how we interpret the data from our perception, it would seem that something nonphysical is in charge of and controls both ends of the process that creates experience – and transforms aware intent into action that can learn from that experience. Is it clear yet that our experience, including the physical experience that defines our local PMR-based reality, is sandwiched between, dependent on, and created by two wholly nonphysical processes carried out within, and created by, consciousness itself?

Is this simple or what? You and I are clumps of individuated consciousness engaged in a dance of energy packet exchanges through an interface that maintains the rules of the game. The book you are reading in your mind is the book I wrote in my mind. The paper and ink and the hand you are holding it with and the eyeballs you are reading it with are the required effects of the space-time rule-set that defines the form and structure of our interaction.

If you think the constraints of space-time are annoying because you are constrained to read word by word what a more natural, less constrained, mind could transmit, comprehend, and thoroughly absorb in a few quick big gulps, criminy, I had to type the damn thing with just two stubby little physical fingers and a pair of drugstore glasses. That is simply the nature of space-time – simple, direct, slow, detailed, and relatively linear – as the experience within any good elementary school should be.

This puts AUM and TBC in the driver's seat when it comes to defining our sense of reality within PMR. How could our cute little individual fleshy bodies and all the other physical things (critters, rocks, bushes and earthquakes) that seem solid be nothing more than constructs of consciousness? How could our solid PMR reality be described as mind, a dream, a delusion, or as extant only in the mind of God (as it might be put by an imaginative PMR poet or hopelessly trapped PMR scientist)? How can our physical and nonphysical parts be integrated into one being? How is it that all earth's beings, critters, objects, and energy are connected? How can all this be on a big communications net or part of a grand digital simulation? If you have been paying close attention, you should know the answers to these questions.

The AUM and TBC consciousness-system-thing control all the inputs, and create our 3D space-time experience of individuated separateness – all in our mind, all in our consciousness, all in our thought-form-fragment-being chip from the old block of AUM consciousness. Everything started out as simple uniform consciousness potential energy. With the encouragement of the Fundamental Process of evolution, consciousness expanded into every potentially profitable state, profits were consolidated, losses cut, and the Big Dude was on an evolutionary roll. Everything is still only digital potential synergy and organized digital content (consciousness), but now, due to the steady decrease in system entropy, many highly synergistic complex configurations have evolved. Everything that seems physical to you is an experience of a consciousness constrained to experience space-time.

The solution to the mind-matter problem is embarrassingly simple. In the Big Picture, there is no matter – everything is mind. There is only the little picture experience-of-matter within mind. "Physical" does not exist – the term "nonphysical reality" only has meaning relative to a nonexistent physical reality. Once you leave the delusion of a local physical reality, everything appears physical, or equivalently, nonphysical, and the distinction between the two vanishes. All reality has solidity of form and function that obeys the causality enforced by its governing rule-set. The physical-nonphysical and mind-matter dichotomies are an illusion created by a limited local PMR viewpoint.

Wave particle duality, uncertainty principles, and the seemingly instantaneous communications between entangled pairs become simple to explain once you realize that PMR is a virtual reality created by a digital simulation implementing the space-time rule-set within TBC. Given a digital PMR simulation, which is stepped forward by time increments that appear infinitesimal to us, and a virtual reality that must obey only the rules driving its digital computation, these paradoxes disappear along with the illusion of absolute space. Once the limiting belief that all possible reality is exclusively defined by measurements within PMR is abandoned and the true nature of consciousness is grasped, the mysterious paradoxes of physics, philosophy, and metaphysics all melt away like ice cubes in the summer sun.

All that is needed to find solutions to the Big Questions of our time is a simple shift in perspective – a casting off of erroneous scientific, cultural, and religious belief inherited from those who were unable answer the same questions. Isn't that how it always turns out? New paradigms deliver an expanded reality as we outgrow the old ones. The digital mountain raised up by the approaching information age has simply afforded us a better view at this time. Progress, like quality and ability, is developed through a bootstrapping process. Every new success is built on previous successes.

Nascent understandings of the digital nature of the Big Picture are erupting all around us. Dozens of top scientists are today hot on the heels of discovering that PMR is actually a little digital picture existing within a computed reality. That is a necessary first step that leaves the Big Picture just around the corner. It appears that this is an auspicious time for humanity to take yet another of its occasional grand leaps toward a greater understanding. *My Big TOE* provides the theoretical foundation that supports the phenomenology and hypotheses that are currently being investigated by scientists and philosophers worldwide. Grand leaps (forward or backward) are always the result of a confluence of many forces and urgings that together produce a unique opportunity. These are exciting times with great success and great failure sitting on opposite sides of the same fantastic opportunity. Human beings, are you ready? Drum roll please!

Once you understand what and who you are, and how you relate to the whole, the resulting Big Picture perspective produces one consistent reality with no paradoxes. Note that the first nonnegotiable requirement of a fully correct Big Picture Theory Of Everything (that it produces one consistent reality with no paradoxes) has been fully met by *My Big TOE*. Also note that the second nonnegotiable requirement of a fully correct Big TOE (that it subsume what is known as a special case of a more general understanding) has also been fully met by *My Big TOE*. Furthermore, that the science contained within *My Big TOE* does not support the limited view of traditional scientific beliefs, which are unable to produce a bigger picture, is a necessary strength, not an unavoidable weakness of this Theory Of Everything.

When you are in NPMR, it appears to be every bit as physical as PMR, but because it operates under a different set of rules, one interacts with it differently. The operational differences between PMR and NPMR simply represent the differences between their rule-sets and the unique causality that each rule-set imposes. Each particular reality dimension has evolved a rule-set to support its own use, function, and purpose. The space-time rule-set supports human function and purpose within OS.

There is no significant distinction between physical and nonphysical realities: Reality is reality. I employ that artificial distinction and terminology (PMR vs. NPMR) as a communications aid. To communicate with you effectively, I need to start (conceptually) from where you are (or think you are). The fact is that most of you are certain that you exist within a physical reality, hence that is the initial perspective we must take. The PMR-NPMR distinction within *My Big TOE* is used to help you conceptually sneak up on a bigger picture. We will continue to use the PMR-NPMR terminology, especially in the next section, because it greatly facilitates the grasping of inherently difficult Big Picture concepts – like thinking of an atom as a billiard ball with BBs zipping around it – patently incorrect, but useful at an elementary level.

Local reality is an experience of individuated mind interacting within the limitations of a given causality. If there are multiple minds interacting within a given local reality, there exists a shared common (public) experience we define as objective, as well as a personal experience that we define as subjective. The subjective and objective components of reality are both extremely significant – their purpose and function are simply different.

The larger reality is all consciousness (All That Is) evolving toward greater profitability, existing to improve itself through entropy reduction. Aware consciousness is created by the **organization** of a fundamental potential energy that we have (for reasons of conceptual familiarity) named Absolute Unbounded Oneness – the nature of this organization is digital. The larger reality is a huge interactive digital consciousness system; it is a consciousness-evolution fractal ecosystem that we have named AUM.

To summarize: Physical and nonphysical are relative to a point of view and therefore do not support a fundamental distinction. The mind-matter, normal-paranormal, physics-metaphysics, and science-philosophy dichotomies are likewise simply illusions of perspective created by a limited understanding that is exclusively focused within its own local reality. The experience of our physical matter reality is the result of a particular set of constraints (space-time rule-set) placed upon the interaction of individuated consciousness with other players, which include other sentient beings as well as the environment. Matter is a simulated mental effect that we, as mind, experience because it helps put us in a virtual environment that makes the evolution of our consciousness more efficient and effective.

As constrained constructs of consciousness, we have the imperative to lower our entropy (evolve our consciousness) because that is the fundamental nature of the greater consciousness-evolution fractal ecosystem of which we are an infinitesimal part. We personally and as a species reflect the pattern of consciousness evolution because we are the result of that pattern and an integral piece of a larger consciousness system that evolves by iterating recursively upon itself to generate All That Is.

We control the experience of a simulated AI Guy in the same way the space-time rule-set controls our experience. We define what he can perceive (what data he can access) and the rules by which he processes the information he collects. We prescribe the boundaries of his experience and reality in order to create the optimal (for our purpose) simulation tool.

We do not enable AI Guy to perceive beyond his local reality (such as most of the computer hardware and software used in his simulation, the people who made it, the facilities they made it in, all of PMR and NPMR) because it is irrelevant to his mission, invisible and unthinkable to his cognitive awareness, outside of his local reality, and beyond his logical causality. To AI Guy, these higher level things would appear (if they were explained to him) to be nonphysical mystical nonsense existing within a different dimension. Computer hardware, power cords and electrical outlets, programmers and the software they produce, and simulation laboratory facilities simply do not exist from his limited point of view and if he is anything like his human brothers, there is no way to convince him otherwise because he simply does not have the conceptual framework to expand his reality enough to perceive and understand the Bigger Picture from which he has been derived.

You might as well explain to a fish how to dance an Irish jig as tell a man that he is nonphysical consciousness. On second thought, that is a poor analogy: The fish has a good excuse (it has no legs), while the man, at least theoretically, has a mind.

34

■■■

PMR as a Virtual Reality Game

■■■

Let's look at reality from an entirely different viewpoint. We may create or customize our own local reality through our personal interpretations, but we certainly do not create all reality: A larger reality exists apart from us that appears to be centered in the nonphysical because it exists outside our local physical reality dimension. We are a subset of that larger reality and we interact with it through our individual personal minds. Our bodies and their physical experiences are a product of our minds interacting within the constraints of the space-time rule-set with other players (both sentient and non-sentient) and other minds in a mutually interactive dance of aware but limited consciousness exchanging discrete energy packets in a process called interactive experience.

A good way to get a rational grip on this concept is to perform a *gedanken* experiment of your own: Ponder a future virtual reality game. Before this virtual reality game begins you are (your body is) put into a perfect sensory-deprivation tank where you blissfully float. The advanced and powerful computer running this game is connected directly to your brain. No special gloves, helmets, pressure suits, or tilting, shaking, rock-n-roll platforms are necessary.

The computer hosting the game is connected wirelessly to the nerves or brain-areas where each and all your sensory data input is received on its way to being processed. This virtual reality bio-computer game machine has been programmed with an advanced understanding of biology, physiology, physics, and of how the senses interact.

Such an advanced, super duper, totally cool, virtual reality game machine can simulate and then stimulate your central nervous system with such accuracy that you have a complete, scientifically exact, and absolutely real experience. This virtual reality machine produces an artificial or virtual experience that is indistinguishable from real experience. You cannot tell the difference.

Because the natural inputs from your actual body are blocked while you are hooked up to this machine, if you lingered too long as a participant in the "Gourmet Foods Of The World" virtual reality game – regularly ate your fill of the world's best virtual filet mignon with the world's freshest virtual steamed vegetables and most delicious virtual fresh fruit – you could physically starve to death without noticing the real you was hungry. You get the picture. This virtual reality game is a marvel of technology that produces absolutely realistic experience.

Imagine that this virtual reality game is a multi-player game. You and a group of your friends, along with many thousands if not millions of others, are playing this game together. The computer tracks the interactions between the players and integrates their experiences. Some multi-player computer games do a limited version of this type of virtual reality simulation now. You and your friends chose the "Jungle Safari" game; consequently, the computer supplies the appropriate rain forest environment for your party and populates it with all the critters, objects, and energy (weather, climate, earthquakes, wind, volcanoes, and so on) that would naturally be there.

Your mind and the computer's rule-set together create a rule based, consistent, causal, objective space-time experience where the free will initiative of you and your friends drives the action to its logical conclusions and simulated physical ramifications. The final results are determined by the computers rule-set and the actions or lack thereof that you and your friends take. Your seeming reality (local virtual reality) is created by your interpretation of your virtual perceptions. These virtual perceptions and interpretations create a virtual experience that provides opportunity for you to learn from the results of the actions that express your intents. This virtual reality experience-game is a good place for you to evolve the quality of your consciousness: It makes a great training machine. All the while there is also a larger reality that contains your actual floating body, your spouse, mortgage payment, and the new car that you left sitting in the parking lot of Sam's Virtual Reality Emporium. This outside reality is not causally connected to your virtual reality, and from the point of view of your virtual reality, it is non-operational, nonphysical, and does not exist.

Do you get my point? The technology I am describing is near enough to our reality that you should be able to follow (imagine) the story line without difficulty. Telling this story sixty years ago would have left the audience without a clue as to what I could possibly be talking about. It would have appeared to be pure fantasy, absolutely impossible, idiotic wild concepts beyond comprehension. Sixty years ago, when Albert Einstein was pondering relativity theory, people would not have known what a digital computer was (the first digital computer, ENIAC, was developed at the University of Pennsylvania for the US Army between 1942 and 1946). Sixty years from now, computers will be (assuming Moore's Law) one trillion (that's twelve orders of magnitude or 10^{12}) times faster and more capable than they are today. Better yet, that improvement factor of one trillion is likely to be an outrageous understatement given the high probability that multiple breakthrough technologies will be discovered during that time span.

That is more number crunching power than we can conceive of. The only thing we can say for sure about what we will be doing with a trillion times the present computational power is that it is beyond our comprehension to imagine. Can you imagine this: Our children and grandchildren will be living in a world that is today totally unimaginable to us? That is how quickly things are changing and the process continues to accelerate. Only ninety years from now, near the end of the present century, Moore's Law predicts our computers will be a million trillion (10^{18}) times faster than today's computers. What do you think your grandchildren, great grandchildren, and AI Guy are going to be doing with that much digital capability? On the other hand, even with breakthroughs, processing speeds could go asymptotic long before they reach an improvement factor of 10^{18} – who knows? What I do know is that within a single human lifespan, AI Guy and the future applications of digital computing will most likely be vastly different from anything that we could possibly imagine, even in our wildest dreams.

Today, a person with a technical education might reasonably ask when a close approximation to this virtual reality game might be expected to hit the market. If this concept seems theoretically doable to little ol' dumbed-down us just sixty years after outrageously slow and clunky digital computers were invented, what kinds of digital magic do you think AUM might be able to pull off with his puddles of individuated consciousness that don't need to be wired, fed, pay mortgages, drive cars, or rub up against each other for personal gratification?

AUM actually has a much simpler problem. Granted, AUM's sets are larger and more detailed, but hey, that requires only some additional computer memory and crunch-power – no problem for an apparently infinite, brilliant, digital-consciousness that operates in a frequency-space that has a basic time increment that is eighty orders of magnitude smaller than our second. In fact, it as so easy there are many, many versions of PMR humming along in parallel – and The Big Dude never breaks a sweat. B.D. makes the coolest games, man. Totally cool!

35

■■■

Real Mystics Don't Smoke
Ciggies in the Bathroom

■■■

What about the scientists and mystics who already knew everything I have explained about the Big Picture? You know, the individuals who are reading these books just to see if I got it right. Do these people represent a glitch in the system? Are they screwing up because they are peeking behind the scenes, looking on the other side of the energy packet exchange interface instead of obeying the rules of space-time like the more normal citizens of PMR?

No way! We are not put in space-time like a zoo keeper puts an animal in a cage. We are not caged at all. We are consciousness – no more, no less. We have at our command all the attributes and abilities of a sentient individuated consciousness with free will. We are a part of AUM and contain the characteristics and potential of the whole in our part. We are in space-time to learn, to grow the quality of our consciousness, to evolve. Once we have evolved our consciousness to the point that the space-time construct is no longer an efficient tool for evolution, we go on to other things. Space-time constitutes a learning lab, an educational environment to grow in, not a jail.

It is more like an elementary school than a detention center. The point is: You are supposed to graduate eventually, not merely hang out with your friends, smoke ciggies in the bathroom, and skip classes. If you pay attention, try hard, do all your homework, and taste test lots of experimental pudding you will some day grow-up and be one of the big (picture) kids. Then you will realize a closely held secret that only the big kids know. Listen up! I am going to spill the beans! This is **the** major secret of life. Are you ready for this? Here goes – drum-roll please! **You can learn**

more if you try, pay attention, study, and practice, than you can if you just wander around in the school hallways waiting for gratuitous insight, or by hanging out with the smart kids. That's it.

That is the biggest and best secret I have. I blab that secret to people who want to know something deep and meaningful, but most of them don't actually get it. All life's great secrets share this attribute: Merely voicing the secret does not divulge the meaning; it only becomes profound, and therefore makes a difference to your life, when you are ready to absorb its significance within the context of a bigger picture.

We make choices based on the quality of our consciousness and the opportunities our apparent situation presents to us. We need such an apparent situation because of the optimal learning opportunity it presents – as discussed in Chapter 22 of Book 1, Chapter 14 of this book, and Chapter 2 of Book 3. Thus, we (and others) represent a logical and evolutionary necessity for AUM. We are configured from AUM's consciousness to allow AUM to optimize its evolutionary potential. We may be an experiment, but we are an experiment that is integral to the being and evolution of the aware consciousness that is AUM.

Come on Jake, put out that cigarette, give up trying to convince Susie that you are as cool as you wish you were, and let's get back to class.

36

■■■

The Politics of Reality

■■■

Each individual partially defines his or her own local reality. To the extent that our perceived environment, sensors and interpretations are similar, our experience will be similar. We of common experience, large ego, and limited understanding subsequently come together and declare that our shared reality is the one true reality and that everybody who doesn't understand that fact is dumb, confused, or delusional. This position concerning the accepted notion of reality becomes just another cultural, scientific, and religious belief system. Be careful: It is an easy trap to fall into.

Our local reality is defined and limited by our senses and our interpretation of the data our senses collect. What lies beyond our local reality is believed to not exist, believed to be mystical, or described as nonphysical. Imagine the reality we would collectively construct for ourselves (believe in) if every human on this planet were (and had always been) blind and deaf. (Assume plenty of accessible food and beer for everybody – we are not probing survival issues.) Imagine what our culture, political boundaries, and civilization would be like under those circumstances. Think of all the things that we now experience and understand as part of our physical reality that would disappear into non-existence or appear to be mystical or nonphysical. How do you think we would collectively interpret our interaction with critters and with each other? How would we deal with sunburn, snow, tornados, fire, tigers, birds, fleas, bumblebees and good-feeling babes?

▶ While your subconscious mulls over the concept of "good-feeling babes," let's explore the degree to which logic and rational analytical process can provide a more correct interpretation of your perceptions. Here we are speaking of fundamental sense perceptions as well as your perception of the quality of sentient interaction (mood, intent, motivation, attitude, feelings, relationship, emotion, and meaning).

Are all interpretations of perceptions equally valid? Can anyone distinguish between logical and non-logical interpretations? If a given interpretation is logical for one perceiver, will it be logical for all perceivers? The point of experience is growing the quality of your consciousness, not get the right answers. You can learn to make more profitable interpretations with more experience – wisdom can be developed. However, do not put too much hope in the power of logic to lead consistently to the optimal, best, or correct interpretation. Logic can be applied only when there are enough good data to support it. Most of the interpretations of our perceptions, particularly those that support our most significant decisions, must be made without enough data to come to a definitive logical conclusion.

This beyond-logical, uncertain state of affairs is by design. Otherwise, choice, free will, and intention would become moot issues if all interaction within our local reality was essentially deductive or tightly logical; all problems and challenges would have a unique analytical solution. Logic would replace judgment; existence and choices would be automatic and machine-like within a closed solution set. Even the extreme left-brainers, who longingly fantasize a more rational world, would eventually get bored. If life were a **logical** puzzle to be solved, learning would come to an end as soon as someone found a solution and shared it with others. Life is not logical – even if you pretend you are. You cannot use your intellect to get the most out of it. Trying to optimize your life by primarily applying your intellect (what most intellectuals do) is like a blind person with exceptional hearing trying to drive an automobile or fly an airplane.

We have the space-time rule-set (PMR physical law) to provide basic order and causality as an objective foundation. Do not expect logic to govern personal learning, interactions, and relationship in the same way that physics governs cannonballs – these are not logical processes even though left-brainers, and many relationship-challenged individuals, would like to pretend that they are or should be. (Why do all the men have this lost look on their faces – and why are all the women nodding their heads and rolling their eyes?)

Typically, your sense of being rational is produced by the self-justifying belief traps you are caught in. Your appearance (to yourself and others) of rationality and logical process is, for the most part, an illusion, a feel-good delusion of the ego that makes you appear to be competent and thus delivers a sense of correctness, and personal security to the self. Each of us has a tendency to define the local truth to be whatever feels good to our ego and boosts our self-esteem. We justify our actions, feeling, attitudes, and beliefs and interpret events to support our needs, wants, desires, and expectations.

Let's tie this discussion of assumed logic and rationality in with some of the things we learned in previous sections. Do you see why randomness (or pseudo-randomness), uncertainty and the psi uncertainty principle are a necessary part of the space-time rule-set? Is it clear why divination, mind reading, telepathy, remote viewing, precognition, psychokinesis, and other psi effects are detrimental to the potential growth of a low quality, high entropy consciousness while generally irrelevant to the growth of a low entropy, high quality consciousness? Little boys, say five to ten years of age, would dearly love to be as strong as full grown men, but fortunately evolution is not that careless.

If you still do not get it, imagine your boss, spouse, mother-in-law, children, or telemarketers having direct access to your mind. Great power in the hands of an irrational ego or manipulating intent is always frightening and usually destructive. For the most part, we are thankful for the natural limitations on **other people's** power, as are they, no doubt, thankful for the limitation on ours. That huge difference between "us" and "them" is an illusion of ego. Irrationality and illogic are the norm, not the exception; belief that the opposite is true (at least for us) is a commonly held delusion. Take a moment to ponder how this discussion might apply to you and the people you know.

Almost everyone will agree that ego typically ravages the rationality of others because we are all reasonably secure in the knowledge that we are an exception to that rule. You and me amigo, we're not like all the others. Right?

Are a gaggle of pre-schoolers rational? Are they logical? Are they highly interactive? What motivates them? Why do you think that you (at the fundamental level of interactive consciousness) interact substantially differently than they do? Think about that for a moment – I want a good, thoughtful answer. Are you sure the perceived difference is not either superficial (you are better at math, a better planner) or generated by an ego justifying itself and its significance (the things you do are more important)? Most people simply define themselves to be rational and that is that.

When you find somebody who thinks that they are particularly rational and logical, often you have found instead somebody who is out of touch with their deeper motivations and intents. Simple analytical thinking often masquerades as basic intelligence and is used to support a superior claim to correctness – a self-serving logic and rationality that justifies dominance, wants, needs, and desires.

People who live entirely out of their heads and exist primarily in intellectual space often are sadly shallow and severely limited by the belief that they are primarily logical beings and that the employment of rationality and logical analysis is the highest and loftiest goal they can aspire to. The most important things in life are not things that can be adequately dealt with or experienced through analysis and logical process. Such self-directed impoverishment and limitation is held up as an ideal in Western culture.

Do not get carried away. I am not implying that all logical process is fraudulent and useless. It can be a wonderfully productive tool – I live and work by it every day. Science is based upon it – it is the foundation of My Big TOE. I am merely asserting that we in the West have elevated the value of belief-based rational process to the point that we are fooling ourselves most of the time and as a consequence, we have blocked our view of a more holistic process that reaches much deeper into the well of truth than mere logical analysis. Our sense of rationality has become twisted, self-referential, and based upon circular logic – a marvelous tool extended beyond its useful function.

The non-rational, non-logical world that we actually live in is entirely different from the rational, logic-driven world that most of us pretend that we live in (particularly intellectuals and technical or scientific types). It seems typical that the information available to support making a logical interpretation or decision about the meaning or significance of our collected perceptions is inversely proportional to the importance of the correctness of that interpretation or decision. The majority of life's important, significant, path-changing decisions are the ones whose outcomes are the most uncertain because of a lack of information.

This state of affairs was not designed to frustrate you, but is a result of the fact that the physical causal world is simply a theatrical set (a playground with rules) provided to you to help you unfold your personal drama by forcing you to make significant subjective choices based upon your intent, not objective choices based upon causal logic. This arrangement allows you to evolve your consciousness, not just practice the relatively sterile art of correctly applying logic. The most important growth opportunities of your life will always be beyond your causal logic – will always be subjective and intuitive gropes dressed up in as much pseudo-logical justification as you can muster in order to make your life appear as orderly and rational as possible. The appearance of an orderly rational process driving our lives forward is a delusion that lowers anxiety and makes us feel better. Beyond that, the appearance of order in your life provides a coherent media or frame of reference for your experience that infallibly reflects the quality of your being. It would seem that our drive to rationalize our choices is a necessary part of what makes us work.

By highly valuing the well behaved, dependable, easily understood objective aspects of your existence while discarding, devaluing, or bumbling through the subjective aspects, you are focusing upon the chaff and throwing away the wheat. This misguided assessment of where we should focus our effort wastes huge amounts of time and energy in logical objective cultures such as ours. The effort that we focus on our careers, status, and material success greatly outweighs the effort that we invest in raising our personal quality. The result is that most people live their lives within a continuous soap opera that seems to have no final episode until death liberates them from that particular part.

The physical virtual reality set (PMR) is not intrinsically important to your purpose except that it provides the structured learning experience you need. The iterative expression of your intent as it assimilates feedback derived from the results of your interactions with others is what allows you to pull yourself up by your bootstraps (lower your entropy increment by increment through a long-term personal program of self-improvement). That you can solve logic problems is helpful in mastering your rule-based space-time environment, but it is only the foil, a supporting, enhancing, enabling structure, not the main goal. Understanding the objective causality of your virtual learning lab is important like your house and car is important; understanding the subjective and intuitive nature of your most significant decisions is important like your children or parents are important.

Big decisions, important decisions, are usually complex and span many uncertain issues and are therefore least amenable to a logical solution. Where did you leave your glasses? Use logic as best you can. Who should you marry? How should you go about improving the quality of your consciousness? Forget logic, it's not going to help much. Because we seldom know how things will change or how relationships and interactions with others will progress (even if we could fully specify present states), how could our logical analysis penetrate very deeply? Our assumed rationality and logical process is a thin veneer, while love, truth, fear, want, need, and desire, run deep.

How do we interpret our perceptions in the midst of this unknowing? Mostly we guess! We make assumptions and rely on beliefs. We go with a hunch, from the heart, or with a gut feeling. We pretend (usually without intellectually knowing that we are pretending) that we are logical or that we know more than we do. We develop theories; we extrapolate past experience into the future. We use our intuition, which is our normal connection to the nonphysical part of our being. How we ultimately interpret our perceptions depends on our knowledge, previous experience, understanding, wisdom, and the quality of our consciousness. We try the best we can to be rational, or at least to appear to be rational.

I expect that you may have noticed the many feedback loops and functional interdependencies that connect perception, interpretation, logical analysis, experience, wisdom, belief, and the quality of your consciousness. If not, take a moment to ponder the maze of interdependent connections and interrelationships. Don't rush, take as along as you need, I'll wait for you. ◀

Interpreting your experience can be tricky if the quality of your consciousness is low. Belief and ego can strongly color your interpretation as well as your perception. Many of man's most horrific experiences – war (including holy wars), genocide, racism, ethnic cleansing and so forth – are motivated by ego in the service of belief. Humanity's worst crimes are typically committed to maintain, preserve, and spread particular beliefs and individual power, or as an expression of ego-arrogance. Many ordinary, perfectly nice people become upset if a bigger picture (or someone else's little picture) threatens their comfortable concept of reality. They will rationalize their attitudes and produce many good reasons why their particular delusion represents the only correct view. Such is the power of fear, belief traps, a closed mind, and a small picture combined. This is the politics of reality.

Selectively ignoring the facts of objective and subjective experience to justify enforcing a common belief (scientific, cultural, political, or religious) of what constitutes official reality sanctioned by the proper (scientific, cultural, political, or religious) authorities is required to maintain the delusion that we are logical, rational people living in an objective physical world. Fear, control, and conformity make ignorance their friend.

The preceding paragraph was rather complex and you may need to read it a few times to get what it implies about other people.

▶ Everyone likes democratic politics these days. If you really want to know how real reality really is, all you need to do is take a vote.

"All those in favor of PMR being all there is to reality raise your hand. I guess that settles it folks, the ayes have it – PMR is all there is.

"I mean …if people as intelligent, open, and with it as you and your friends are haven't experienced this larger reality, what are the odds that anyone has? Not high, I am afraid, not high – especially if we discard the goofy unreliable types – the ones that are not like us. If this foreign sounding AUM gobbledygook were actually true we would all have heard about it by now – everybody would know. Right?

"Look at all the smart people in the world – do they **believe** this nonsense? No way! Where is the hard physical evidence? I am not buying this consciousness mumbo jumbo until I can put my hands on some good samples of nonphysical energy to study in the lab. Scientists cannot allow themselves to fall into this subjective quicksand – that's where science was hundreds of years ago when doctors were bleeding people with leaches to cure them. You cannot go wrong if you stick to objectivity. Right?

"There is nothing you can do about it anyway. How could I ever know the truth? Jeez, weird people are everywhere. You name it and there is some bunch of wacko people somewhere that believe it. There seems to be no limit to people's capacity for goofiness. This nonphysical baloney is all unsubstantiated opinion. It is **objectively** not provable. Right?

"You need to be careful of what you are willing to **believe**. Make a note: Thinking thoughts that are not 'normal' can be dangerous. I should be more careful about what I expose myself to. I think I should toss this disconcerting TOE-jam book in the fireplace and go watch TV. What could be more harmless than TV? Right?" ◀

That's politics folks! The majority rules. Run with the crowd – it is much safer that way and there is no personal responsibility to worry about. Kick back and let it go. If a mistake is made it is no big deal because everybody else will have made it too. If something is especially important, someone will tell you about it. Right? And when they do, you will listen and understand. Right?

37

■■■

Weird Physics Requires
Weird Physicists

■■■

What about the sense of touch? Isn't that the sense that gives us our most trustworthy feel for reality? The eyes and ears (our dominant sensors) can be tricked rather easily. Illusionists make a living by tricking us into believing something that is not true. Mass banging into mass, now that feels real! If you can get your hands on it, you know it is not an illusion, right? There is a classical law of physics that says two masses cannot occupy the same space at the same time. That simple physical law alone can account for our individual sense of separateness within space-time. Everything – rocks, fish, people, hockey pucks, and the planets – must all be and remain separate entities within a shared space. None can encroach on the other's personal space.

TBC undoubtedly has that rule expressed somewhere in the space-time rule-set that defines and limits our perception. Yet, when things become big, fast, or small the game changes. Our law abiding bodies that vigorously lay claim to their specific volume and mass wouldn't dream of sharing that same space with anything else. Yet a neutrino, neutron, or a high energy photon sees our bodies as we see our universe – mostly empty space with a few chunks of matter scattered about here and there. Now the concept of no two masses existing at the same point at the same time begins to take on a different meaning. At a smaller (quantum) scale where the classical view breaks down completely and a particle seems to exist as a smeared out probability distribution, that particular physical law seems to have developed a statistical loophole.

Wherever the mechanisms and processes of our perception are coarse enough to disturb what we are attempting to perceive, direct observation becomes impossible. If this situation occurs because we are probing the boundary between experienceable and un-experienceable reality, we should expect the results to be strange because essentially we are probing the boundary between our local reality and the algorithms and mechanisms that TBC uses to implement its rule-set from outside our causal system.

The boundary between what we can perceive (experience) and the un-experienceable reality, which is the source of that perception but at the same time forever beyond our perception, is the boundary between our local reality and a mystical reality (from the view of PMR). This is the boundary between physical objects and consciousness, between what appears (from the view of PMR) to obey our law of causality and what appears to flaunt that law. It is also the boundary between our bodies and our mind, soul, sprit, and intuition. This boundary separates the normal from the paranormal and, if a bridge between the two is developed, defines and enforces the psi uncertainty principle discussed in Chapters 13 and 14 of this book.

Modern physics in general and quantum mechanics in particular will always be mired in mystery and produce results that seem inconsistent, unexplainable and counter-intuitive as long as it clings to its PMR-only little picture belief system. Quantum physics will remain confusingly abstruse as long as it stubbornly requires the $NPMR_N$ reality camel to be forced through the eye of the PMR reality needle – or the $NPMR_N$ elephant to be pulled out of a PMR acorn. Until the self-imposed belief blindfold is removed, the outer boundary of little picture science will remain confused, out of focus, and apparently mystical. Inside that boundary, scientists will continue to unravel the space-time rule-set one fact and relationship at a time.

Discovery constitutes a journey that is much longer and more personal than most people think: Take your time, and focus on where you want to go. Understanding the rule-set that governs your local reality so that you can manipulate material existence to suit your needs is all well and good, but understanding the Big Picture is vastly more significant.

38

■ ■ ■

Section 4 Postlude
Hail! Hearty Reader,
Thine Open Mind and Force of Will
are Truly Extraordinary

■ ■ ■

If you have made it to this point (unless you have skipped around a lot) you have proved yourself to be no shrinking metaphysical violet. By now those with little to no experience beyond PMR have had almost everything they ever believed in thoroughly trashed or turned upside down and inside out. That could cause an uncomfortable, lost, sad, or empty feeling – or maybe a "drifting free with no roots" feeling. Has some nasty person torn up your comfortable old roots? How rude! Fortunately for me, the culprit is you. I simply supplied the hoe, trowel and rototiller (or was that a bulldozer?) and gave some encouragement. Don't worry, such feelings are often the doorway to a better place than you inhabited before. Award yourself four more of those highly coveted beautiful golden stars; paste them in your book next to your name and you will feel better.

On the other hand, those with considerable experience outside the confines of PMR will have found a conceptual structure and context that makes sense out of all those unusual experiences that they knew were significant, but simply could not explain or integrate into their worldview. For these folks, *My Big TOE* holds the promise to transform the incomprehensible into the well understood, the mystical into the mundane, the fear of being strange into the assurance of being normal, and far-out seekers searching blindly by trial and error into well reasoned individuals with a good explanation of what they are doing and why they are doing it.

From the opposite point of view, let me remind you that this book is flammable, and you can always forget the entire thing. Hey, that's not so bad; you get a great fire-starter for your fireplace, and can easily dismiss *My Big TOE* as *My Big Delusion* – the ravings of a wacko physicist who has obviously lost his way.

Either way, you ought to read the next Section. Section 5 is the result of everything we have accomplished in the previous sections; it's where you begin to see how everything previously mentioned begins to pull together into a coherent (that's my opinion) model of reality. Section 5 reveals the mechanics of how the larger reality functions and describes many of its processes. It will tell you what's out there, why your unusual experiences are as they are, and how and why they are rationally bounded. Thus far, only the conceptual foundation has been laid; now we will build the model that operationally describes the larger reality upon it.

Ahead the trail gets steep in a few places (because the structure and processes of reality can get complex), but most of the conceptual heavy lifting is behind us. To get the most out of Section 5, you will need to continue to be an intrepid explorer. Open minded skepticism, perseverance, and dogged personal stamina will be required in Section 5 at least as much, if not more, than they were in the previous sections.

Now let's go straightaway to Section 5 and discover what reality looks like from the inside.

Find the other two books of the *My Big TOE* trilogy:
http://www.My-Big-TOE.com
http://www.lightningstrikebooks.com
Phone orders: 1-800-901-2122